A
HUGH HENRY BRACKENRIDGE
Reader

1770–1815

With appreciation for all
feel she done for me,

Dan M.

A HUGH HENRY BRACKENRIDGE *Reader*

1770-1815

Edited, with an Introduction by

Daniel Marder

University of Pittsburgh Press

SBN 8229-3184-2

Library of Congress Catalog Card Number 69-12332

Copyright © 1970, University of Pittsburgh Press

All Rights Reserved

Manufactured in the United States of America

Acknowledgments

I am grateful for the guidance of Professor Robert E. Gale of the University of Pittsburgh and for the aid of Professor Clara Thoman of Slippery Rock State College and of Barbara Humphrey Marder. Each contributed uniquely at various stages in the prolonged production of this book.

Contents

A Note about the Collection

The work of Brackenridge collected here falls into three roughly discernible periods of the writer's development: (1) the period of "rising glory," which includes his work at Princeton, in the army, and on the *United States Magazine* (1774–1779), all dominated by American revolutionary ideas both in government and in art; (2) the period of the early American frontier (1781–1801), which includes his major work, dominated by democratic realities impinging upon and tempering his early idealism; and (3) the period of collection and recollection (1801–1815), which includes the bulk of his reflective work and his collections, dominated by a wistfulness as he reviews his early ideals and his frontier life.

Pieces that are too confined in time and place for application today have been excluded. Because of this criterion, neither of his dramas has found a place in this collection, nor have the majority of his journalistic bickerings with his political enemies. His Hudibrastics and most other awkward verse have also been excluded. The dramas offer little action; the verses and essays not included offer little sense of composition. In the editor's opinion, this volume contains most of the work that is worth saving. However, all the original work that merits inclusion could not be represented in a single volume. In all instances the editor has tried to select the nub of the literary experience. Thus, only a third of Brackenridge's part of *The Rising Glory* is included and only the narrative elements of *Modern Chivalry* and of *Incidents of the Insurrection* are presented. In general the shorter pieces are offered without deletions.

Editorial Devices

Editorial comments preceding the major selections are indicated by italic type and brackets, as are explanatory insertions within the text. Textual insertions that supply missing words are in roman type and

ix

brackets. Some of the selections are introduced by Brackenridge's words taken from another source; these are unbracketed.

Numbered notes are those of the editor. Brackenridge's notes bear symbols rather than numbers and are followed by his initials to further prevent confusion.

Missing letters and minor words, such as articles and simple prepositions that were obviously unintentional omissions, have been inserted without brackets. The editor has modernized punctuation, spelling, and paragraphing in Brackenridge's works.

Short ellipses indicate omitted words or sentences; full-line ellipses indicate omitted paragraphs. Arabic chapter numbers within *Modern Chivalry* and *Incidents of the Insurrection* have been inserted in numerical order for the convenience of the reader.

D.M.

Bibliographical Note

Brackenridge has received little critical attention. A biography, Claude M. Newlin's *The Life and Writings of Hugh Henry Brackenridge* (Princeton, 1932), is devoted to the events of his life. A second biography, *Hugh Henry Brackenridge* by the editor of this volume (New York, 1967), brings the works into critical focus. A few historians of American literature have regarded Brackenridge as a central figure in our literary development. Some evaluation of his work appears in Moses Coit Tyler, *The Literary History of the American Revolution*, Volume II (New York, 1897); Vernon Louis Parrington, *Main Currents in American Thought*, Volume I (New York, 1927); Alexander Cowie, *The Rise of the American Novel* (New York, 1948); and Robert E. Spiller and others (eds.), *Literary History of the United States*, Volume I (New York, 1948). Other accounts of the insurrection are Henry Marie Brackenridge, *History of the Western Insurrection in Western Pennsylvania, Commonly Called the Whiskey Insurrection* (Pittsburgh, 1859); William Findley, *History of the Insurrection in the Four Western Counties of Pennsylvania* (Philadelphia, 1796); and Neville B. Craig, *Exposure of the Many Misstatements in H. M. Brackenridge's History of the Whiskey Insurrection* (Pittsburgh, 1859).

D.M.

A
HUGH HENRY BRACKENRIDGE
Reader

1770–1815

Introduction

Along with Mike Fink and Simon Girty, Judge Hugh Henry Brackenridge is one of the eccentrics in the legend of the early frontier west
of the Alleghenies. There is the abiding image of the circuit rider
charging the jury, beard unshaven and hair disheveled, tie askew,
shirt sprung open and soiled almost to the color of his rusty black
waistcoat, and his bare feet propped on the bar of justice. It was said
he owned no stockings. Caught riding naked through the rain he
pointed to his only suit tucked under the saddle, "The storm, you
know, would spoil the clothes, but it couldn't spoil me." In the East he
had become notorious as the "worst of the Whiskey Rebels," and in
the West as the elected representative of the backwoodsmen who
sold them out "for a dinner of some stockholder's fat beef." Appointed
a Justice of the Supreme Court of Pennsylvania for his role in
Jefferson's victory (1799), he was congratulated with a summary account of his career, beginning with an exposé of the new "Supreme
Judge and sapient philosopher too . . . seen 'stark naked' and nearly
'stark mad' from too much tipple in the face of open day." The
description touched upon his role in the Whiskey Rebellion, his ad-
vocacy of the French Revolution and of the Federal Constitution, his
sermons to correct his countrymen's morals, and his reputation as a
writer: "President of the Jacobin Society . . . Biographer of the
Insurgents . . . Auctioneer of Divinity . . . Haberdasher of Pronouns." And because he had hired a Jewish editor for his Jeffersonian
newspaper, *Tree of Liberty*, "Brackenridge of late seems to have
a hankering after the Jews. . . . Like his friend Jefferson the philosopher and the Rogues of France . . . that he should turn Jew in his
old days and build him a synagogue in his own ground surprizes
nobody. . . . If in one of his crack-brained magazines Hugh has submitted to the Knife of his High Priest, is it expected that every
man, woman and child will do the same? Are we all to be circumcised
without benefit of clergy?"

There were, however, softer images: the vigorous orator standing on a hillside overlooking the town . . . "fine voice . . . fine person . . . eagle eye . . . ," beseeching his rough countrymen to accept the new Federal Constitution that would limit their liberties, "O Israel, thou art destroyed for the lack of knowledge"; the suitor who paid ten dollars annual fee to Sofia Wolfe's father for a substitute to shrub the meadows; the husband who sent his bride to Philadelphia "under the governance of a reputable female character . . . to polish the manners and wipe off the rusticities which Mrs. Brackenridge had acquired whilst a Wolfe"; the moralist who responded to a gentleman's challenge by printing it

Sir,

I will thank you to take a walk with a friend and meet me at the back of the graveyard about sunrise tomorrow morning. After what has happened, you know what I mean

Your humble servant, etc.

along with his reply

Sir,

I know what you mean very well; you want to have a shot at me but I have no inclination to hit you, and I am afraid you would hit me. I pray thee therefore have me excused.

Judge Brackenridge the legend has absorbed the literary reputation of Hugh Henry Brackenridge, author of *Modern Chivalry*. Until the middle of the nineteenth century, Brackenridge's massive satire of the fumblings and foibles of the new Republic was read over the frontier, by some back East, and in Europe—at least by the King of France. In 1815, a year before his death, Brackenridge boasted that five publishers had already made their fortunes on his book and that a copy could be found in every parlor in Pennsylvania. In June 1839, the editor of the *Pittsburgh Literary Examiner and Western Monthly Review* unabashedly claimed *Modern Chivalry* was "to the West what Don Quixote was to Europe . . . the humorous textbook of all classes of society." John Quincy Adams was so taken with the satire that years later on a visit to Pittsburgh he sought out the descendants of Brackenridge. Professor Arthur Quinn's *American Fiction* tells us that the author's name "became a household word for half a century." Apparently the satire competed well in the West with the various romances of Charles Brockden Brown and James Fenimore Cooper, and with the rather tranquil satires of Washington Irving. But its power to attract the imagination weakened about mid-century when American genius had ripened sufficiently to produce such works as *The Scarlet Letter* (1850), *Moby Dick* (1851), and *Leaves of Grass* (1855).

Although *Modern Chivalry* was read in the East, it had never been accepted by the literati who championed the cause of an independent literature while their ears were attuned to the accustomed sounds of England and the continent. In the coastal culture the preferred view of frontier life was that of the noble and paternal Leatherstocking, whose inventor wrote from secondhand knowledge after the frontier had passed.

Brackenridge's portrait of our early frontier—swollen with heavy-handed bluster, uncompromising directness, violent humor, and savage conflict—is clearly out of phase with the nation's literary development. When attention finally focused on events to the West, it was a farther West than the Ohio Valley. *Modern Chivalry* was subordinated to the flourishing legend of its author. It became an ill-understood relic. To one recent critic it typifies "neo-classical thought and form," although Brackenridge stated that it was written to instruct "Tom, Dick, and Harry in the woods." *Duyckinck's Cyclopedia of American Literature*, highly influential at least throughout the early years of the twentieth century, listed it as a "century old piece of Scotch wit and wisdom." The legend of Judge Brackenridge has so absorbed the author of *Modern Chivalry* that even the careful *Literary History of the United States* (1963) states: "For years a judge in Pennsylvania, he knew at first hand the rough politics of democracy, yet his point of view in *Modern Chivalry* is generally that of an objective observer." Brackenridge became a judge six years after the first volumes of the novel were published and very soon after returned East.

If the legend of Judge Brackenridge absorbs *Modern Chivalry*, it smothers the rest of his work. Yet it is only in terms of his other satires, his narratives, his essays and poems that we see the full portrait he draws of the new country far from English dominance. The frontiersman is always in the center, always pulling against eastern influences, constraints, and propositions. Not only does the portrait bring into focus the disunity of national ideals but also the image of an American cultural pioneer planting seeds of education, art, communication, and a sense of political responsibility on the frontier and reaping personal defeat in return.

The problem so urgent today—how to be both free and orderly— is the same that consumed the life of Hugh Henry Brackenridge at the beginning of the democratic experiment. He was totally committed and utterly involved. He had come to maturity at least a generation before American writers could devote themselves to art. Almost everything he wrote constituted a public art, even his massive satire *Modern Chivalry*. He was committed completely to the requirement of an educated and sensitized population, and he was involved, therefore, in overcoming ignorance and licentiousness. In England the major social problem concerned the people's right to rule; in America the problem had abruptly changed to the development and qualifications of a people who would rule. The pursuit of this problem is basic to everything Brackenridge wrote.

Although his purpose was seldom artistic, he was always aware of literary values. Many of his essays and narratives and even some of his poems have enduring power both in what they say and how they say it. Taken together his best efforts have a sweep and a penetration unequaled before the work of Emerson. They also comprise a story of an American literary man of the eighteenth century—a trained classicist—who ventured West in the last days of the Revolutionary War to teach his bumptious countrymen how to realize man's oldest dream. This is not the American success story of Ben Franklin in another setting. The industriousness of Brackenridge was not commercial and was not driven by a thinly-buried Puritan ethic. He had come to the West, he said, "to advance the country and thereby myself," much as a modern-day existentialist might say in assuming responsibility for society in his individual acts. And the outcome of the story is not success. In the West, the dream clashed with the harsh realities of frontier life. His twenty years in the frontier town of Pittsburgh (1781–1801) were one long embroilment that tested and tempered his democratic idealism.

As history, the writings of Brackenridge reveal a dominant strain of the American spirit evolving out of English tradition into Jacksonian democracy. For Emerson this transition was abrupt and occurred at a definite place: "Europe extends to the Alleghenies," he said; "America lies beyond." As literature, the works of Brackenridge enrich the sparse period of American literary output between the Revolution and the first quarter of the nineteenth century, the period of the early Republic, of national incubation.

I

Brackenridge was thirty-three years old when he came to the end of the horse trail at the junction of the Allegheny and Monongahela rivers. He had left Philadelphia because he saw "no chance of being anything in that city. There were such great men before me." Behind him were short careers as a Philadelphia man of letters, an army chaplain, a schoolmaster. A decade had passed since he had been exposed to the Whiggish political philosophies at Princeton. With classmates Philip Freneau and James Madison, Brackenridge had been immersed in the empiricism of the senses and the ideals of common sense as taught by Dr. John Witherspoon. Democracy was a test of man's rationality, and its practice required sensibility, intelligence, and knowledge of the past. "The function of government," Witherspoon taught, is "the protection of liberty as far as it is a blessing."

These ideas were absorbed with ideals of Greek democracy, particularly those of Thucydides, and with the satirical habits of Lucian, and fortified outside of class with the "modern wits such as Cervantes, Le Sage and especially Swift." Although he considered satire a ludicrous way of thinking and writing, he was impelled to imitation. First results were in a series of poems, *Satires Against the Tories,* written with Freneau, Madison, and William Bradford and employed in a paper war between the Whig and Tory student societies. A more enduring result was the first American short story, a satire of marvelous adventures included in a longer manuscript, *Father Bombo's Pilgrimage to Mecca,* again written with Freneau.

But there was no satire in the poem he delivered on Commencement Day, 1771. In epic verse, imitating the grandest style of Milton, Brackenridge and Freneau viewed the progress of mankind, its hopes and its dreams fulfilled at last in the westernmost land of the civilized world:

> 'Tis but the morning of the world with us
> And Science yet but sheds her orient rays.

It was a vision of individuals who had at last reached that degree of sensibility and intelligence where a *Rising Glory of America* was possible. And standing before the assembly in Nassau Hall, this graduate symbolized every sense of the vision. Only eighteen years before, he had emigrated at the age of five with his family from the poor farmlands near Campbellstown, Scotland, to the "Barrens" in York County, Pennsylvania. By day he had cleared, planted, and harvested the fields, and by night devoured every book within walking range. At Princeton he supported himself by teaching grammar school classes and by ghosting orations for his fellow students.

The Rising Glory of America was a welding of all his passions—

politics, classical literature, oration. It was also his summons to take part. But he remained at Princeton to study for the ministry, partly because his parents, and perhaps he too, considered this role the very consummation of intellectual pursuits. The ministry also promised opportunity for oratory, which to Brackenridge was probably its most appealing aspect.

Rather than a pulpit, Brackenridge was offered the leadership of an academy on the eastern shore of Maryland at a good salary. According to Freneau who went along as assistant, Brackenridge delighted in his position of eminence in the "wealthy and highly polished society." (Freneau himself could not abide the students who "prey upon me like leeches.") Returning to Princeton for his Master's degree, Brackenridge read a second version of his *Rising Glory,* this time called *A Poem on Divine Revelation* (1774).

Hearing the news from Bunker Hill, Brackenridge reacted with a drama that wrings a moral victory out of the defeat, and the following year he wrote another drama that screams his outrage at British atrocities in the siege of Quebec. The subject of both is valor and the manner is grand; there is much oration and little action. But the emotion is genuine. That same year (1777) he gave up teaching and joined the troops in the field as an army chaplain, assuming the neglected role he had prepared for.

The chaplain, however, was no minister of God. He saw himself as a combination of druid (the chaplain "of our ancestors among the Germans"), of heroic bard, and of propagandist. His sermons seethed with Hemingway-like descriptions of enemy atrocities, yet the hateful images of British and American Tories were woven with purpose, with hopes for a rising American glory and modulated ironically with appreciation for the cultural attainments of the enemy. Clever devices of analogy, the sermons substituted patriotic and civic passions for religious ones. Only in the dark hour when it was rumored that their French officers had been called home did the chaplain allow God to enter. God blessed America and "the Armies of the universe were not sufficient to resist his providence."

No sooner had the British evacuated Philadelphia in 1778 than Brackenridge abandoned his role of chaplain and set off for the city to seek a literary career. Immediately, he published the best of his sermons, precisely titling them *Six Political Discourses Founded on the Scriptures.* His larger purpose, however, was to try his own hand at publishing. In the battlefields he had conceived of a periodical that would ingrain the value of literature in the American civilization.

"For what is man without taste, and the acquirement of genius? An orangutan with the human shape and the soul of a beast." Not only did he fear an empty victory, but he wished to serve the cause of American independence by fostering a native literature which at least would convince the British that Americans were able to cultivate the belles lettres. But the fundamental role of the periodical would be educational, aimed particularly at the "mechanic of the city or the husbandman who ploughs his farm by the river [and who] has it in his power to become one day the first magistrate of his respective commonwealth or to fill a seat in the Continental Congress."

The *United States Magazine* would not only make the mind capable of judgment but also provide entertainment to "unbend it from study and severe application." In December 1779, after a full year of publication, he blamed its failure on that large class who "inhabit the region of stupidity and cannot bear to have the tranquility of their repose disturbed by the villainous jargon of a book." He studied law. Then in the spring of 1781 Brackenridge abandoned America's center of culture and politics and turned west where he prophesied fulfillment of man's oldest dreams.

II

Most of the settlers at the fork of the Ohio River had emigrated from Scotland and the lowlands. By degrees they had extended the frontier. Many had come from the harsh land of York County called the "Barrens" where Brackenridge had spent his childhood. Enticed by advertisements that the governments of Pennsylvania and Virginia would recognize pre-emptive rights, the settlers pushed over the mountain and exposed themselves once again to the Indian warfare that had become a way of life. But then the governments themselves began a squabble over the rights to this new land. When it was ceded to Pennsylvania in 1779, the settlers moved to secede from a nation that was hardly yet in existence and which had ignored all their needs including defenses against Indians and rights to navigate the Mississippi.

Brackenridge arrived from Philadelphia at the crescendo of the secessionist movement. No sooner was he admitted to the rural bar than he displayed his yet untarnished devotion to the new nation, acting according to ideal and thus against the popular will, a way of behavior that was to become characteristic. He took it upon himself to show the State Assembly that secession would deprive Pennsylvania

of public lands needed to raise revenues. On the frontier to oppose
the will of the frontiersmen was to oppose oneself. He appeared to be
the fool of ideas and books; a man who kept too much to himself
and his candle late into the night; who talked about the "good of the
nation" meaning the land grabbers of the East; surely a man who
didn't know his own good, who told clients "no man of sense goes
to law, did you ever hear of my going to law?"

To Brackenridge the secessionist issue was a test of rising America
which depended totally on the proposition that men could be brought
to reason. In this instance, reason showed clearly enough how local
and individual good must be subordinated to the national good in
order to have a nation. Not attacked when the Assembly declared
any agitation for secession a treasonable act, Brackenridge should
have felt somewhat justified in his faith; their restraint indicated at
least a strain of patience in the frontiersmen.

The more they observed the attorney, the more he perplexed them.
He thought East indeed, but also West. If language, logic, and law
confused the newcomer about the land disputes, he saw the Indian
situation in the same light as any other man on the frontier. Since his
youth in the "Barrens," where he may have witnessed the cruelties
everyone talked about, Brackenridge consistently referred to the native
Americans as "animals vulgarly called Indians." In the *United States
Magazine* he had ridiculed the European views of the noble savages
and found a rationale for denying Indians rights to the soil: the land
belonged only to those who cultivated it, according to the dictates
of God as revealed in the Bible. This same rationale served to deny
the British any claims to American land, but somehow the attorney
had forgotten this argument when he looked at the issue between
the squatter and eastern titleholders.

In the summer of 1782 when Colonel Crawford's punitive exposi-
tion against the Indians ended in the capture, torture, and murder of
Crawford and many of his men, Brackenridge reacted with sensational
reports to eastern newspapers. They were raw retellings of eyewitness
accounts of two survivors. In a prefatory note to *The Narratives of the
Perils and Sufferings of Dr. Knight and John Slover* (1783), he expressed the hope that the shock of these first communiqués from the
frontier would open eastern eyes to the real nature of Indians and to
the uselessness of dealing with them. As his first writing efforts in two
years, the reports revealed to him that the realities of his frontier
existence had at least jarred the literary attitudes nurtured during
his years in the East.

But on a vacation at Warm Springs, Virginia, the following year, he reminded himself that he was still a man of letters and, as if to prove it, produced a masque in the courtly style of Ben Jonson. It was intended to honor General Washington who was also visiting there. Its spirits of the springs and rivers, its water nymphs and happy godlings refused to dance for Brackenridge as they had for Jonson a century earlier. Washington's diary for the day of the performance records hours spent arranging for construction on property the General owned near that town but contains not a word about the masque written in his honor.

The following year Brackenridge opposed General Washington in court. Usually he had defended eastern land speculators against the squatters but when the General tried to remove thirteen squatters from land he had just purchased from a Colonel Groghan, Brackenridge argued that Groghan himself had not owned it legally since he purchased it from Indians who didn't have rights to any land and therefore couldn't sell. The squatters were ejected.

Having vindicated himself somewhat as a man who stood for the people, which meant against Indians and eastern subtleties, Brackenridge suddenly turned on them. He undertook the defense of an Indian who had ended a drunken spree by killing a carpenter working on the Brackenridge house. "I was curious," he explained, as any artist would. Trying to understand the mind of this animal vulgarly called Indian, the narrator achieved an objective view that allowed penetration of the Indian's character rather than condemnation of it. "The Trial of Mamachtaga" is a rare narrative of the frontier in which the sharp selection of environmental detail and of action compel sympathy for the Indian who is quite ugly by most ordinary standards; and the story renders the white man's inability to comprehend an inbred honesty in the American native. But such sensitivity hardly suited the mood of the frontiersmen who threatened to storm the prison and hang the Indian awaiting trial.

Although the realities of the frontier had invaded his literary attitudes and changed his style, they had not proved effective against his stubborn idealism. Like artists and philosophers in general he saw no reason to change his attitudes to correspond with those of his fellows; but unlike these staunchly independent minds, he sought direct rather than literary action to change the attitudes surrounding him. He had come there to adapt the frontier to his personality, not to be adapted to the crudities and bumptiousness of the frontiersmen. When he left Philadelphia he had in mind "being among the first to bring the press to the West of the mountain," in order to provide a forum for the democratic process and also to get elected to the State Assembly. By 1786 he at last had found two printers willing to undertake the venture and arranged to have the presses hauled over the Allegheny trail. The first issue of the *Pittsburgh Gazette* contained his saccharine account of the idyllic life at the confluence of the Allegheny and Monongahela rivers. Very much in the vein of the earliest American reports to Europe a century earlier, the *Gazette* offered distortions of fact and with the same propagandistic aim—to induce migration. Subsequent issues were dominated by his sober lessons for democratic behavior, civic responsibilities, and cultural developments. These culminated, according to plan, in the announcement that the author had been compelled to seek a place on the ballot. During his campaign, he had promised to promote the people's interests by establishing the village as a borough and around it a county and there creating a seat of justice, an academy of learning, a library and bookstore, and a church for all denominations.

But the people really wanted to hear what he would do about getting troops to defend them against the Indians, about securing their rights to navigate the Mississippi then held by Spain, and about winning the titles to their lands. On the most urgent of these desires Brackenridge equivocated sufficiently to be elected; but when the bill to allow them purchase of the land came before the Assembly he opposed it. The price was too high, he told them; the certificates of indebtedness they would have to sign imposed too great a hardship. The *Gazette* roared objection, demonstrating its success as the democratic forum Brackenridge had envisioned. The feeling of betrayal was captured most clearly and calmly by William Findley, Brackenridge's political opponent. The people's representative was "a gentleman who professes the greatest acquired abilities and most shining imagination [but who] makes a prey of the people's confidence, betrays their interests and trifles with his own solemn professions. . . ."

Typically, Brackenridge responded with a lesson in democracy: a representative is not a machine but a thoughtful man who is sent to hear from others and who is qualified to decide for himself what is in the best interests of the people. He reminded them that all his promises had been kept except one, which he judged to be against their interests. But, the people felt, churches and academies were niceties compared to the owning of land. They were mixed blessings, in fact, containing seeds of eastern effeteness. And Brackenridge's abstract philosophizing about representative government was downright insulting. The more he explained on the pages of the *Gazette,* the more he condemned himself.

III

Returning for a second year in the Assembly, Brackenridge recognized that reason alone was ineffective with the people. Ostracized by the other western representatives and their leader William Findley, Brackenridge had to align himself with the eastern representatives who considered the constitution weak and called themselves anti-constitutionalists. Largely because of this alliance, Brackenridge was able to push through the Assembly the legislation he had promised his constituents. But the significance of bills advancing the western country faded in the light of the great debate on the new Federal Constitution that now occupied the representatives. To the westerners, the proposed document of government was treachery. It undermined the very cause of the Revolution. Whether in London or Philadelphia, a strong central government would limit their liberties and impose unjust taxes. To Brackenridge, however, a strong government was essential to unify the nation, "to consolidate the government of the union which, after all the pains taken, was with great difficulty brought about." Now is spirit, as well as fact, he joined the easterners, summoning all his literary powers to secure acceptance of the new Constitution.

When the western representatives, led by Findley, absconded from the State Assembly to avoid a quorum and thus delay a vote on a constitutional convention, Brackenridge saw no distinction between their burlesque of the democratic process and the invented burlesques of Samuel Butler. Consequently, he lashed out at the ridiculous representatives with the first of a series of verse he called Hudibrastics: "On the Running Away of the Nineteen Members of the Assembly from the House, When It Was Proposed to Call a Convention to Consider the New System of Congressional Government; and on the Apology Made by Them in Their Address. A Hudibrastic." In the burlesque, Findley who had been a cloth-maker became Traddle, the ambitious but ignorant weaver who should have stayed home at his treadle. Later, when Findley rather than Brackenridge was elected to the ratifying convention, the infuriated idealist substituted the lowest common denominator of the time for his Assembly colleague, Teague O'Regan, the people's choice:

> What wonder then that Teague O'Regan
> Like Asteroth, or idol Dagon,

Should here receive our reverence,
In spite of Truth and common sense;
Men in all ages are the same,
And nature is herself to blame.
Who has not given to all an eye
Of Sapience and philosophy.

Thus, out of the whirling events that set national attitudes in motion, the theme and leading character of *Modern Chivalry* were born.

In June 1788, the new Constitution was finally ratified. In spite of their former opposition the citizens gathered on a hill overlooking Pittsburgh to hear Hugh Henry Brackenridge lead them in celebration. Imagining his policies vindicated and himself once more in favor, Brackenridge sought to oppose Findley as a candidate for the first Congress of the new government. But the Federalists refused him. Had he not defended the twelve rioters who had amused themselves at the expense of the exciseman, William Graham, "Singeing his wig, cutting the tail of his horse, putting coals in his boots," and later "besieg[ing] him in a public house"? And even worse, he had not only defended but won the case for the seventy distillers who attacked Graham's successor when he seized their stills.

Distrusted by all, Brackenridge absolved himself from all political engagement and withdrew from public life. Seeing him at work in his law office in the village, the settlers no longer thought him a menace, merely an eccentric. "He always denied the charge," according to his son, Henry Marie, "and asserted that he was the only one of his acquaintances that was like everybody else." The following year he broke his silence to chastise the villagers. Because no clergymen assumed responsibility for the town's moral tone, he took it upon himself to lecture to them in "A Sermon on Village Slander." And challenged to a duel several months later, he responded with another, a sermon on dueling. In 1790 he took time out from his work on *Modern Chivalry* to get married, but immediately sent his bride off to Philadelphia for training.

In his first effort at satirizing modern times in America, Brackenridge imagined that he could produce a masterpiece in imitation of Butler—an American Hudibras. The ignorant weaver Traddle was given a foil, a modern chevalier who travelled the country observing and commenting on politics, social institutions, and manners. Meeting the weaver, the chevalier suggests that he take advantage of the new democracy and become somebody—a statesman. Rising ambition is immediately cancelled by Traddle's wife who interrupts with a cudgel

on the weaver's rump. And the chevalier, resisting a knightly impulse
to draw his sword, learns that this lowly creature has already attempted
politics and would be the champion of the people were it not for the
restraining cudgel of his wife. An observer then castigates the chevalier for neglecting his duty in educating the people:

> It would do service to the state
> If such a noble Knight as you
> Would teach them what they ought to do,
> And give them seasonable lessons
> Respecting such their wide creations
> That on the one hand while they pass
> The ignorant though monied ass
> So on the other should avoid
> The chusing such amongst the crowd
> As are unqualified, though less
> They may in property possess.

After thirty pages of such lessons, Brackenridge abandoned the
Hudibrastic form, but not the thought. It was with some regret that
he gave up the verse. Apparently, he was not aware of the sawdust
characters and artificial language of his *Modern Chevalier*. In his
opinion the verse was "not without some felicity . . . yet never having
been complemented to the same extent by others, I thought proper
to change my composition to prose . . . which was a more humble
and might be a safer walk." The novel form allowed Brackenridge
to impart the vigor and reality of the life he had experienced. Teague
O'Regan pushed Traddle into the background as he stepped into
full view, blazing with ignorance and ambition. And the chevalier
also took on dimensions of a real character as the author divested
him of the conventional trappings and transformed him into Captain
John Farrago, a hodge-podge of education and ideals and gentleman
at leisure. Instead of the abstract region of the author's political
thought, the picaresque adventures of the Captain and his bog-trotter,
Teague, carry the reader through real country, from the western
frontier to Philadelphia and back again.

In 1792 he took the first two volumes to a publisher in Philadelphia. A year later he completed another but this time he published
it in Pittsburgh where it became the first literary work to be written,
printed, and issued west of the mountains. He felt that he had
fathered a kind of classic, but a statement at the end of the third
volume reveals some disappointment. He wished he could get his
book to make a little more noise. "Will nobody attack it and prove

that it is insipid, libellous, treasonable, immoral or irreligious? . . .
Will nobody speak? What? Ho! Are ye all asleep in the hold down
there at Philadelphia?" But why should they listen? Literature was
produced in civilized places like New York and Hartford, not Pittsburgh. What would they hear? Bluster? Slapstick? Exaggeration? Such
noises would be heard later from farther west, but now the easterners
were too busy to listen, too busy championing the cause of a distinctive
American literature.

Four years later Brackenridge resumed his picaresque novel and
did not stop until the end of his life.

IV

While he was in Philadelphia to arrange the publication of
Modern Chivalry in 1792, Brackenridge called on his old friend
Freneau, who had become Jefferson's propagandist and ran a newspaper, the *National Gazette,* in opposition to the *Gazette of the
United States* supporting Hamilton. Before he left Philadelphia
Brackenridge was drawn back into public life. Freneau's *Gazette*
published a series of articles by the westerner, attacking the Federalists
who had rejected him. One struck out at Washington's foreign policy
by accusing the British of arming and provoking the Indians to attack
frontier settlements. Another directly attacked the new excise law,
insinuating that the government was a coalition of money interests
and aristocrats in the rich capitals, and was "opposed to the bed of
simplicity and true republicanism." The article pleaded for "a little
time to breath[e] and recover loss and feel vigour." And if the
frontiersmen then did not submit to the law, Brackenridge would be
the first to testify against them as he had in the past. If the Federalists
acted wisely they would in the end reap great benefits from the
western country both in trade and taxes; but if not, the frontiersmen
would "resist with intemperance what they ought to resist with
reason." It was not difficult to read this warning as a threat of
insurrection.

The tax on whiskey had actually existed in the province of
Pennsylvania since 1756, but attempts to collect it had always been
futile. When the new nation continued the tax and in fact tried to
enforce it, the westerners were offended, as the American patriots
had been offended when Britain tried to enforce the Stamp Act. Until
they could navigate the rivers and sell their grain downstream (Spain
held rights to the Mississippi) or until roads were built to carry

their products east, the farmers would have to reduce the bulk of their grain by converting it to whiskey. A horse could carry two kegs, some sixteen gallons, over the mountains and return with valuable staples. Stills were standard equipment on all large farms. Any excise man who tried his powers of search and seizure was certain to meet with violence. To the more peaceful settlers he may have had a nuisance value worth a few shillings, but for most he was a target of amusement, usually violent. Brackenridge himself may best represent the frontier attitude in his excuse for defending the tormentors of William Graham, the financially-ruined tavern keeper from Philadelphia who bravely undertook the office of Collector General in 1783: "It is to be presumed that I had been of the same opinion with my clients, that excise laws were odious and that an honest fellow ought not to be severely treated who had done nothing more than to shave the underhairs from the head of an excise man who wore a wig at any rate."

The new United States excise law passed in 1791 served to test the new Constitution. Enforcement of an unwanted law in the farthest reach of the Republic would demonstrate to all factions at home and all nations abroad the unity and strength of the new government of the United States. In western minds the identity of the new tax with aristocratic power and dominion was reinforced by the war between the French Jacobins and England. The French cause, Brackenridge declared, was the American cause. Washington's proclamation of neutrality hardly concealed the government's sympathy for the British crown, and the excise tax became the symbol of the enduring conflict between democracy and aristocracy: between France and England abroad, and between West and East at home. Although he had opposed the tax since his first days in the West, Brackenridge did not join any of the democratic groups formed in imitation of the French Jacobin societies which promoted American aid to the French cause along with resistance to the excise. A man of law, he sidestepped active entanglements with the budding insurgents but abetted them with his ironic satires and fiery sermons. When Louis XVI was executed, Brackenridge celebrated with a bite-size satire, "Louis Capet Lost his Caput," and he accused Washington and his Federalists of "desertion" of the democratic experiment. On July 4, 1793, he soared to an apogee of French fervor:

> Shall kings combine, and shall republics not unite? We have united. The
> heart of America feels the cause of France . . . approves her wisdom . . .
> blames her excesses . . . feels the same fury in her veins. . . . Is not our fate

interlaced with hers? For, O' France, if thy republic perish, where is the honour due to ours?

Freneau published the oration in the *National Gazette* where it drew so much attention that it was later represented as the work of "Citizen Brackenridge" along with another essay by "Citizen Robespierre." Such talk may have misled the members of the ultra-democratic societies whose own talk grew more violent, endangering the union itself. Brackenridge shuddered at the thought of a second revolution.

Today the actual events of the Whiskey Rebellion would not be considered even first-rate rioting. In the year 1794, however, poor communications over the mountains and fearful imaginations combined in eastern minds to produce images of drunken wildmen raging through the countryside determined on destruction. Physical violence was confined to the burning of Inspector Neville's house and to gunfire in which a leader of the attacking party was killed. The mood for violence had suddenly hardened when General Neville, who pretended sympathy with the westerners, accepted the excise office. After the violence at the Neville house, anyone who paid his taxes or favored the federal government in any way was in danger. Bracken-ridge had dissuaded the frontiersmen from opposing the government as certainly as he had denounced the excise tax. Now he was caught between conflicting demands of his conscience—sympathy with the cause of the insurgents and his sense for law. His internal conflict led him into the role of mediator which earned him the scorn of both sides and exposed him to charges of treason.

At the root of the conflict were opposing assumptions about human nature. Most Federalists believed that men could not be persuaded by reason, that the knowing and the wise had to lead them. The westerners assumed that good men were innocent of knowledge, that learning corrupted. Independence to them was freedom from eastern codes and culture and trust in man's ability to take care of himself with God's help. The conflict in its broadest terms was essentially between the myth of innocence and the myth of knowing. With Hamilton, Brackenridge agreed that innocence was ignorance and that freedom led inevitably to licentiousness. But unlike Hamilton, Brackenridge assumed that human nature could become rational and knowledgeable through education. That was the great burden of the democratic experiment. Unless men became qualified for democracy, the rising glory was doomed.

In spite of Brackenridge's efforts to remain aloof, each side solicited his support on the pretext of seeking legal advice. Drawn at last into the public meetings, his singular purpose was to guide his countrymen along the narrow path of protest short of violence. The fact that the rebellion did not materialize is due largely to his efforts. Using devious tactics in meeting after meeting and during a march on Pittsburgh, he was able to delay and ultimately divert action. As the insurrection dissipated with the advance of the New Jersey troops, Brackenridge persuaded the westerners to accept an amnesty. Ironically, the name of Brackenridge became a rallying symbol for some eastern patriots who joined the militia and marched over the mountains to subdue the imagined rebellion and to hang the leader— "the worst of all the scoundrels," Hugh Henry Brackenridge. When he heard that the troops were shouting "Brackenridge" at the bushes as they thrust bayonets into them, he quickly printed a handbill to explain his position and sent it for distribution to the rank and file. As the militia approached Pittsburgh, he thought of taking refuge with the Indians. But his handbill had promised he would be there when they arrived. After several sleepless nights, he found in Plutarch's *Lives,* particularly in that of Solon, the courage to await assassination. Waiting, he put his papers in order and wrote a sketch of his role in the affair so that his name would be clear in the event of his murder.

Perhaps Hamilton more than anyone had given Brackenridge the reputation as the worst of the insurrectionists. Stopping at Bedford along the way to Pittsburgh, the Secretary sent a letter stating that Brackenridge had failed to sign the amnesty until after the deadline, which proved indeed what he was.

When the militia arrived, they found the insurrection already suppressed, and Hamilton discovered that the conduct of the "chief insurgent" had been "horribly misrepresented," that Brackenridge had been riding through the countryside persuading people to sign the amnesty and had not reached Pittsburgh until it was too late for him to sign. After a brief hearing, Hamilton decided not to trouble the defendant with "even a simple inquisition by a judge"; but warned, "what may be due to yourself with the public is another question." It was in response to this remark that Brackenridge expanded the notes he had scribbled while awaiting execution.

In writing *Incidents of the Insurrection in Western Pennsylvania in the Year 1794,* he hoped to exonerate his conduct with the people, East and West, as he had with Secretary Hamilton. Working to render the situation in which he acted and to show the motives for the action, Brackenridge produced a narrative that is unlike anything he had written before, a suspenseful drama of individual versus mob psychology, a realistic portrait of a social movement, and a story of individual sensibility.

V

Once more Brackenridge retreated from the political storms and for a while wrote, read, and reconstructed his law practice mainly as collector of debts for eastern merchants. In 1797, two years after he published *Incidents,* he completed a fourth volume of *Modern Chivalry.* It reviewed the events of the insurrection, this time with a satirical eye. This volume was the last sustained satire he produced. Writing it, he said, prevented the mind "from corroding or gnawing upon itself."

When David Bruce, a country storekeeper who called himself the Scots-Irishman, sent him a dialect poem criticizing the insurgents for having refused to pay the excise on a blessing so precious as whiskey, Brackenridge ignored the challenge but was overwhelmed by the native sound of the verse. His reply started a correspondence in Scottish verse that continued until he left Pittsburgh five years later. Calling himself "Aqua Vitae," Brackenridge also praised whiskey and agreed that law and order were necessary. But his interest was not in the issue. Brackenridge used the Scottish poems to reflect upon his boyhood among the Scots of the Barrens. And beginning with these poems, his writings take on a wistfulness about his early idealism as well as his boyhood. His satirical powers waned and he sought solutions for the problems of democratic society in terms of the law. The reflective tone dominates the introductions to his *Gazette Publications* and *Law Miscellanies.* It is the mood for his *Epistle to Walter Scott,* which pleads for a poet similar to Scott who can do justice to the beauty and spirit of the western country. These, plus extensive additions to *Modern Chivalry,* mostly didactic, comprise the major production in the last fifteen years of his life.

In spite of his literary mood, Brackenridge was again drawn into the thicket of politics and did not escape even when he backtrailed East. His opposition to the Federalist theory and practice had solidified in the events of the insurrection, but those same events had served to shift the opinions of most westerners towards those of the Federalists. His son observed that after the insurrection, "but fifty Democrats [anti-Federalists] could be mustered in Pittsburgh, and not all these were entitled to put a ticket into the ballot box." Under such conditions it was natural for Brackenridge to reenter politics as a Jeffersonian Democrat. He was the founder and leader of the party in western Pennsylvania. In opposition to the *Pittsburgh Gazette,* he undertook a new journalistic venture to give a voice to the Jeffersonians in the West. In the *Tree of Liberty,* Brackenridge attempted to combat the shocking accusations of the *Gazette* with the condescending manner of a man brushing off an annoyance. After an extremely vituperative campaign, Brackenridge managed to win support for Albert Gallatin, the party candidate for Congress, and for Thomas McKean, the candidate for governor, although he lost his own race for the State Assembly. He was rewarded for this effort with an appointment as Justice of the Supreme Court of Pennsylvania. Before leaving the frontier to assume his judicial duties at Carlisle, Brackenridge started a correspondence with Jefferson that inspired him to attempt a poem eulogizing the future president in the grand style of his idealistic days at Princeton. In the leaden verses of *Jefferson: In Imitation of Virgil's Pollio,* Brackenridge was still seeking the fulfillment of the hopes expressed in *The Rising Glory.*

On the bench, Brackenridge found himself opposing President Jefferson's policies of judicial reform. The general distrust of educated persons in the West was abetted by Jefferson's own fear of the judiciary, and came to focus on lawyers and judges. In this atmosphere, impeachment proceedings were brought against three justices of the Supreme Court of Pennsylvania. If Brackenridge had been sitting at the time, there would have been four impeached justices. He tried to assume an equal share of the alleged offenses; and somewhat through his support, his colleagues were acquitted. The proceedings and the attitude of the nation provided the impulse for Part Two of *Modern Chivalry,* which began as a satire on the "blackguard journalists" but changed after a few chapters to lengthy arguments in favor of the judiciary and the common law.

Attuned to reflection in Carlisle, he seemed more interested in collecting works than in producing them. In 1806 he published some poems, articles, a play, and other odd pieces, not because they were his best but because he had been able to locate them in the lockers and drawers where he stuffed his papers. The introduction to *Gazette Publications* reflects disappointment that literature was not the "means of emolument or the way to honor" in this "age or country." Thus, his collection amounts to no more than "scraps for amusement." Yet he did not regret his pursuits: "Though I would rather be the poet than the Maecenas as to after-fame, yet it is better to be the Maecenas as to present enjoyment." He published the collection, he said, to show in what "manner the human mind had employed itself in the past."

In addition to *Gazette Publications* and *Modern Chivalry,* Brackenridge occupied himself at Carlisle compiling a book of articles taken from American journals which he called the *Spirit of Public Journals; or Beauties of American Newspapers for 1805.* There appears to be no rationale or criteria for his selections. Between 1801 and 1814 he worked on a far more significant collection, his *Law Miscellanies.* He had intended to produce a "Pennsylvania Blackstone," showing how the state's law differed from English law, but as he proceeded he realized the extent of knowledge required. He settled for a collection of miscellaneous essays. They criticize the unenlightened use of traditions and precedent, the feudal principles which still survived, and the tight naturalization laws—tracts appealing primarily to legal students. But the Introduction speaks to all, of ethics and values, of the need for graceful expression, and of student problems, including their finances and their languishing attitudes. Although his hopes of a new cultural empire rising in the west had dwindled through experience, there remained a sedate desire for order in the democracy as it was: a desire for proper law, peace, safeguards. He had seen that law and the force behind it, not ideas, ultimately won the people's respect. Yet, he "despised the law," according to Horace Binney who observed him in the Supreme Court for seven years. "He once said to me as I was standing by his chair on the bench, 'Talk of your Cokes and Littletons, I had rather have one spark of the ethereal fire of Milton than all the learning of all the Cokes and Littletons that ever lived.'"

Returning to Pittsburgh on circuit duty in 1811, Brackenridge read "by chance" Walter Scott's *Lady of the Lake.* Scott's images of his native Scotland recalled to Brackenridge his own early ambition to express the spirit and beauty of the new country at the headwaters of the Ohio. Finally, the emotion became a poem, *An Epistle to Walter Scott,* in which Brackenridge regrets that this beautiful wilderness has no Scott to immortalize it. These were the last years, the years of the disheveled judge riding the circuit, the legendary years.

VI

"What I am patriotic to is a just notion and just policy—when the nation changes from this, I find myself standing in opposition to it." These are not the words of Brackenridge but of a graduate of the class of 1968 as quoted in *Time*. Like the graduate, Brackenridge appreciated consistent ideals and sentiments. When the nation diverged from its revolutionary principles after the War, he found them fully alive in the violent protests of the frontiersmen, but there he opposed the violence itself, the roaringness and anti-intellectual sentiment. And he succeeded. For all the talk, little blood was spilled; and after all the government's neglect, troops were sent to protect the settlers, the Mississippi was freed for navigation, and the tax became equitable.

Racism was then as urgent a national problem as it is today. But Brackenridge's hatred of the red man is not racial; it is self-defense. The noble savage romance was to him European poppycock. Still he could examine the red man with sympathy when he was an under-dog as in "The Trial of Mamachtaga" or in "The Lone Indian." The Indians he sympathizes with do deserve their fates; one, Mamach-taga, is a murderer. As for the race of "animals vulgarly called Indians," let them roam elsewhere; there is after all a good deal of room. The black man was another issue, not the victim of his own brutality but of social injustice. It was altogether consistent for Brack-enridge to demand immediate freedom for the black man and to propose a solution that may have worked at that time—a state of freed black men carved out of the red man's territory as the white man had carved out his states.

Underlying these yet unsolved American problems was the funda-mental issue of the qualifications of a people determined to rule themselves. This question is the burden of all that Brackenridge wrote. His novels, his essays, even his poems and plays are elaborate answers. The two qualities that make man unique—his reason and his refined sensibility—qualify man for self-rule. The problem on the frontier was not the establishment of freedom but the control of it. Brackenridge saw clearly that uncontrolled freedom does not return us to the primal forest as Rousseau had imagined but to the tangled jungle.

Pursuing this American problem, Brackenridge produced literature that imitated his English models in form only. He never satirized with Swift's bitterness nor with Butler's malignity. His earliest story, the picaresque *Father Bombo's Pilgrimage,* shows the fundamental good nature of his satire and demonstrates that the emerging writer has already sighted his major theme. Travelling to Mecca, Bombo is taken prisoner by an Irish privateer and is given the freedom of the ship by the captain because of his ingratiating display of wisdom.

But the ignorant sailors, fearing him as a wizard, bind him in the hold. A storm arises and he is thrown overboard in a barrel which washes up on a North Ireland shore. In throwing Bombo overboard during the storm, the seamen symbolize all the ignorant who grasp their freedom with a licentious spirit and throw away their cultural inheritance. But Bombo is a con artist of indomitable spirit: he is confident as he emerges from his barrel that he will reach Mecca where his spirit can fulfill itself. He is an ambiguous symbol of knowledge and fakery.

Father Bombo's Pilgrimage anticipates the theme of all the author's work. We see that he was absorbed in the fundamental democratic problem even before he celebrated America's rising glory. Wit and learning allow Bombo to overcome one barrier after another, each at its base a form of ignorance and undisciplined spirit. The story, which appears to be the first written in America, also anticipated the elements of his satiric style—the use of commonplace detail, low language, and exaggeration. These were to become the distinguishing characteristics of American western humor.

Faith that man will solve the fundamental problem of democracy, that its solution is the very meaning of America, underlines the epic vision of *The Rising Glory*. America's inheritance is the light in all history's acts. On the American continent even the geography is destined to accommodate the diverse glories of man. The land and its waters sing the "final destiny of things." Man is at last fulfilled in the freedom that nourishes to fullest bloom all the arts and sciences and the commerce and technology they germinate; but still they are only blooms. The poem never soars out of the grasp of reality; it ends with the sure knowledge that the ultimate glory of man is itself doomed since man will "run his long career" and finally be "lost in chaos and the womb of night."

It was only after the success of the Revolution that the other American epics appeared. The best of them, Timothy Dwight's *Conquest of Canaan* (1785) and Joel Barlow's *Vision of Columbus* (1787), later worked into *Columbiad* (1807), are tedious hindsights, one full of religious and the other of patriotic commonplaces. Not until the appearance of *Leaves of Grass* is the spirit of *The Rising Glory* given fresh life and restrained, in spite of its "barbaric yawp," by a sense of realistic prophecy. Although not a great literary achievement when compared with the work of Whitman or with the poems of Virgil and Milton that inspired it, *The Rising Glory* has the significance of preserving American mood, thought, and hope that lived on the eve of the Revolution. Brackenridge's lines are loaded with cultural rather than political idealism. They dream of a profusion of arts and commerce and they "bid fair science smile." Years later, when Freneau rewrote these lines for his own publication, he revealed a fundamental split at the root of American culture by omitting the commerce and fair science and by championing instead a rural reign in which men would no longer shed blood "For metal buried in a rocky waste."

Like the dramas he wrote upon receiving the news of Bunker Hill and of the death of General Montgomery at Quebec, *Rising Glory* is imprisoned by its grand language and heroic allusions. When he joined the troops as a chaplain in the field, however, Brackenridge forgot about art. Moved to utterance, he was able to achieve the effects he imagined his contrived style and hollow drama provided. The passion of his sermons was fueled with British atrocities but modulated with deliberate thought and appreciation for the culture of the British past. He told the troops how he was "touched with the magic sound of Milton's harp and the lyre of a Gray modulating soft music to my ravished ear." After the Battle of Brandywine the modulation weakens, the sermons seethe with hatred of British brutality. The English have gone the way of Cain, like their antecedents, the Pharaohs, Ahabs, the Alexanders, the Genghis Khans, the Huns, the Vandals, and the Goths. "I pass them by, and hasten on, for I have an object of greater wickedness in view—an object of such accomplished fraud, perfidy and murder, that every one heretofore mentioned is lost and disappears. I mean him of England—the fierce, cruel, unrelenting, the bloody king of Britain." Here is the negative side of *Rising Glory*, the roll call of man's acts of darkness.

The Preface and Introduction to the *United States Magazine* are essentially continuations of his sermons to the troops. The real war for Brackenridge was always cultural. With the British troops retreating from Philadelphia the next step was apparent: he launched the battle for literary independence. "We hope to convince them the [British] that we are able to cultivate the belles lettres even disconnected with Great Britain; and that liberty is of so noble and energetic quality, as even from the bosom of war to call forth the powers of human genius in every course of literary fame and improvement." For the mechanic of the city and the husbandman on the farm, the magazine would be a kind of literary coffeehouse of public conversation where men too busy or too poor for college could prepare themselves for self-government.

A large portion of the contents are the editor's own contributions. In one of the more enduring pieces, "A Letter to Poets, Philosophers, Orators, Statesmen and Heroes of Antiquity," the editor playfully appeals for contributors to come to the aid of the country via the pages of the magazine. Following the eighteenth-century journalistic tradition of writing under classical pseudonyms, Brackenridge asked the ancient worthies for practical advice on the proposed structure of Congress as a one-house assembly unchecked by a senate. Although the subject was hotly debated, Brackenridge presents it with scientific coolness, appealing to reason through a sense of historical distance. The piece demonstrates his view of journalism as an instrument of education, of inquiry, of the uses of the past in attacking the problems of the present. This idea of journalism as an unbiased and penetrating inquiry into social problems rather than as propaganda, or opinion, or the listing of facts was unheard of then; and even today it is still an ideal rather than a reality.

The *United States Magazine* digested foreign and domestic news in regular columns, an innovation that remains fixed in American journalism. The focus was on the meaning of events, on education, and on entertainment. Sermons that Brackenridge had not published in *Six Political Discourses* and which connected the struggle to man's eternal battle were included along with a serialized history, "Establishment of These United States," and a story also serialized, "The Cave of Vanhest." Brackenridge contributed no satire to his periodical nor did he publish any from other contributors except a dull mock heroic called "The Cornwalliad." There were travel articles, scientific expositions, accounts of Indians, recipes, advice on moral conduct, and the early and perhaps best poems of Freneau such as the "Beauties of Vera Cruz" and "The House of Night." Published in the spirit of celebration rather than protest, it is not surprising that we find so little satire in the *United States Magazine*.

In place of satire, Brackenridge entertained his readers with installments of "The Cave of Vanhest," a symbolic story of sensibility, a strain unheard in American literature up to this time. It is his second piece of fiction and written at a high point of patriotic passion, yet the impulse that moves it is the urge to escape society and its gruesome warfare. The soldier-narrator and his comrade, having fled the Battle of Monmouth, come upon a cave inhabited by a hermit. In the manner of Poe, the narrator disarms the reader's credulity by directly addressing it: "I have been a thousand times disappointed in my expectation and never had the pleasure to descry any mortal of this stamp [the hermit] until lately on a tour through the Jerseys. . . ." The ominous tone also suggests Poe: ". . . and immediately the door was opened to us by a man in a long white linen robe, who desired us to walk in and be happy, if we could be happy, in the Cave of Vanhest." And within we are treated to the richest of furnishings again à la Poe but, instead of the sickly atmosphere of decaying life, Brackenridge immerses us in a sense of joy. It is the literature of light, not of darkness. We begin to perceive that our narrator is seeking the meaning of personal life. Apparently, the hermit has found a way to happiness. He has removed himself from society only that he may form his own society, his own family. But he is thoroughly educated in the culture and history of the greater society and very curious about it. He wishes to know all about the life of his visitor and the Battle of Monmouth, although he will not tell his own story. Instead he trusts experience. The goodness and the joy prove themselves as the visitor partakes in the hermit's life, very much as Fraser allows his visitors to perceive the behavioral utopia in Skinner's *Walden Two* (1948).

The fine company of his intelligent and sensitive daughters and the sweet plums from the trees he has planted in the wilderness sustain the hermit who emerges as the ideal pioneer. Not only is his social unit cultured and beautiful, but tender, protective of the weak, as symbolized by the treatment his daughter renders to a half-wit servant who has broken a bone. The harmony of life in the cave, contrasted in the narrator's mind with the destructive and frustrating life of a society at war, force him to review his own desires and ambitions. He has confused his former ambitions—Miss Theology, Miss Muse, Miss Law—with love. Before him are all the subjects of true love—most noticeably the ladies of the cave. Beginning in a mood of mystery, the story moves into the light of personal satisfactions, for that is really what the fighting is all about. And realization of man's dreams of personal satisfaction are again in the wilderness. "I have been told," says the hermit, "there are fine plumbs on the creeks to the westward."

Running concurrently with "The Cave of Vanhest" in the first seven issues of the magazine, "Establishment of These United States" sought a rationale for the Revolution. But the author is far more interested in justifying the American conscience for the grasping of Indian lands than in disqualifying British claims. Although he considered the Bible as one of man's literary achievements rather than God's, it is the authority of the Bible that sustains his reasoning. The land, he argues, belongs to men who will cultivate it, not to animals who remain in the savage state of hunters. Economically, an animal who lives by means of his hunting requires too vast an extent of land for his livelihood. Men who cultivate the land, however, require but little land. It is only by means of agriculture that mankind shares God's bounty, as directed by His very word: "And God blessed them, and God said unto them, be fruitful and multiply and replenish the earth, and subdue it." God's mandate is to cultivate the land so that all men may be accommodated, not merely the good hunters. Ultimately, the argument does apply more to the British than to the Indians who practiced a fair amount of agriculture, ignored by Brackenridge.

The contents of later issues of the magazine deteriorated; the last were filled with state constitutions. Buried among them in the final number, December 1779, lay an article of surprising vigor and fresh significance, "Thoughts on the Enfranchisement of the Negro." Here Brackenridge exposes the nation's main fissure even before nation-hood is achieved. Not only is slavery inhumane; it is irrational and by the same reasoning that denies Indians the rights to the land, "it casts a shade upon the face of this country that some of those who cultivate her soil are slaves." Slavery continued to thrive because of the American blight of Calvinism that predetermined pain and misery for the non-elect. If Brackenridge could not root out the blight itself, he at least could propose a solution to its horrible effects: "Cast out the bond-woman and her son." He proposed to give them not only freedom but the land in the wilderness beyond the Ohio which the Indians had forfeited through their hostilities and which the white man had not yet settled.

VII

On the frontier the *Pittsburgh Gazette* became Brackenridge's substitute for the *United States Magazine*. Although his contributions were motivated by his political ambitions, he identified these ambitions with the cultural advancement of the frontiersmen. His first efforts were satiric. Gently, slyly, Brackenridge wooed support for his ideas through ironical observations under the guise of frontier characters. Those signed William Donachy ("Value of a Newspaper") congratulate the *Gazette* for printing trivia. Donachy hopes instead to find in the paper "something of the upper world," meaning not only the "discoveries of philosophers who teach us at what distance the bulls, goats and rams depasture from each other in the firmament," but even "what is going on in our state, particularly what our representatives are doing." If the *United States Magazine* had been a necessary instrument of cultural instruction, the newspaper as the prime source of information was even more vital to the republic's survival. For how could the uninformed rule themselves?

Although the criticisms of the burgeoning country found in the *Gazette* are significant, the local color glimpses of frontier life in which they are imbedded are more interesting: "I have been a subscriber from the list," reads the letter from Angus MacMore, "and I sent in a dollar the other day by William Guy when he went to the contractor's store to buy an ounce of snuff for his wife. . . . I see the Congress have appointed a superintendent of the Indians to give them presents to keep them in peace. I am persuaded it is meant well and the men may be capable that are nominated to this station, but I am apprehensive. . . ." Without the perverted spellings or grammar of the later humorists of the West, Brackenridge conveys the flavor of speech and the tone of mind of the early frontier characters.

Since satire is indirect, it assumes some literary sensibility and therefore could not be trusted to do the job. Reaching for all the audience that could read, Brackenridge reverted to direct prose. In a series of articles he called "Observations on the Country at the Head of the Ohio River," he expanded the spirit of *The Rising Glory* to all the population. His motive was to instill desires for learning, for literary art, and civic establishments—an academy, a library, a church. These were the materials that would realize the abstract vision of his commencement poem. Grossly mistitled, the "Observations" share the passion of his sermons to the troops and are empowered with the same style of fiery metaphor: "Academies are the furnace which melt the natural ore to real metal. . . . Cultivated genius has the power of electric fire." Establishing these desires in the electorate, Brackenridge hoped to be elected by promising to satisfy them. And the plan worked, at least for one term.

Even after he realized that his promises to "work for the people's interests" were understood not as he intended and that his opposition to their demands for rights to the land was considered treachery, he persisted according to his vision. When he managed to get a bill passed establishing a non-sectarian church for the town, a Pittsburgh minister manipulated a change to a Presbyterian congregation. Approaching the threshold of despair, the people's rather wayward representative defended himself in the *Pittsburgh Gazette:*

> I had hoped that seated on the utmost verge of the inhabited globe, and separated from the Old World by a great mountain, you would have taken up things on the first principles, and represented a church like those in the time of the first apostles, distinguished by the name of *Christian* only, and have left to divines in future times to dispute, as they now do, about those of Smyrna or Ephesus, whether you are Presbyterian or Episcopal.

His argument in the "Defense of the Church Bill" was economic as well as democratic. Not having enough people in the town to support more than one church, the Presbyterians would be discriminating against the other denominations unless they established a church for all. The tone of the argument is impatient with the rhetoric of reason. And when the great debate over adoption of the new Federal Constitution arose in the State Assembly, Brackenridge abandoned his faith that the people could be moved by reason. Instead he tried to move the frontiersmen through the ironies of satire and through the passions of sermon. Years later he reflected on the political use of satire: "Ridicule is not the test of truth, but it may be employed to expose error and on this occasion it seemed not amiss to use it a little, as a great object was at stake, and much willful misrepresentation to be encountered. . . ."

But the use of satire required no defense. The events in the Assembly that occasioned Brackenridge's *Hudibrastics* were so ludicrous in themselves that a mere report would appear satirical. In a letter "To The Dissenting Assemblyman" he again assumed the role of a constituent whose straight-faced ignorance ironically reduced the actions of the absconding representative to the absurd: "If a member is not swift in running off, the check may be lost, the vote being taken before he fairly disappears. There will hence be two kinds of motion in the House, that to the speaker and the other to the door." In other letters he attacked opposition to the new constitution more directly. "What is the nature of a bill of rights?" Brackenridge's character asks in "Cursory Remarks on the Federal Constitution." The answer shows its redundancy: "It is a schedule of inventory of those powers which the Congress do not possess. But if it is clearly ascertained what powers they have, what need of a catalogue of those powers which they have not?" This answer had also been given by Patrick Henry and Albert Gallatin, speaking for the low-income population, by the New Yorker George Clinton, whose *Letters from Cato* (1787–88) pointed to the new document as a means to renewed tyranny and corruption, and even by the Virginian Richard Henry

Lee speaking for the more affluent sectors of the population. Still Brackenridge considered the opposition as mainly western and blamed the lack of knowledge.

Failing with reason and with satire, both poetic and prosaic, he turned at last to sermons: "O Israel," he lamented, "thou art destroyed for lack of knowledge" and "Oh my people, they which lead thee cause thee to err and destroy the way of thy path." His "Sermons in Favor of the Federal Constitution" were later versions of his impassioned *Political Discourses*. Now the evils of American demagoguery replace those of the British king and his parliament. But the history recited in the sermons opposes their purpose. In all western civilizations the people have been uninformed and they have always rejected the leadership of the knowing and the dedicated and followed the demagogues. Distrusting the appeal of reason he nevertheless pursues it, hoping that the lesson will be induced, that now at least all history will be reversed, that demagoguery will no longer be the way. His pride reduced by political loss, Brackenridge pleads in these sermons with the wayward to follow the righteous path of democracy, which had become tantamount to a religion, and to follow him, its humble prophet.

VIII

When Brackenridge abandoned the Hudibrastic modern chevalier and transformed that noble into Captain Farrago, the thoughtful, knowledgeable, and sensible conscience of *Modern Chivalry,* he fell back upon a situation already established years earlier in "Memoir to the American Philosophical Society." But not only do we see the prototypes of Farrago and his ambitious servant in the "Memoir," we also perceive a highly significant and easily overlooked dimension of *Modern Chivalry*. The ambitious and ignorant Teague O'Regan is considered not only for membership in the Society but also for a professorship and the satire is directed as much against the puffed-up academician as against the ill-prepared, indentured immigrant. *Modern Chivalry* takes aim not only at the unduly ambitious but also at the duly educated, the pretentious fact-laden heads of the cultural establishment. A third target was the vulgar successes, the "monied asses" as Brackenridge called them. Opposed to all three types is the thoughtful man, Farrago, who assumes social responsibility for democratic action, not the usual scholar but, as Emerson later put it, "a man thinking."

In the travels of Farrago and his bog-trotter from the western frontier to Philadelphia and back again, Brackenridge reveals the foibles and follies of an amorphous America and points steadily to the need for knowledge and the discipline of the senses. The lessons are usually rendered by Farrago either to crowds or individuals who propose Teague for some high position, or to Teague himself. Those to Teague are concocted out of Farrago's farcical imagination. They deceive the bog-trotter into obedience by appealing to his fear rather than his reason. The servant is not described "because the very name imports what he was." The theme is presented in the opening episode where the captain declines to enter his horse in a race on the grounds that he is not qualified to run against racehorses. In the chapters that follow, the captain's rhetoric is taxed again and again to dampen Teague's ambitions to become a legislator, a member of Dr. Franklin's Philosophical Society, a clergyman, actor, lawyer, professor, and even chief of the Kickapoos. It is as a lover, however, that the captain finds him most irrepressible. Managing to free himself from the captain, Teague assumes the role of Major O'Regan and inspires "a kind of Teagueomania among the females." Only the captain's plotting with fathers and spurned suitors separates Teague from the fullest rewards of his triumphs.

There is some development through the picaresque episodes. By the end of the second volume, Captain Farrago is no longer able to hold back against popular demand for his ignorant servant. Capitulating, he attempts to mitigate what he cannot prevent. Teague is educated for a government position. But the education itself—in the niceties of the French language and the dance—implies Brackenridge's view of government officials and is typical of his double-edged satire. At the end of that volume Teague is presented with fitting buffoonery to the President of the United States and receives an appointment. In the fourth volume—delayed by the events of the Whiskey Rebellion—Teague is given his government appointment. He is made collector of the excise in western Pennsylvania. In his place as servant the captain has taken on a sober and religious Scotsman, and the contrast in dialogue when they meet reveals the author's development of realistic technique. At a crowded inn along the way to Pittsburgh, the captain suggests that his new bog-trotter share a bed with his former one, the present collector of the excise. "Guid deliver me frae sik a prophanation o' the name o' Ferguson as to sleep wi ai excise officer," replies the Scotsman. And the difference between their rather similar characters is brought out in the language as much as the thought in Teague's response, "The devil burn me . . . if I will be often slapeing wid you, you son of a whore, you teef luking vagabon; wid de itch upon your back."

Reaching the western country, the proud exciseman is quickly humbled by the tar and feathers of the insurgents. When the militia arrive, the captain, who has sought to instruct the frontiersmen on lawful means of opposing the odious laws, is accused of traitorous conduct, but is acquitted by an "examiner of sense." At the end, the tarred and feathered Teague is shipped to a French zoo as a rare American species. Though written to "get ease and allay pain," this volume, like the others, is free of bitterness.

Brackenridge's satire is almost good-natured. Still the tone has no more in common with the congeniality of Washington Irving than with the vitriol of Mark Twain. Actually the hopelessness heard in Twain's caustic tones may be an effect of the defeat of Brackenridge's democratic instruction. The satire of Brackenridge is indeed instruction rather than moral indignation—as satire is supposed to be, according to Juvenal and Dryden. As moral instruction, the satire of Brackenridge asserts as much as it ridicules. Its exaggerated representations of events are intended to provide lessons. *Modern Chivalry* is structured to emphasize the positive, the assertions of the author's spokesman, Captain Farrago. Its narrative action is subordinated to its expository lessons in democracy. Nevertheless in the exaggerations of the narrative itself we experience the reality of the cultured and ignorant, the rich and poor, in the commonplaces of their daily lives. We see the politicians, the lawyers, the clergy, and the Philadelphia belles and frontier gamecocks. We respond to the stupidity of the electors, the hypocrisy of the demagogues. We observe meaningless speeches in Congress, trials by ignorant juries, misuses of government appropriations, the snobbishness and artificiality of the East, and the western resentment of law and learning.

Although the picaresque episodes in *Modern Chivalry* develop into a hazy climax when Teague is appointed an excise officer, the action does not change or reveal character; consequently, we have no thematic development. Instead we have thematic elaboration as in an essay. In essence, *Modern Chivalry* is an essay illustrating social habits, abuses, and absurdities. It reveals the substance of early democratic life in order to define its problems. Emphasizing scene at the expense of concise statement permits Brackenridge to render the speech, mind, and habit of frontier people. The satire bears little resemblance to *Don Quixote* or to any other work of the European continent or

England. Nor does it share many common elements with the few American satires before it. *Modern Chivalry* is a new literary product and it anticipates the satire as well as the sentiment that would sound out of the Far West late in the following century.

"From the days of Brackenridge and Royal Tyler," writes Arthur Dobson Quinn in *American Fiction*, "American novelists have not been unaware of locality. . . . It is a mistake to speak of Bret Harte as though he discovered something new. . . ." The exaggerated and boisterous settings, characters, and actions of later local color stories are the very substance of the Brackenridge satire. In *American Humor*, Constance Rourke finds that the satirical views of the nation's affairs presented by Petroleum P. Nasby and Artemus Ward actually belonged to the earlier figures in the Ohio Valley. Certainly the most prominent of these figures and the most articulate is Hugh Henry Brackenridge. The adventures of Teague O'Regan are prototypes of the western tall stories.

Although sentiment is not as prominent in *Modern Chivalry* as in the local color story of the later West, it is present. Before sentimental love is burlesqued in Teague's affairs among the Philadelphia belles, Brackenridge treats it seriously. Farrago's search for the missing bog-trotter leads him to a brothel where he finds a young woman who has unwillingly been maneuvered into that life. Promising to find a home for her, he returns the next day to discover that she has killed herself. The surprise of her suicide reveals her extreme cynicism of men. This touch of realistic irony in *Modern Chivalry* is absent from the sentimental novel of its time and restrains the sentiments from the excesses found in the heart-of-gold stories of Bret Harte.

The character of Bret Harte's local color was consciously composed to illustrate, as he said, "an era replete with a certain Heroic Greek poetry, of which perhaps none was more unconscious than the heroes themselves." This purpose resonates in Captain Farrago and is completely burlesqued in the American society which he attempts to instruct. The expanded attitudes of self reflected in *Modern Chivalry* and other Brackenridge satires work as parodies of Homer's heroes. The boasting and amorality of Homer's ancient figures are renewed in the frontiersmen who can perform almost any feat in their freedom: burn a church or an academy, or tar and feather an exciseman. The parallels, though not exact, bring the weight of man's history to bear upon contemporary American follies.

While Bret Harte's purpose was poetic, Brackenridge's was social. More in the manner of Mark Twain's young rogue, Teague O'Regan provides social criticism. But in *Huckleberry Finn* and throughout Twain's fiction, the criticism is without hope for a rising glory of America. We can view the corrupt politicians in *The Gilded Age*, for instance, as successful Teague O'Regans. Consequently, it is too late to press for reform. Instead Twain retreats into the personal innocence of Huck Finn. Teague is also innocent but his ambitious acts are a constant threat to society, while Twain's rogue is an individual faithful to himself in a society of Teagues who oppress him. *Huckleberry Finn* suggests what is; *Modern Chivalry* states what ought to be. Taken together, these novels reveal what has happened.

The attitude of social hopelessness is borne out in Twain's *Autobiography*, in which he describes politicians as "dust-licking pimps and slaves of the scum," and asserts that his first duty is to his family, not to his political consciousness. Only the innocence of boyhood and the virtues of women as witnessed in *Joan of Arc* compel Twain's sympathies. The Brackenridge ideals of culture, of democracy, and of manners are targets of his bitter satire. Genteel literature was abhorrent to him. Of Jane Austen he wrote, "It seems a great pity that they allowed her to die a natural death." And Sir Walter Scott's "sham grandeurs, sham gauds, and sham chivalries [represent] a brainless and worthless long-vanished society." European arts and cultures were his targets in *Innocents Abroad*. Churches as well as monarchial vestiges were his targets in *A Connecticut Yankee in King Arthur's Court*. And ultimately in *The Mysterious Stranger*, Twain's satire was directed at man himself, particularly at democratic man who has the opportunity of choice, "and in nine out of ten cases he prefers the wrong." Brackenridge suffered personal disappointments as severe as Twain's but his satires are still based on hope.

IX

The larger-than-life-sized attitudes parodied in *Modern Chivalry* are also woven into the *Incidents of the Insurrection in Western Pennsylvania in the Year 1794*. But the author's intention is no longer instructional and his method is no longer satirical. Beneath the realistic treatment is an air suggestive of epic events and heroic poses. For example, in the scene introducing young Ormsby and young Neville, Brackenridge assumes a protective role which the heroes reject with Achilles-like postures:

I felt concern for them; and taking what liberty with the young man [Ormsby] which I could not take with others, I addressed him abruptly, "What!" said I, "Armed?"

"Yes," said he.

"You will not ride with us armed."

"You may ride as you please," said he. "I am armed."

Neville, the younger, who was mounted on a gray horse, pistols in his holster, spoke. "We are not all born orators," said he. "We are going to fight, you to speak." I thought him a better chevalier than a judge on this occasion.

Still working within the framework of *The Rising Glory*, Brackenridge associated the glorious past with the events of the moment. Warriors are characterized through their histories. They contest oratorically to build courage for the battle. Disasters are prophesied through omens. Even the similes are heroic: "When a scud of wind takes the standing corn of the farmer and on the field bows the stalks to the earth, so languished my brother at the bar." But these are heroic, not mock-heroic, devices. We find no exaggeration here. The report is realistic. There is humor and sentiment but these are perceived in the world being reported, not imagined. Like "The Trial of Mamachtaga" written ten years earlier, *Incidents* is a true narrative that seeks an artistic effect through the selection and dramatic arrangement of observations. And like the earlier piece, its treatment brings to mind the fiction at the end of the nineteenth century that we call realistic.

Evidence of haste—misspellings, omissions of pronouns, and digressions into excessive evidence—might have hidden from early readers the intense experience rendered in the narrative. Yet one of the most important of those readers, Peter Porcupine (William Cobbett), a journalistic enemy of Brackenridge, found that the author's "perspicuity, his simplicity, his picturesque minuteness conduct his reader into the scene of action. You see, hear and feel just as the author actually did, and this itself is a talent of high excellence." Porcupine's description of *Incidents* could easily be applied to the whole mode of realism which was certainly out of phase with the literary norms of the year 1795.

Cold reason could not exonerate Brackenridge from the accusation of treasonous collusion with the insurrectionists. The explanation of his conduct had to appeal emotionally through a total recreation of the situation in which he and the others had acted. Intensity is achieved though selection of critical scenes rendered with sensual detail and woven to develop action and character and to combine motifs. The tension increases as the narrator attempts to moderate the rebellious action that he cannot prevent, often with his own life at stake. The focal point of the book is the psychology of the narrator, a well-intentioned public figure forced into a public stance under the stress of social upheaval. He is also a Farrago attempting to moderate the violence of a horde of Teagues, while internally his sympathies with the insurgents are at war with his duties as a patriot.

Incidents is also a story of the people whose tumult the narrator attempts to assuage by subtle manipulation of them. On the eve of the march to Pittsburgh, for example, the narrator walks from fire to fire on the field of rendezvous attempting to undermine the resolution of the rebels although he must appear to favor their intended action:

> Their query everywhere was, were we to take the garrison? I answered always that we were. The query then was, could we take it?
> It was answered, "No doubt about that."
> "But at a great loss?"
> "Not at all; not above a thousand killed, and five hundred mortally wounded."
> This loss, to the more thinking part, appeared very serious.

The unfolding characterization of the insurgents and their leaders and the structuring of events carry the narrative beyond reportage. Brackenridge's technique suggests the contemporary artistic treatment of journalistic material which Truman Capote has claimed as a new art form. The events are presented not as they actually occurred but at the most pertinent point in the narrative, as they impinge on the narrator's thought and action. The story opens, for example, with the U.S. Marshall seeking advice from Attorney Brackenridge on serving writs to delinquent distillers and to the persons who have attacked the excise collector, General Neville. The scene establishes the major thread of the story—the lawyer's conflict between the law and his sympathy for the cause of the mob—and it also introduces the prevailing atmosphere, the tensions and dangers of dealing with the mob as well as the authorities. Scenes of violence that have already occurred are brought in as the narrator is drawn deeper into the affair.

The leaders of both sides are portrayed sympathetically. Most of them appear to share the narrator's reluctance to become involved. Our first view of David Bradford, a leader of the insurgents who later proves cowardly, is a grand portrait of a man astride a horse, full of both confidence and power. The reader is repelled by Bradford's bristling military manner but as the action reveals his character and his necessity for posing, the reader's sympathy grows. Bradford knows that his conduct is treasonous but does not know how to act otherwise and still maintain his position as an affluent man of the people.

The main character, the narrator, employs all his psychological insight to preserve his own image while prodding the inflammatory mob to forsake violence in favor of formal redress to the government. Any misstep or misstatement might lead to personal harm. His delicate treading is suspenseful yet is often the source of humorous irony. The perception of ironies, however, is part of the author's characterization of Attorney Brackenridge, who observes:

> A clergyman was not thought orthodox in the pulpit unless against the law; a physician was not capable of administering medicine unless his principles were right in this respect; a lawyer could have no practice without at least concealing his sentiment, if for the law. . . . On the contrary . . . in order to be recommended to the government as a justice of the peace you must be against the law.

The character, Attorney Brackenridge, also uses humor as a rhetorical weapon. When the members of the Jacobin society at Mingo Creek threaten violence he arouses laughter and diverts action with amusing anecdotes. The effort is painful and the effect of the humor is to enhance rather than disrupt the serious tone and the tension of the narrative.

Among all the characters—insurgent and patriot—only the attorney seems to understand the consequence of the struggle. He equates his own destruction at the hands of the rebels with disruption of the Union, and the consequence is war—civil war—between East and West. Yet he vacillates between government loyalty, community loyalty, and personal loyalty. He appears to be a Federalist in the eyes of insurgents and an insurgent in the eyes of the Federalists. Forced to commit himself at the risk of his life, the attorney leads the insurgents to believe he will act with them but actually states only his sympathy for their cause. As the thrust of events amplifies the vacillations, he contemplates emigration to the East and later, when his efforts at conciliation have made him a symbol of insurrection in eastern minds, he weighs the possibilities of waging war against the government with the aid of the savages. Finally, when the Jersey troops are approaching, the attorney fears assassination and contemplates a run to the woods and a life among the people he had referred to as "animals vulgarly called Indians."

Deciding rather to accept his fate at the hands of the troops, the attorney reads Plutarch's *Lives* for philosophic comfort. There Solon tells him that his fate was unavoidable; that citizens must take some role in a civil tumult or be put to death. But Solon speaks of a civilized society, Athens, where his effort to moderate the conflict will be understood. On the frontier, far from the center of government, moderation was not a recognizable human act. Solon's law was absurd. Heroic concepts were for civilized minds. On the frontier the first law was to preserve self, not society. The attorney condemns himself for his foolish belief in heroic ideals.

With the arrival of the troops and the promise of amnesty, the ironies converge. Avoidance of the ultimate violence, the attorney's aim, is achieved, but instead of personal victory it brings personal defeat. Still he is not assassinated as anticipated. He is merely humiliated. General Lee, whom he had known at Princeton, is head of the militia and immeasurably increases the attorney's pain by choosing to quarter at the Brackenridge home while his host awaits a hearing before Secretary Hamilton to determine whether he should be charged with treason. He is exonerated in a dramatic sequence of hearings but the taint of treason adheres: Turned state's evidence, the citizens say, "Most artful fellow." Walking the streets, the attorney "contemplated the buildings a good deal." Mrs. Brackenridge, too, is ostracized. The narrative part of the book ends in a delicate domestic scene in which the attorney and his wife fortify themselves against social snubbing. A ball was being given and Mrs. Brackenridge was "not sent the usual card." Seeing the "flush of indignation in her cheek and sparkle of fire in her eye," the attorney compares his own position with that of Phocion: "Would you not think it more honorable to be the wife of Phocion, under these circumstances, than of a common Athenian, though you had received a card, and been called upon to lead the first dance? . . . By this address to the pride of the human mind, I had a philosophress in a moment."

Grasping at the example of Phocion's heroic conduct, the attorney reverts to the belief he abandoned the night he awaited the troops. Now it appears he has forgotten the primacy of the rule of self-preservation and the separate peace that he had declared, "If the like scene should happen again, I will not conduct myself on the principle of Solon's law. . . . let the Executive and insurgents settle their own negotiations; I will have nothing to do with them."

The naked view of man's responsibility to himself is uncovered at the heart of the story, but it is too base a view for a man of ideals and ambitions. Consequently, the momentary glimpse of the naked self passes with the dangers that unveil it. On a more obvious level the narrative elements of *Incidents* combine into a story of the individual will exerted upon social forces in tumult. And on the level of the author's overt intention, *Incidents* comprises an explanation of a man's conduct in the frontier turmoil called the Whiskey Rebellion.

<h1 style="text-align:center">X</h1>

Reflecting upon his life and time in his later years, Brackenridge gathered his available work into a volume called *Gazette Publications* (1806). The introduction and conclusion are reminiscent essays evaluating his literary accomplishments and aims. Although he referred to the collection as scraps for amusement, he considered himself a literary man. But his was "not an age or country that will make it the means of emolument, or the way to honor." These essays render the feelings of a man of affairs who achieved some station in life, but at the expense of the dream he had set out to fulfill in youth. His purpose in publishing the collection was to see in what "manner the human mind had employed itself in the past." A narrative and a number of poems preserved in the collection illustrate dimensions of feeling unsuspected in the public life of Brackenridge. Neither satirical nor oratorical, these pieces reflect strains of sensibility that eventually came to drench the local color fiction of later frontiers. They may be representative of other unpublished works now lost, since Brackenridge was in the habit of stowing his work in trunks and drawers and other out-of-the-way places and forgetting them.

The sensibility in the narrative "The Trial of Mamachtaga" (1785), like that found in parts of *Modern Chivalry* and in the later *Incidents of the Insurrection*, is never idealized as in the standard novels of seduction that began to appear about that time. In *Power of Sympathy* (1789) and *Charlotte Temple* (1791), for instance, sentiment raged unchecked. In the narratives of Brackenridge it is always restrained by a quality lacking in the sensibility writers—a sense of reality. "The Trial of Mamachtaga" is distinguished by an objective observation of scene, character, and action, and an arrangement of these observations to yield a climax.

The story concerns an Indian brought to justice for killing a white man. In spite of his loathing for the American native, Brackenridge was intrigued with this savage who had been rejected by his own tribe. Curious even about the name Mamachtaga (which means trees blown in a tempest), the author penetrated beyond his own predetermined notions. Brackenridge brings the reader so close that he can almost hear Mamachtaga thinking. As a result, a real portrait of the Indian character emerges perhaps for the first time in American literature. And through our immediacy with the Indian, we perceive in the hearts of the respectable white men who try him little capacity for understanding a man of another culture, and even more fundamental, a basic lack of sentiment for a fellow human being.

The narrator, Attorney Brackenridge, offers to defend the Indian for a few beaver skins, even though he knows the town will ostracize him for it. The Indian imagined that he was "giving the beaver as a commutation for his life." The beaver, in turn, is used to procure a blanket and food to comfort the Indian in his dank hole underground. The attorney's interpreter, fearful for his own reputation, refuses to make the purchases. But the townsmen discover the interpreter's involvement, nevertheless, and almost succeed in hanging him. The pursuit of the interpreter provides comic relief to an otherwise somber mood. At the trial Mamachtaga confuses his judges with God and Jesus Christ. He cannot plead guilty because he does not really know what he did since he was drunk at the time of the murder. If white men made him drunk, then he understands he would not be guilty. Without leaving the bar for deliberation, the jury returns a verdict of guilty. Asked why he should not be hung, the Indian replies that he would rather "run awhile," which is the tribal custom for the condemned. Ironically, he does get a chance to "run awhile" as he awaits execution. He is asked to gather herbs for the jailor's sick daughter, and he is given a second opportunity for escape when he goes to gather paints to prepare for a warrior's death. In jail a white prisoner also awaiting execution asks Mamachtaga to kill him, but the Indian replies that he has killed enough white men for awhile. He has apparently accepted the white man's justice. As his body is released on the scaffold the rope breaks and he falls to earth alive. Climbing back up he smiles, as though excusing himself for being so clumsy. He is hanged then with this smile upon his lips. The author does not interpret the smile. The story tells us that it comes from the depth of his honesty, an honesty possible only in a creature so fundamentally innocent of the white man's mores. But it is not ironical for the Indian who is ignorant of the virtue he has come to symbolize.

In spite of its seriousness there is an undercurrent of grisly humor through the story. In selecting the jury, for example, the court officer directs:

> "Prisoner, look upon the juror: juror, look upon the prisoner at the bar. Are you related to the prisoner?" One of them, a German of a swarthy complexion and being the first called, took the question amiss, as thinking it a reflection and said with some anger that he thought that an uncivil way to treat Dutch people, as if he could be the brother or cousin of an Indian.

Although the account of backwoods justice with its gruesome ending is edged with humor, the humor never interferes with the serious overtone and, instead of subduing our sympathy for Mamachtaga, increases it. This little-known story produces its effect with the economy of modern short fiction. The theme is never stated, but is revealed through the viewpoint of a major character. Through Attorney Brackenridge the reader recognizes in the savage some fundamental qualities of civilized individuals, and in the civilized white men, a fundamental savageness.

Two of the poems preserved in *Gazette Publications* were composed about 1790, when he was deep into the satirical mode of *Modern Chivalry*. They are occasional pieces, one generated by the death of his friend, the wife of Doctor Nathaniel Bedford, and the other by the celebration of St. Andrew's anniversary. After the clumsy jolting of the Hudibrastics, the reader is surprised by the control of rhythm and sound in these poems. In "Ideas at the Interment of Mrs. Bedford," the subject is indeed sentimental and though the treatment relies on Greek and Roman allusions, there is nothing of the grand manner here. The run-on line and the caesura give him instead the natural tone of a man ruminating:

> Whether the spirit doth survive
> The body and doth live
> In the Elysium of the Greeks
> Or heaven of which the Christian speaks,
> I know not; but, if there be. . . .

Even the rhymes of the couplets are muted. And rather than ornament and display, the classical allusions are functional. The motifs of sensibility—purity and innocence—are woven with the ancient ideas of fate and idealistic love:

> For pure as Innocence and Love
> She felt the will of Jove,

With proper forbearance complied
And like the unstain'd lily dropp'd her head and died.

"To the Sons of Saint Andrew" was written for the Pittsburgh
inhabitants of Scottish descent who celebrated the date, November
30, with a festival. The poem is an inner retreat from the embroilment of frontier politics. His first effort in Scottish dialect, it turns
the poet in on himself where he finds the most painful of his
inadequacies:

> Ah: had I but the soul o' sang,
>   My kintra kens fu weel,
> The pleasant melody ere lang,
>   Wad sound o'er vale and hill.

By far the most significant verse preserved in *Gazette Publications*
are the "Scot's Poems Addressed to David Bruce." Six years after the St.
Andrew poem, Brackenridge returned to the Scottish dialect in response to the country storekeeper who called himself the Scots-Irishman. The Scottish poems reveal a thorough knowledge of Robert
Burns, who died that year (1796). Brackenridge owned a large collection of Scottish poems and songs and consistently retreated to them.
But even if he possessed the talent of a Burns he could not achieve
the spontaneity and the naturalness since he had no chance to immerse
his senses in the actual sounds of the vernacular as Burns did. Where
Burns could directly represent, Brackenridge could only reminisce.
The attitude throughout the poems is indeed that of nostalgia. The
humor is warmed by reflections of the Scotsman on the frontier and
of his boyhood in the Scottish settlement of the Barrens. The satirical
impulse is checked by a lyrical urge; the poems express less the
wisdom derived from life than the experience of life itself.

XI

Brackenridge attempted to write satire until the end of his life,
yet he knew as he worked on the second part of *Modern Chivalry*
that his powers had dwindled. His inclination was to reflect and
philosophize: "Were it not that I am afraid of . . . losing readers,"
he confesses in Part Two, "it would be more agreeable to my own
mind to moralize more." The second part of *Modern Chivalry* is less
a novel than a collection of his ideas, fancies, and criticisms written
from 1801 to 1815 at Carlisle. It began in reaction to the newspaper
battles between his *Tree of Liberty* and the *Pittsburgh Gazette*. But
he soon found himself opposing President Jefferson's policies on

judicial reform which abetted the western distrust of educated persons, and consequently Brackenridge changed his target to the opposers of the common law and its judiciary. Teague, who had become an editor in the intended satire on frontier journalism, was now given a seat on the bench where Brackenridge ignored him. The satire dissipates in didacticisms, those of the author relieved by those of his Captain Farrago.

Yet the author's prevailing mood of reflection frequently overwhelms the instruction and as a result some of his best writing occurs here and there in the farrago of Part Two. As in the Scottish verse, the humor is resigned and serves to warm the arguments that it frequently interrupts. Captain Farrago's wisdom has changed; it is exercised rather than offered. When a spirited mob threatens to burn the professors along with their college unless they stand out of the way, Farrago no longer seeks to reason with them but appeals to their desires: "Why burn the college? The building will serve useful purposes when the professors are driven out of it."

The nostaligia of the Scottish poems is also evident in patches of Part Two, but the early days of the frontier replace his early days in the Barrens. Trying to recapture his past, Brackenridge preserves rare portraits of frontier life. The descriptions of a settler taking a wife and of the process of actually settling in the new country are refreshing oases of sensibility. Looking back, Brackenridge also sensed the mythical qualities of the insurrection and he was moved to find an adequate form of expression. Appearing suddenly among the dull observations of Part Two, we find a ballad called "The Song of Clonmel." The singer, Clonmel, has taken to the woods with the whiskey boys where the outcasts have established a "madcap settlement." Like the Scottish verse, the ballad is conciliatory:

> But give me the whiskey, it makes one so frisky,
>   But beating, and bruising make sore;
> Come shake hands, my cronies, come near my dear honies,
>   And think of your grudges no more.

The tone of Part Two is mostly that of a man remembering, confessing, advising. The system of finance and unequal wealth in America had destroyed the spirit of *The Rising Glory* and planted "that of the lottery in the human heart." But Brackenridge valued still the knowledge and tastes stored within one man, for use in his private world. There the actual development of the country need never touch his ideal. He could dwell in the spirit of past aspirations.

An Epistle to Walter Scott, written five years before he died, reveals Brackenridge's private world. On a return to Pittsburgh after

ten years absence he read Scott's *Lady of the Lake* and was moved
by the thought of his own failure. It is a last effort to make good a
promise to himself; and the very crudity of the non-poet so desperately
seeking to fulfill the poetic need and realizing his failure is itself
poetic:

> My gift is only to admire;
> In madness I attempt the lyre
>   . . . .
> Of this I dream and when awake,
> I read the Lady of the Lake.

The poet is driven by reaction to "the lottery in the human heart."
He wishes to mirror nature for individual pleasure and exaltation,
not social utility, which is the only purpose his society seems to
recognize in life:

> Inglorious I must bend my head,
> And think of something else than fame,
> Though in my bosom burns the flame
> That in a happier age and clime
> Might have attempted lofty rime.

These lines extend his personal failure to that of the American
spirit, which began in the vision of a rising glory, a poetic vision.

XII

Brackenridge is consistent in thought from his literary beginning
at Princeton through his last efforts at Carlisle. Although the rising
glory dimmed, it was never extinguished, but glowed in his private
world long after society ignored it. Very much in line with Emerson's
notion of self-reliance, Brackenridge urged all to realize the potentials
which would equate them with the heroes of history. The opportunity
for realizing man's potential is America. If his *Rising Glory* rings
with the exuberance of Whitman's *Leaves of Grass,* its yawp is not
barbaric but quite the opposite.

Brackenridge's satires were aimed at social instruction and therefore could not afford the bitterness of his English models nor the
relaxation later found in Washington Irving. The absurdities of
American life that amused Irving threatened Brackenridge. The cultivation of men's minds was the most important work of the moment.
That was the way man earned his freedom just as the right to the soil
was earned through its cultivation.

Until the mass of men had become educated, the concepts of the
Federalist party most closely approached the republican ideal, which

was the natural political form for refined and free men. But as the French Revolution loomed, that party abandoned the American experiment. With the ideals of republicanism at stake, Brackenridge had to join the Jeffersonians even though his fellows mistook its freedoms for license, its desires for rights. But republicanism was not a visionary philosophy. In Brackenridge's eyes, Thomas Paine was "an uncommon but uninformed man"; Rousseau and Godwin were examples of the "mere philosopher [who] is but a fool in matters of business . . . [and who] imagines nonsense." The dream would be defeated as much by such visionaries as by the aristocratic concepts of the Federalists whose "pride and arrogance . . . desires to be checked by the populace."

He applied the same principle to his style. Pride and arrogance generated the prose of Samuel Johnson whom he called a "literary dunce." He chose to emulate the simplicity and natural grace of Swift, Hume, and Fielding. "Nothing could surpass" Swift's definition of style—"proper words in proper places"—not even his own definition—"good sense expressed in clear language." The apparent ramble of his work is by design. He admired the wandering structure of Montaigne's essays, and Fielding's introductory chapters charmed him. "Good moral observations and anecdotes are the important elements," he claimed. In spite of digressions, the loose organization in his works does guide the reader to the point, which is usually made ironically. As he matured in the West, the biblical and classical allusions faded from his work and his sentences approached the simplicity of his models. His thought tended to move between sentences rather than within them as in the rigorously balanced prose of his time. Still he struggled against a heaviness that he could not quite overcome. His style did not satisfy him. Near the end of *Modern Chivalry*, he confessed, "Style is what I never could exactly hit."

His work fuses the literary modes beginning in the eighteenth-century tradition of epics and mock-heroics and travels the avenues of sensibility and realism. Practical and idealistic, Brackenridge directed his criticism at the abuses of the democracy he found in action so that the term "people" might assume genuine meaning rather than decay into the jargon of demagogues. If his satires chastised the electorate, his realistic and reflective work spoke to the individual man. Success of the democratic experiment depended wholly on wise and sensitive individuals, "the first springs of happiness in a republic."

I

The Rising Glory

from *Father Bombo's Pilgrimage To Mecca in Arabia*

[*Collaborating with Philip Freneau at the end of his junior year in college, Bracken-ridge projected an extended piece of epistolary fiction addressed to "My Dear Brethren." The fragments that remain of this work are contained in the Bradford Papers. They may comprise the first prose fiction written in America. Book III, Chapter I, is signed H. B. and tells a complete story. It shows Brackenridge's concern for immigrants and an interest in imitating their dialects. The story reveals that Brackenridge was absorbed from the very beginning of his literary career in the problems of maintaining cultural values in a democracy and in the rela-tions of these values to democratic success. Bombo, a picaresque rogue, extricates himself from one difficulty after another by means of his wit and learning. He is a prototype of the confidence man but justified by the forces of ignorance and superstition that oppose him everywhere. The story foreshadows* Modern Chivalry. *In the novel, however, Teague O'Regan assumes the qualities not of Bombo but of his obstacle, ignorance combined with freedom of choice. Teague, the generic term for the ignorant Irish immigrant, first appears in "Father Bombo's Pilgrim-age."*]

Dear and worthy brethren,

The name of the French Captain who took the Commodore was Monsieur de Pivot. He appeared to me to be a very brave and worthy gentleman, and I began to promise myself some happy days in the sunshine of his favor. For, as he was an extravagant lover of the polite arts, I became a very acceptable prisoner to him as he found me to be a great connoisseur in the various parts, branches and systems of moral philosophy as it is taught in all the learned nations of Europe. He frequently applied to me for instructions whereby he might regulate his conduct in life. But all my fine hopes were soon blasted by a surprising instance of the ups and downs of fortune. For as the Captain and I were walking on deck the same evening on which we left the Commodore one of the Sailors from the round top called out to the Captain that he spied a sail on the larboard bow making toward us. "Zounds," said the Captain, "it is one of the enemy," and immediately gave orders to clear the deck, throw the hencoops [1] overboard, and have the guns in readiness. By the time this was performed the enemy, who proved to be an Irish privateer, gave us a broadside. Monsieur de Pivot, standing on the quarter deck in ten or twelve coils of the cable, gave orders with great alacrity and courage.

Here I found myself in a miserable plight, for should I seem to act the coward on the present occasion my fate would be unavoidably fixed, if the Frenchman gained the victory; but if I fought gallantly and suffered myself to play the hero I would be treated as a prisoner, if the privateer should conquer. I therefore resolved to steer a mean between both for according to that wise Philosopher Ovid, "in medio tutissimus ibis." The midway is the best. Accordingly while the privateer was at some distance I thought proper to assume an air of fortitude and valor and after that shape my fortune according to the day. Now taking off my wig I swang it round in the air and gave the men three cheers. "Courage, my boys," said I, "the day is ours!"

Monsieur de Pivot, beholding my courage and bravery, commended me to the skies and promised me advancement in life according to the services I should perform that day. But now the cannon of the other ship beginning to rain a shower of winged messengers upon us, I thought it the most prudent method to withdraw, lest my pious resolution should be nipt in the bud by an immature death. So, I whispered to the officer who stood next to me that I would just run down into the cabin and drink a glass of rum and gunpowder and come up again as courageous and bold as a lion. But however, I was not the fool to return so suddenly as I pretended, but waited there till I could find how the play was going above. In a short time the Irishmen boarded us and began to carry all before them, and upon hearing Monsieur de Pivot call out, "Strike the flag, the day is lost!" I made down through a trap door into the hold and there wrapping myself in an old fishing net, I so entangled myself in it that I seemed to have been fast bound like a prisoner. Here I lay struggling and groaning and making the most piteous lamentation when the privateer's men came down to search the vessel.

Upon seeing me one of them called out to his comrade, "Arrah, dear Bryan, here is the Divil!" "Oh no," replied I, speaking in a very

---

1. Hencoops were barrels.

hoarse and hollow voice, "I am an Irishman, a countryman of your own. My name is Reynold McDonald. I was taken by these accursed Frenchmen about seven days ago, and here they have kept me in this vile dungeon, from the light of the sun, moon, and stars without a drop of drink or a bit of victuals to cross my throat, so that I am almost famished to death with hunger."

"Ah, dear O'Donnel then," said the Irishman, "rise up and come away, and by Shaint Patrick you shall fare as well as any one of us, for we have taken da vessel."

"Arra, my Shewel," [2] quoth I, "I might as well fly away with de ship tro' de air as to get out of dese ropes wid which I am bound."

"Arra, my honey, den," said the Irishman, "I will cut them open with my gully." Upon this, opening his knife, he cut the net from around me and set me at liberty.

Pretending to be worn out with famine and ill usage, I clambered to deck with my hands and feet. I saluted the Teagues [3] as my deliverers, and my friends. They indeed treated me very kindly and when the French vessel was ready to be dismissed—for Monsieur de Pivot had ransomed her with the very same money he received from the Commodore—I say when this was done I was put on board the Irish privateer, which hoisted sail that very evening and stood away for the North of Ireland.

For several days after the battle I entertained them with a relation of the cruel usage I received from the Frenchmen. "Not a day passed," said I, "but I was hauled up to the Halyards to receive four and thirty lashes with the rope's end."

"Arra but," said Nus McSwine, the fellow that found me. "Did you not tell me you neither saw sun, moon, nor stars the whole time you were prisoner? I tought by day you had never been out of de hold at all."

"Very true," replied I, "neither did I see de light of the blessed day, for tho' I was hoisted up on deck, they took care to have my wig drawn over my face, and braced round mine head with a piece of a tarpaulin so that I could neither see nor hear no more than if I had been at the bottom of the sea."

By this time the Captain of the privateer, whose name was Lacklin MacSwooly, heard of me and coming to see me asked where I was born. I answered him, "In Canickfergus." For tho' this was far from

2. A scarecrow made of feathers to frighten deer.
3. Popular name for uneducated Irish immigrants in America; later used for the major character in *Modern Chivalry*.

being the truth, yet I found it the most probable method to curry favor in the present situation of my affairs. "Arra then," said he, "you are a brave Irish boy."

"In truth I am," answered I. "And it is no wonder, if I don't speak my own country dialect as I left it when I was a boy and have never been there since."

"Ah-h-h," said he. "That's a great pity. But you shall be kindly used by us, and if you go along wid us in the privateer way you shall share in our fortune and if you are anything of a scholar you have a chance to be advanced to some office when we return from our cruise."

"Scholar!" said I. "I am a most profound scholar. I have learned navigation, astronomy, astrology, and all the occult sciences with the greatest attention. I can tell you the names of the seven planets [4] and count you all the stars from the tropics to the Tartric circles.[5] I know the names of the twelve constellations of the Zodiac, and the times of the risings of Orion and the bear star." The Captain by this time began to stare at me as a prodigy, for these sublime sentences were the same as Latin to him. Upon this all the sailors came crowding about me and set themselves to listen with their mouths and ears wide open, for the word had gone out among them that I was a man of wonderful scholarship. "Yes, gentlemen," continued I, "I have had opportunities of knowing a great deal. I was put to school when I was young, to the best masters in the kingdom. I have since travelled thro' the whole world. I have conversed with the Mufti of the Persians, the Bramins of India, the Mandarines of China, the Mussel-man of Turkey, and the priests of Busiris in Egypt. Twas there [*Egypt*] I received this wig which you now see me wear. Some of them told me it sprang from the mud of the River Nile, enlivened by the prolific heat of the sun, others again told me that it was the wig which Noah wore in the ark and which Saint Patrick consecrated on the head of Ptolemy Philopater [6] seventeen hundred years ago. This staff which I carry in my hand I received when I was at Rome from Pope Urban [7] who told me it was the very staff which the Patriarch had when he travelled to Padan-aram. These books which you see in

4. Only seven planets were known in 1770. Neptune was discovered in 1846 and Pluto in 1930.

5. In this coinage, Brackenridge appears to be associating the frigid region with Tartarus.

6. Ptolemy IV, who reigned in Macedonia from 221–204 B.C. He earned the reputation of a debauchee.

7. Urban II (1042–1099) was Pope during the first crusade.

my wallet are of a religious kind. These, showing them my dictionaries, contain the history of St. Consten.[8] This, showing them my Lucian, is the Life of St. Patrick. This, pulling out my Xenophon, contains a set of Ave Marias wrote in Latin and a copy of indulgencies which I received from the Pope's own hand.

When I had finished my harangue the Captain treated me with the greatest respect, invited me down in the cabin and having furnished me with an elegant supper then asking me very politely if I was for bed, I answered in the affirmative. "Patrick O'Konnel," said he, "Conduct this gentleman to your berth in the steerage and lay him down by your messmate, Carney McGuire, and do you shift for yourself a night." The fellow conducted me to the berth but went away grumbling, very much displeased to be so turned out of his berth. And I must confess it was something hard for him, for as I understood afterwards he was obliged to lay all night in a coil of the cable rope.

This circumstance, small and trifling as may seem at the first, proved the source of my future disasters; for the fellow, beyond measure enraged, spared no pains to work my downfall. The first thing he did the next day was to signify by nods and whispers to his messmates that he did not like my appearance. "I am much mistaken," said he, "if he is not a wizard conjurer or something worse. I was troubled all night long," continued he, "with something running up and down the ropes and strange noises in the bow and stern of the ship." Then nodding his head, he seemed to signify that he knew more than he would discover at that time. Hereupon they all began to hint that they had likewise seen something lest they should seem behind hand in sagacity and penetration. "By my troth," says one, "when I got up very early this morning I saw a crow on the topmast as big as my head though I did not care to speak of it before." "Upon my faath," said another, "I saw two hares run through the scuttle holes of the ship. I tought den dey were rats, but now I find dey were hares." "If that is the case," says a third, "and I verily believe it is, we must take care what we do with him. Last night I saw something on the prow of the ship in the shape of a woman which I took to be Sheelay, the wife of Neal Ogen, the cook. Now in troth I could take my oath it was a witch. But as I say, let us take care what we do with him for if we were to throw him overboard he would blow up a storm which would sink us to the bottom." "Ay faith,

8. St. Constantine, who had been a penitent in Ireland, then a missionary in Scotland where pirates murdered him in Kintyre in the sixth century.

and that's true," replied another. "For I remember when Sheelah Mochklonnikhan with two or three more witches raised a whirlwind and carried away an oat stack of my father's, and did much more mischief to the country by Elve, shooting the cows and bewitching the people of the neighborhood till Tuccan O'Klarty shot her with a pair of silver buttons." "Let Donnel O'Loyd, immediately then," said they, "acquaint the Captain that the man who he took for a priest we have found to be a wizard."

The mate having told the Captain the report of the sailors and added a great deal more to it—that he himself had seen me all night long up among the shrouds, sometimes hauling and reefing the sails and at other times dancing like a witch out on the waves with his wig in his hand—"Egad," says the Captain, "if that is the case, keep a good look out after him and order him not to stir out of the steerage on peril of his life." When I received this command I found it was most expedient to obey it, for it was in vain to persuade them to anything else but that I was a wizard. I had unluckily forgot my wallet above deck; not daring to venture on myself, they resolved to wreak their fury on it, thinking they should destroy as much of my power as was contained in the books. Accordingly they burnt them to my unspeakable grief and mortification. Here I was obliged to lie in a miserable plight for some days, none daring to come near to fetch me victuals, nor durst I venture out myself. For the Captain had sworn if I did, he would shoot me with a silver bullet. In the meantime, by long fasting, a violent cholic came upon me. I wreathed myself to and fro and groaned most woefully, for indeed I was in extreme misery. The sailors overhearing me fancied that they heard me pronouncing strange and uncouth expressions and were firmly persuaded that I was about to call up a ghost or raise a spirit.

About this time a gale happened to spring up. "Ay Fa-ath," says one, "now it comes we'll go to the bottom presently." "Something must be done," says another, "something must be done!" There happening to be an old French priest on board, it was agreed to call for him to put a stop to the impending destruction. The priest coming with a piggin [9] of holy water threw the half of it down the hatchway on my face. I was in the meantime in the greatest misery, not much regarding them. But what even at that time gave me some concern was this, that one of the sailors, putting down a fish gig, drew up my wig and consumed it along with my books.

9. A small wooden pail or dipper.

The storm still increasing, they began to be terribly afraid. The Captain sometimes threatening me, at other times with fair words strove to persuade me to call down the storm. But it was all in vain, for had I been never so much inclined, 'twas not in my power to do it. Finding now, as they imagined, that I was deaf to all intreaties, they thought proper to throw me overboard. Accordingly, hoisting me up with a block and tackle, they lowered me down into a tobacco hogshead,[10] and the cooper immediately heading it up and clapping on three iron hoops, they tossed me into the ocean. Here I rolled, as Martin [11] says in his philosophy, obsequious to the waves and swelling tides. After a long time I found myself at rest on some shore; and knocking out the bung, I saw two men coming down towards me. By their voices I knew them to be Irishmen. "Arra, Dennis," says one of them, "I'll lay a groat [12] yonder is a hogshead of onions or potatoes coming from some wreck!" "Arra by my troth," says the other, "I believe it is."

And now, being come up, they hoisted up the hogshead on one end and concluded it was about half full. Then knocking out the end, they made way for me, and taking me I suppose for a witch, took to the hills. I followed them to some distance, endeavoring to persuade them that I was a man; but having got up into the mountains, they were lost to my view. I now found myself, my dear brethren, in the North of Ireland, without house or home, books to read, or a wig to my head. But the manner in which I behaved and the adventures which befell me among the wild Irish shall be the subject of the ensuing chapter.

[*Princeton, 1770*]

10. A barrel.
11. Perhaps St. Martin, bishop of Tours, who is regarded as the patron of drinking and jovial meetings, as well as of reformed drunkards.
12. English silver coin worth fourpence.

from *The Rising Glory of America*

[*On September 25, 1771, Brackenridge recited* The Rising Glory of America *at the Princeton commencement. Until then his poetry consisted of humorous and juvenile satires directed against the campus tories. Written with Freneau and patterned after the works of Virgil and Milton, the commencement poem rang with epic qualities and august tones. But it was excessively long and repetitious. The speakers, Acasto, Eugenio, and Leander, repeat the same materials with varying emphasis. They describe the American beginnings, struggles, heroes and peoples, and they point all this history towards a manifest destiny of man's glorious fulfillment on these shores. In 1786, Freneau recast the poem, omitting the Brackenridge lines. The verses of Brackenridge look forward to a commerce that is profuse, and they "bid fair science smile." Those of Freneau speak of a rural reign and of no longer shedding blood "for metal buried in a rocky waste." The selection below is roughly the last third of the poem devoid of the Freneau lines.*]

Eugenio

'Tis true no human eye can penetrate
The veil obscure, and in fair light disclos'd
Behold the scenes of dark futurity;
Yet if we reason from the course of things,
And downward trace the vestiges of time,
The mind prophetic grows and pierces far
Thro' ages yet unborn. We saw the states
And mighty empires of the East arise
In swift succession from the Assyrian
To Macedon and Rome; to Britain thence
Dominion drove her car, she stretch'd her reign
O'er many isles, wide seas, and peopled lands.
Now in the west a continent appears;
A newer world now opens to her view.

She hastens onward to th' Americ shores
And bids a scene of recent wonders rise.
New states, new empires and a line of kings,
High rais'd in glory, cities, palaces,
Fair domes on each long bay, sea, shore or stream,
Circling the hills now rear their lofty heads.

Far in the Arctic skies a Petersburgh,
A bergen, or Archangel lifts its spires
Glitt'ring with ice, far in the West appears
A new Palmyra [1] or an Ecbatan [2]
And sees the slow pac'd caravan return
O'er many a realm from the Pacific shore,
Where fleets shall then convey rich Persia's silks,
Arabia's perfumes, and spices rare
Of Philippine, Coelebe and Marian isles,
Or from the Acapulco coast our India then,
Laden with pearl and burning gems and gold.
Far in the south I see a Babylon,
As once by Tigris or Euphrates stream,
With blazing watch tow'rs and observatories
Rising to heav'n; from thence astronomers
With optic glass take nobler views of God
In golden suns and shining worlds display'd
Than the poor Chaldean with the naked eye.
A Nineveh where Oronoque [3] descends
With waves discolour'd from the Andes high,
Winding himself around a hundred isles
Where golden buildings glitter o'er his tide.
To mighty nations shall the people grow
Which cultivate the banks of many a flood
In crystal currents poured from the hills
Apalachia nam'd, to lave the sands
Of Carolina, Georgia, and the plains
Stretch'd out from thence far to the burning line,
St. Johns or Clarendon or Albermarle.[4]
And thou Potomac, navigable stream,
Rolling thy waters thro' Virginia's groves,
Shall vie with Thames, the Tiber or the Rhine,
For on thy banks I see an hundred towns
And the tall vessels wafted down thy tide.
Hoarse Niagara's stream now roaring on
Thro' woods and rocks and broken mountains torn,
In days remote far from their ancient beds,
By some great monarch taught a better course
Or cleared of cataracts shall glow beneath
Unnumbr'd boats and merchandize and men;

1. The biblical Tadmor (Book of Mormons) which was built by Solomon on an oasis and was destroyed by Emperor Aurelian in 273 A.D. after the revolt of its queen, Zenobia.
2. Capital of the Median kingdom and afterwards the summer residence of the Persian and Parthian kings.
3. River in South America.
4. The image is confused. "St. John" refers to the river in Maine and "Albermarle" to the sound cutting into the coast of North Carolina, but "Clarendon" refers to land rather than a body of water. It is a county in South Carolina.

And from the coasts of piny Labradore,
A thousand navies crowd before the gale,
And spread their commerce to remotest lands,
Or bear their thunder round the conquered world.

Leander

And here fair freedom shall forever reign.
I see a train, a glorious train appear,
Of patriots plac'd in equal fame with those
Who nobly fell for Athens or for Rome.
The sons of Boston, resolute and brave,
The firm supporters of our injur'd rights,
Shall lose their splendors in the brighter beams
of patriots fam'd and heroes yet unborn.

Acasto

'Tis but the morning of the world with us
And science yet but sheds her orient rays.
I see the age, the happy age, roll on
Bright with the splendors of her mid-day beams,
I see a Homer and a Milton rise
In all the pomp and majesty of song,
Which gives immortal vigor to the deeds
Achiev'd by heroes in the fields of fame.

A second Pope,[5] like that Arabian bird
Of which no age can boast but one, may yet
Awake the muse by Schuylkill's silent stream,
And bid new forests bloom along her tide.
And Susquehanna's rocky stream unsung,
In bright meanders winding round the hills,
Where first the mountain nymph, sweet echo, heard
The uncouth music of my rural lay,
Shall yet remurmur to the magic sound
Of song heroic, when in future days
Some noble Hambden [6] rises into fame.

Leander

Or Roanoke's and James's limpid waves
The sound of music murmurs in the gale;

5. Except for "Windsor Forest," the poetry of Alexander Pope is seldom associated with physical nature.
6. Probably John Hampden (1594–1643), who consistently opposed the crown and became an opposition leader during the short parliament of 1640.

Another Denham [7] celebrates their flow,
In gliding numbers and harmonious lays.

Eugenio

Now in the bow'rs of Tuscororah hills,[8]
As once on Pindus [9] all the muses stray,
New Theban bards high soaring reach the skies
And swim along thro' azure deeps of air.

Leander

From Allegheny in thick groves imbrown'd,
Sweet music breathing thro' the shades of night
Steals on my ear, they sing the origin
Of those fair lights which gild the firmament;
From whence the gale that murmurs in the pines;
Why glows the stream down from the mountains brow
And rolls the ocean lower than the land.
They sing the final destiny of things,
The great result of all our labors here,
The last day's glory, and the world renew'd.
Such are their themes, for in these happier days
The bard enraptur'd scorns ignoble strains,
Fair science smiling and full truth revealed,
The world at peace, and all her tumults o'er,
The blissful prelude to Emanuel's reign.

Acasto

This is thy praise, America, thy pow'r,
Thou best of climes, by science visited,
By freedom blest and richly stor'd with all
The luxuries of life. Hail, happy land,
The seat of empire, the abode of kings,
The final stage where time shall introduce
Renowned characters, and glorious works
Of high invention and of wond'rous art
Which not the ravages of time shall waste
Till he himself has run his long career;
Till all those glorious orbs of light on high,

7. The reference is to Sir John Denham's "Cooper's Hill" (1642): "Oh could
I glow like thee. . . . "
8. In North Carolina. It is the land of the Tuscororas, a tribe of Indians conquered by the British in 1713.
9. Mountain chain in northwest Greece.

The rolling wonders that surround the ball,
Drop from their spheres extinguish'd and consum'd;
When final ruin with her fiery car
Rides o'er creation, and all nature's works
Are lost in chaos and the womb of night.

[*Princeton, 1771*]

from *Six Political Discourses Founded on the Scriptures*

I. The Bloody Vestiges of Tyranny

Let not the word *scripture*, in the title page, prevent that general attention to these discourses which they might otherwise receive. I know it is natural for us to be anxious in looking into any thing that borders on religion, lest we should meet with some sly insinuation *like a bayonet point to dart upon the conscience*. For this reason, in the very *patibulo*, or entrance, I am careful to assure my countrymen that these discourses are what they pretend to be, *of a nature chiefly political*. They were written at different times, since the opening of the last campaign in Pennsylvania, and were intended for the military. The three first were delivered on some occasions. If they shall now more generally serve the great cause in which we are engaged, it will be an ample recompense for the time spent in transcribing them for publication.

Discourse

I. The Bloody Vestiges of Tyranny.
"Woe unto them, for they have gone in the way of Cain." Jude i, 11

II. The Nature and the Artifice of Toryism.
"And ran greedily after the error of Balaam for reward." Jude i, 11

III. The Fate of Tyranny and Toryism.
"And perished in the gainsaying of Core." Jude i, 11

IV. The Agency of Heaven in the Cause of Liberty.
"And there was war in heaven." Rev. xii, 7

V. The Blasphemy of Gasconade and Self Dependence in a Certain General.
"And there was given unto him a mouth, speaking great things and blasphemies." Rev. xiii, 5

VI. The Great Wrath of the Tyrant, and the Cause of it.
"Having great wrath, because he knoweth that he hath but a short time." Rev. xii, 12   *[The Preface]*

"Woe unto them, for they have gone in the way of Cain." Jude i, 11.

It is very usual in any language, when we mean to draw a character to the highest point, to compare it with one already known and confessedly eminent in virtue or in vice. This is the ground of the expression in this place, "Woe unto them, for they have gone in the way of Cain."

Cain, we know, was a bloody-minded man. The fierceness of his nature did very early show itself in great vehemency of passion and in the sullen gloom of a reserved countenance. He was very wroth and his countenance was fallen. No wonder, for he was indeed a very bloody man. He shed the first blood that ever crimsoned the earth. He bathed his hands in a brother's blood. These two circumstances of his guilt place him first in the line of murderers. He is so infamously famous that when we mean to say of anyone that he is fierce and savage to a high degree we may strike off his character at once by saying, he hath gone in the way of Cain.

I shall not detain you with a longer introduction but proceed to say,

I. What it is to go in the way of Cain.

II. Who are they who have most eminently gone in the way of Cain.

I. What it is to go in the way of Cain. It is to give indulgence in the least unlawful measure to the anger and resentment of the breast; for whoso hateth his brother is a murderer. The evil principles of envy, malice, and ambition, like so many younger Cains, lurk within the breast and wait only for an opportunity to show themselves in action. The evil principles of envy and ambition lead to murder; for they seek to end in the death of those who stand in the way of the proposed rise and strike not readily to their superior greatness. Hence it is that the tyrant makes war upon his own or the neighboring nation, because they refuse to live precariously by his bounty and to hold their property, liberty, and life entirely at his disposal. It is the nature of the wicked heart of man to desire absolute dominion. Let a wicked man be made a magistrate and he will desire to be supreme in office; and if supreme by the appointment of his countrymen, he will aspire to unrestrained authority; and in order to acquire despotic rule, he will not hesitate to shed the blood of kinsmen, friends, and fellow citizens. This is to go in the way of Cain—to shed blood like him and take the same character upon the earth. But I am to say:

II. Who are they who have most eminently gone in the way of

Cain. I need not tell you that such is the degeneracy of human nature that we all some time or other have gone lengths in the way of Cain. The rich man hates him that is richer than himself because he is unwilling that anyone should be equal or superior to him in the same line of eminence. The learned for the same reason hates him that is more learned still, and the candidate for office hates the brother candidate. A temper of this cast is not so rare as men unattentive to themselves and to others may suppose it. What man is there among us who is not conscious to himself of having too much indulged the passion of resentment against a brother from some improper cause and principle? What man is there among us who has not found in himself a sentiment of some revenge against a brother because he had not submitted to him in a dispute in conversation, or in a competition for a magistracy, or place of public trust and appointment of some kind or other? Every man has his ambition, and in the frustration of this particular hope, by the competition of a rival, he is vulnerable. The lady envies dress, precedency, and degrees of honor in the sphere peculiar to herself. The gentleman is troubled at the mention of superior fame in weather, wit, learning, or honor in some other way. Envy, malice, hatred, and revenge may be found in some degree, at some time or other, in almost every breast. We have therefore all proceeded frequently too much in the way of Cain.

But who are they who have most eminently gone in the way of Cain? From the day that Cain slew Abel to the present hour there have been many who have [trod] in the same path of blood, concerning whom history is silent. One half of the wickedness of mankind is buried in oblivion. From the day of Cain to the deluge we have particularly the name but of one man who shed human blood. Lamech, by his own confession, slew a man to his wounding and a young man to his hurt; and with such circumstance of aggravation that in his own judgment he had deserved a punishment seventy-fold greater than the punishment of Cain. In this long period we have the name but of Lamech on record, though no doubt there were many more who shed the blood of man. The earth at this time was filled with violence—with contention, with havock, with war and bloodshed in every place. Many an unjust tyrant sought dominion and obtained it by the death of thousands. Such was the sense of things before the flood; but by and by the sacred history more and more unfolds itself, and we begin to see many, very many, to take the character of Cain upon the earth. Nimrod first began to be a mighty one; that is, as we may conjecture one who first at the head of a small band made himself famous, but shortly dared to usurp dominion over others that were not willing to allow it. But as we have nothing more explicit concerning him, I pass him by and come down to a more remarkable personage, even Pharoah, king of Egypt, who went with hasty steps and to a great length in the way of Cain. I might say a great deal of this bloody man, and set in high colors the complexion of his crime who to the slavery of the father added the infant son's death. But I leave this instance in my view, and likewise all that happened to the chosen people under the tyrants that made war upon them after their settlement in the promised land. I leave behind me the cruelty of many of their own kings, and in particular the bloody tragedy of Ahab who took the life of Naboth for the sake of the poor man's vineyard upon which he had fixed his covetous desire. I leave behind me the inroad of the Syrians and all that the Chaldean monarch did when he transplanted the ten tribes from their own land to a distant country. I come down to profane history and there I likewise leave behind me all that is told us of the mighty captains and conquerors of ancient time—the Alexanders—the Caesars—the Genghis Khans— the Tamarlanes. I leave behind me all that is related of the Hun, the Vandal, or the Goth, and all the cruel, persecuting, bloody princes and people in more modern times when Europe floated as one sea of blood. I pass them by and hasten on, for I have an object of greater wickedness in view—an object of such accomplished fraud, perfidy, and murder that every one heretofore mentioned is lost and disappears. I mean him of England—the fierce, cruel, unrelenting, and bloody king of Britain. What has this tyrant done? What has he not done?

He meditated with himself in cold blood, and before he had the least foundation of resentment, the enslaving of this rising country. He could view without a tear and without one check of conscience this early land bound in the chains of servitude which he forged for it. This was the prospect which he had painted to his own imagination. It was this which he endeavored to accomplish by the insiduous and, as he hoped, insensible gradation of a slow approach, in bribery and flattering promises to vain persons, and then by distant acts of parliament that did not seem immediately to involve the loss of freedom but did by sure steps lead to it. Those that are the most skillful in the art of poisoning make use of a slow bane which wastes the system gradually and is not discernible in its operation from a natural disease. Such was the first attempt of the king of Britain. But when it failed him to accomplish our destruction by this which might be called a sap, with what composure did he determine with himself to drench with slaughter and imbrue the continent in blood. With what continued and unbroken obstinacy hath he persevered in the design. Let the streets of Boston and the bloody fifth of March be witness of his cruelty, when several lovely and unresisting youths fell by the hands of the bloody Preston who acted the savage pleasure of his still more savage master.[1] Let the streets that were wet with this blood and drank it not, for the flood ran down upon the stones, let the streets that were wet and ran down with this blood speak loud of it and cry to heaven for a day of vengeance. Let the town of Boston be witness to their cruelty. The town of Boston with the cries of infants, and the groans of distressed mothers detained from their relatives and husbands, but for the perfidy of a Gage in violation of his plighted faith.[2] Let the heights of Boston,[3] naked of the sister town which stood upon them, be witness of the cruelty of Britain. Let these call to mind and show the graves of the brave men who fell fighting gallantly for the noble cause of freedom. Let these be witness to the tyranny and, at the same time, some part of the punishment of Britain; for the heroes saw themselves revenged and slept not in death until fifteen hundred of the foe lay vanquished on the soil.[4] Let the heights of Canada and the environs of Quebec call to mind and publish the bloody vestiges of tyranny in that unhappy country. Like the heights of Gilboa, let them be ever recollected, for there the blood of Montgomery flowed upon the plain.[5] Like the blood of Abel, it shall cry from the hostile ground, and God shall require it of the George of England, as he required the like blood of Cain, saying, "Where is my Montgomery, who once drew his sword in thy defence, before these very walls, who continued faithful until the hand of tyranny was stretched to destroy?" From the heights of Canada to the distant barrier of Fort Sullivan,[6] let the intermediate states give in rememberance to remotest times what they have suffered from the Hessian

1. The Boston Massacre. On March 5, 1770, a sergeant's guard of the British garrison, led perhaps by a Sergeant Preston, fired upon a crowd, killing three men and wounding several others, two of whom died later.

2. General Thomas Gage (1721–1787) was in command of the British troops sent to preserve order after the tea party in Boston. He had praised the courage and determination of the Boston insurgents. Brackenridge may have interpreted this attitude as perfidy.

3. Bunker Hill.

4. Battle of Bunker Hill, June 17, 1775.

5. General Richard Montgomery was slain while leading the American attack on Quebec in the fall of 1775.

6. On Sullivan Island off North Carolina.

ravisher and from the inroad of the cruel Englishman wasting their
plantations. Let the Jersey state be witness to their vestiges. Let the
blood of Haslet [7] on the plain of Princeton cry aloud to God for a
day of retribution. Let the fourteen wounds of Mercer,[8] with the
bayonet point, on the same victorious eminence, open their dumb
mouths afresh and cry aloud for justice.

But omitting those who fell in the field of battle, let the unhappy
prisoners of the states declare what they have suffered from the tyrant.
Let the prisoners of Fort Washington [9] relate the hunger, cold, and
every shape of misery to which they were consigned. Sick, emaciated,
dying, let them tell if by their last breath they can give some faint
account of it. How for many days they tasted not food until sharp
famine began to prey upon their vitals, and destroy the love of life.
How for many months they were detained in the wintry and inclement
season of the year, comfortless, in cold rooms, and without fire, until
the blood of the body lost its motion in the veins. Let them tell the
quality and pernicious taste of that unwholesome food which was
served to them and intended for their death. This let those who
suffered speak; but we can testify what was the appearance and
lamentable state of the meagre, faint, and heart-dejected few who
for a time survived the usage, and at length to save some pretense of
an exchange were dismissed from the fangs of such barbarity. We saw
them—oh spectacle of horror and commiseration! The legs swollen,
and from the ankle to the knee of an equal shape, the belly contracted
to the ribs, the eye sunk and hid within the head, the visage narrow,
the cheeks fallen to the bone, the voice shrill, feeble, and not to be
distinctly heard, the dress ragged and scarcely hanging to the body.
Ask one of these what became of his companion whom we see not?
He died the first week partly with hunger and partly with cold. He
recommended his wife and infant children to God, and his death to
be revenged by his country. What became of another whom we see
not? He died the second week on board the ships by the badness and,
as we suppose, poison of the food which was served to us. He hoped
that the God of heaven and the freemen of his country would call the

7. At the Battle of Princeton on January 3, 1777, Colonel John Haslet walked on
foot beside the horse of General Hugh Mercer. When Mercer was killed, Haslet
attempted to lead the troops on into the battle, but they fled in terror. He was
shot in the head.

8. General Hugh Mercer received seven wounds according to Christopher Ward
in *The War of the Revolution,* I (New York, 1952) , p. 314.

9. On the Hudson River. Upon the fall of Fort Washington, 230 American
officers and 2,607 soldiers were taken prisoner.

tyrant to account for this. What became of another known to us but whom we see not now amongst you? He died the third, the fourth, the fifth, or the sixth week of our captivity. He, with twenty more, was found dead one morning amongst our feet. They had perished with cold, being without covering in the night. Many, very many, perished every day. The carriage for the dead came every morning to the door. From 2,500 or 2,700 that were suffered to depart, not perhaps 100, worn out with sickness which cold and famine had produced, are now alive.

Thus, we see, great has been the cruelty of this infernal tyrant; but to add to this, let the prisoners taken by his pirates on the sea be witness of his horrid depredation. Let the prisoners sent by him to India and the burning islands of the East be witness of his inhumanity. There hath he purposed to send [and] there hath he sent our brethren and our fellow-soldiers in the common cause. There hath he sent them, distant far, and hopeless from their native land, to anti-Christian settlements and paganish domains. There hath he sent our countrymen, beyond those settlements and solitary streams at which the captive Hebrew sat and hung his harp upon the willow-tree; for music suited not in such distress. There many a poor American may sit this day, forlorn and deeply melancholy in a distant clime. There may they sit, far on the Cape of Comorin, or on the Malabar or Coromandel shore,[10] looking westward o'er the main to the setting sun where their native country lies. There may they sit and look in vain; for the tyrant hath sentenced them, though fairly prisoners in war, to this unpitied state. This hath he done and this hath he proposed to do, while we have treated those of the enemy, who by the chance of war have fallen into our hands, with every exercise of tenderness, compassion, and humanity. This we have done; but as for them, they have gone in the way of Cain.

This hath come more immediately in later instances before our eyes. Their sad cruelties are now transacted on our own plains. They have landed; they have travelled through a part of the adjacent country; they have burned dwelling houses; they have destroyed provision and the means of life; they have tortured for money those whom they suspected of possessing it; they have driven the peaceful inhabitants from their places of abode; they have violated the chastity of women who fell into their hands; they are bending on and breathing slaughter to the whole state. They meditate destruction, at the

10. Points on the southwest Indian coast. Cape Comorin is at the tip of the peninsula.

risk of their own lives. It is their determination to destroy or to perish. Rather than suffer us to live, they will cease to live themselves. Can anything be more diabolical, more strongly marked infernal, more in the spirit of the first-born Cain?

I conclude with something in the spirit of the words: "Woe unto them, for they have gone in the way of Cain." In the language of a soldier, too often and very iniquitously used, it might be said damn them; but such expression is not to be commended. Let our resentment be leveled against their practice and let our execution be stayed on their bodies, but let us spare the soul. Let us wish them spiritual happiness; but let every thought and exercise of mind draw forth itself against their conduct. Let us endeavor to conceive with strength the baseness of their crime; and let us speak to others what we have conceived, so that we may fix the detestation of it beyond a possibility to be erased. This is laudable, for a just and honest indignation against any vice or evil practice is an evidence of virtue. This is necessary, for we are too apt to lose our hatred of evil from a familiarity and acquaintance with it. Hence it is that they who are once enslaved do very seldom exert themselves to shake off the bondage. It is in this as it is said to be in the charm of a serpent, we fall in love with that which ought to be the object of our hate, as it is the instrument of our destruction. It is therefore necessary to beget, increase, and keep alive an aversion from it, to inkindle our resentment, not by curses and indecent language, but by sensible remonstrances to ourselves and with each other. Let it be woven in our daily conversation; woe unto them for they have intended to enslave us, they have intended to subjugate us to their empire, to make us hewers of wood and drawers of water and, in every base employment, vassals to their despotic power. By this they have intended to prevent the growth of every art and science in this country; for without freedom, learning shall decay and no art can flourish. In the destruction of our freedom they have intended the eradication of every private virtue; for when the soul is unbraced and enervated by the poison of a base subjection, nothing generous or noble can be expected from it. It is a sentiment as old as the poet Homer—

> For Jove decreed it certain, that the day
> which makes a man a slave, takes half his worth away.[11]

Woe unto them, for they have rejected the frequency and humility of our petitions. They have rejected them with a fierce disdain. They

11. *The Odyssey*, xvii.

have been deaf to entreaty and the softest words of soft expostulation. They have pursued, without remorse, the dire intention to destroy us. They have pursued it in a cruel manner. They have warred with a rage unknown to civilized nations. They have mangled the bodies of our heroes on the field of battle. They have defaced our colleges and schools of learning. They have burned houses of religious worship. They have stabbed and shed the blood of an unarmed and supplicating clergyman. This they have done to persons of the same language and religion with themselves. Woe unto them, for they have shed a brother's blood. They have gone in the way of Cain.

Let us be careful to recollect and commemorate their conduct. Let every class of men join to execrate the tyrant and the tyranny; and to rank the George of England with the Cains and the murderers of mankind. Let fathers teach their sons the degenerate nature and the name of Englishmen. Let mothers still with this the children on the breast and make the name a bug-bear. In thought, in word, let the indignation have a place; but chiefly in our actions let strong resentment show itself. Let the aged father send his son to battle with cheerfulness and resignation. Let the wife permit her husband and perplex him not with womanish exclamation or with tears. Let the soldier in the field—and to such I principally address myself— let the soldier in the field behave with fortitude. Let him forget the effeminacy of a tender and luxurious life. Let him summon up the blood, give indignation to the visage, and let the spirit of resentment flash from the enraged eye. Let him, in obedience to his orders, show himself steady, in execution of them prompt, in every enterprise undaunted. Let the arm be stretched with vigor, and give full revenge its scope. Duty, honor, and the love of virtue calls to battle. The wounded soldier and the dying hero calls to battle. The voice of the brigades* so lately injured by superior numbers calls to battle. The happiness and glory of the rising generations calls to battle. Let every man give audience to the voice. Let every man become a soldier. Let every soldier acquit himself as valiant. Let him determine victory or death. Let him be of the mind to fight from hill to hill, from vale to vale, and on every plain, until the enemy is driven back and forced to depart, until the tyrant shall give up his claim and be obliged to confess that free men, that Americans are not to be subdued.

[*Lancaster, 1777*]

* At Brandywine. [H.H.B.]

from the *United States Magazine*

Preface

The preface of a publication means the same with the exordiom of an oration, which is to conciliate the minds of the audience and, in the words of Cicero, to render them teachable, attentive, benevolent. We are so happy in assurances of good will from the public that on this occasion it will not be necessary to detain them with any great compliment and ceremony of this nature. They are themselves well pleased with our attempts (in the language of figure) to paint the graces on the front of war and invite the muses to our country. They will be indulgent to the infancy and progress of the work; and if there are deficiencies, they will be disposed to forgive them until full age shall have supplied every want and brought it to perfection.

We are indeed happy to find a young and rising people so disposed to wish well to the labors of those men who make it their study to contribute to the entertainment and to raise the credit of the age in which they live by useful works of literature that are the solace and at the same time the ornament of human nature. For what is man without taste and the acquirements of genius? An orangutan with the human shape and the soul of a beast.

It was the language of our enemies at the commencement of the debate between America and what is called the mother country that in righteous judgment for our wickedness it would be well to leave us to sink down to so many orangutans of the wood, lost to the light of science which, from the other side of the Atlantic, has just begun to break upon us. They have been made to see and even to confess the vanity of this kind of argument. The British officers who are, some of them, men of understanding, on perusal of our pamphlets in the course of the debate and the essays and dissertations in the newspapers, have been forced to acknowledge, not without chagrin, that the rebels, as they are pleased to call us, had some d-mn'd good writers on their side the question, and that we had fought them no less successfully with the pen than with the sword. We hope to convince them yet more fully that we are able to cultivate the belles lettres, even disconnected with Great Britain; and that liberty is of so noble and energetic a quality as even from the bosom of a war to call forth the powers of human genius in every course of literary fame and improvement.

It is our only doubt that in this undertaking the public will not sufficiently attend to the expenses of the press and from this circumstance will be disposed to complain that our publication is too highly rated. We shall in this case pray them to consider that there is scarcely an article of commerce that is not thirty times the price it was formerly; and that from the great quantity of currency in circulation, they themselves can more easily command thirty prices now than one price formerly; and therefore our publication will demonstrably be lower and more convenient for the public to receive it than anything of this kind ever was at any former period.

These things premised and understood, we shall go on in good humor with the purchaser; and it will not be the fault of our intention if we do not continue in good humor with him as long as we shall publish this magazine.

[*Philadelphia*
January 1779]

Introduction

We regard it as our great happiness in these United States that the path to office and preferment lies upon to every individual. The mechanic of the city or the husbandman who plows his farm by the river bank has it in his power to become, one day, the first magistrate of his respective commonwealth or to fill a seat in the Continental Congress. This happy circumstance lays an obligation upon every individual to exert a double industry to qualify himself for the great trust which may, one day, be reposed in him. It becomes him to obtain some knowledge of the history and principles of government or at least to understand the policy and commerce of his own country. Now it may not be the lot of every individual to be able to obtain this knowledge from the first source, that is from the best writers, or the conversation of men of reading and experience. In the one case it would require a larger library than most of us are able to procure, and in the other a greater opportunity of travelling than is consistent with our daily occupations.

The want of these advantages must therefore be supplied by some publication that will in itself contain a library and be the literary coffee-house of public conversation. A work of this nature is the *United States Magazine.*

It will contain the writings of the sage historian; it will convey the thoughts, remarks, proposals, theories, and reasonings of the politician; it will collect the genuine letters of the hero or the statesman; it will communicate the observations of the curious traveller; it will unfold the new discoveries of philosophers; it will disclose the avenues of trade and commerce; it will record proceedings in the courts of justice; it will select from late and curious publications; it will comprise the most remarkable events in Europe and America; in short, [it] will comprehend a great variety of matter on a great variety of subjects. Instruction will appear in every shape, essays, sketches, schemes, tracts and dissertations. Amusement will disport in every form of letters, tales, dreams, scraps and anecdotes. The first of these will brace the mind and make it capable to judge in matters of the highest moment. The last will pleasurably unbend it from what may border upon study and severer application.

The honest husbandman who reads this publication will rapidly improve in every kind of knowledge. He will be shortly capable to arbitrate the differences that may arise amongst his neighbors. He will be qualified to be a magistrate. He will appear a proper person to be appointed sheriff of his country. He will be equal to the task of legislation. He will be capable of any office to which the gale of popularity amongst his countrymen may raise him.

The honest husbandman and the industrious labourer and mechanic, by reading this at proper intervals of business, may qualify themselves not only for discharging offices of honor and of profit, but also for the conversation of the learned and ingenious. It will supply the want of early education and enable them to speak with great propriety and fluency on any subject. If at anytime they take a journey through a neighboring state or settlement they will be everywhere acceptable. If at any time the traveller visits their abodes, perhaps beyond the Allegheny mountain, he will be pleased to find so knowing and polite a people in this embowered residence. This language may appear romantical, but I have seen the case exemplified in those from other countries. I have conversed with common laborers and mechanics, who by the reading of the magazines had made themselves acquainted with almost every subject. I have been told that there are Whigs amongst the common class of men in Scotland which, I may almost say miracle, is brought about by means of that various and liberal information communicated through the magazine.

It has been said that magazines are oftentimes preventive of the acquirement of more solid literature because that while they make the path to knowledge easy it is more swiftly travelled over and cannot be so accurately examined as when the student is reduced to plod upon it through a tract of long and heavy reading of the authors that are found in libraries. But suppose it may be true that we are likely to become more deep and solid scholars by reading systematic writers and diving deeply to the fountain head of classic information, yet this is not to be obtained by every one and is it not more eligible that the greater part be moderately instructed than that a few should be unrivalled in the commonwealth of letters, and all the world besides, a group of ignorant and brainless persons? But I deny the proposition, for though the general knowledge communicated through the magazines may satisfy some individuals who may have it in their power to make a greater progress, yet men of taste will rather be engaged by it to go farther, so that in the issue there will be at least as many deep and solid scholars where magazines are published as where they are not published, but infinitely a greater number of moderately knowing and instructed persons.

Magazines are greatly useful as repositories of a thousand valuable smaller pieces that otherwise would never see the light, but lie concealed amongst the papers of the ingenious. It is not every man who has the leisure or the inclination to compose a book or pamphlet, but there are many who now and then may write an essay at a sitting, and by the channel of a magazine communicate it to the public.

Magazines are greatly useful as the nurseries of genius. They put it in the power of young and rising authors to make trial of their strength without the risk of being checked in the first stages of their progress by ill-natured critics whose knowledge of the person generally excites their envy and disposes them to censure what they themselves perhaps could not equal. Many men of great abilities have been prevented from venturing into a literary life and reputation from a want of some such means of making their first appearance to the public. In these respects a magazine may be compared to the sun; for as that luminary exhales the water of the ocean and pours it on the hills and valleys, so this miscellany draws forth the drops of human genius that lie amongst society and, as it were condensing them to showers, carries pleasure and refreshment to the plains and mountain tops and forms the rivers that flow down again to mingle with the ocean.

[*Philadelphia
January 1779*]

A Letter to the Poets, Philosophers, Orators, Statesmen and Heroes of Antiquity

[*Contributors to the journals of the eighteenth century often signed their articles with pseudonyms taken from antiquity. The assumed name was usually chosen because of similarity in thought and style between the ancient and contemporary authors. In appealing for contributors to the* United States Magazine, *Brackenridge plays with intentional ambiguity upon this custom. By specifying a particular desire for articles bearing on the problem of a double or single legislature, he reveals his own political perplexity at this time and also a journalistic attitude of unbiased inquiry.*]

Gentlemen,

Happy in the brown shades of Elysium you are under no apprehension from the evils of severe fate or the changes of inconstant fortune. Yet you have the feelings of men, and it is the maxim of each of you, "I am a man, and I think nothing that belongs to man foreign to me."

This appears from the part which you seem to take in all the transactions of surviving mortals. We often hear from you, and you appear to be well acquainted with all affairs in which we are engaged. I suppose the dead who daily go down to you communicate the information. Without flattery, give me leave to say, the ancient world was greatly honored by your presence and benefited by your services. The modern world is also much in debt to you, for though dead nevertheless *each of you yet speaketh*. Almost every day we receive from you some tract, dissertation or essay in history, politics or letters. The gazettes and magazines abound with lucubrations under the signatures of Nestor, Antenor, Trismegistus, Hermes, Mentor, Diogenes, Plato, Zeno, Dion, Hiero, Xenophon, Socrates, Aristotle, Euripides, and others. In looking over the periodical and literary publications of the past century, I find innumerable entertaining and instructive pieces from the pens of Solon, Lycurgus, Numa, Mucius Scaevola, Camillus, Brutus, Pliny and others equally respectable. If the old Greeks and Romans should take away what they have produced in the publications in Britain, that haughty people would have few things left to boast of.

For some time past you seem greatly to have broken off your correspondence with that wicked nation. A late circumstance has put it in my power to make the observation: An armed vessel belonging to the States, having captured a prize near the capes of the Delaware, the cargo consisting chiefly of books, was brought to Philadelphia. Amongst this collection were a number of the *Gentleman's*, the *London* and the *Westminster* magazines; and in these I could observe but very few things under any of your signatures. I presume, having found that nation incorrigible, you have discontinued your epistles to their island. It is indeed high time to abandon them and to turn your attention to the free people of America. Here your correspondence will be much courted and your observations very generally attended to. It is in a great measure for our conveniency that we have set on foot a public paper under the title of the *United States Magazine,* which paper will be a very proper channel to convey your opinions to the public. Anacreon, if he pleases may give us, now and then, a bit of poetry; Pythagoras, a scrap on the doctrine of transmigration. Archimedes may hand us up a problem, and Demosthenes the sketch of some well-written thundering oration.

History and politics, however, will be more to the taste of the present times; and for that reason I am particularly anxious to interest in our behalf those great legislators, Solon and Lycurgus, Numa Pompilius, Minos, Rhadamanthus, Aecus, and others. The sentiments of these great men, upon government, will be of great service at the present day as they will be able from their own experience to inform us whether a single or a double legislature, as we call it, be the most happy constitution of a government. We are excessively puzzled on this head in Pennsylvania. For my own part I must confess that the arguments for and against seem so perfectly to balance one another that I can hardly tell to which I shall submit myself. When a single-legislature man takes me by the sleeve and tells me of a house of Lords, and a King upon the back of them, I am greatly startled and in doubt what to say. When, on the other hand, a double-legislature man asks me to dine with him and begins to push about the bottle pretty freely, I am almost brought to be of his opinion that the multitude in all ages have been devils and that no man nor even they themselves can be safe in a commonwealth that is not checked by a variety of councils in the legislative body. If both of these meet me in the street, as is sometimes the case, I am held between them and alternately shaken by their arguments. First I nod to one and then to another, like a man that is half asleep and reclines and recovers in the angle of a chimney.

It would much oblige us if Solon and some others of your best politicians would send up a few observations on the nature of government in general, which we may use as a compass to steer our opinions in this wide waste of argument.

Cato's letters which he published some years ago I have read with very great pleasure; they were well written and breathed a fine spirit of liberty. He has spoken almost prophetically of the sad effects of coercive measures, should they be adopted on the part of Britain against her colonies. I refer to the first letter of his fourth volume.

Junius (I think it must be Junius Brutus) writes a very noble letter. His style has not been equalled by any of us on the earth at present. The name of Junius is very popular in North America and we should be very happy to hear from him in the great cause in which we are engaged.

Hortensius is a Whig and a writer of the first magnitude; he has drawn his pen with a fine vein of wit and humor in the controversy with the tyrant. His pieces published in *Collin's Gazette* of New Jersey are admirable. That particularly in which he proposed the exchange of General Burgoyne is equal to the best performances of Lucian. If Hortensius spoke as well in ancient times as he writes at the present, I do not wonder that Cicero thought him no mean competitor for the palm of immortal eloquence. Indeed I cannot [but] be of the opinion that Cicero has half the warmth and fire of genius in his compositions that brightly kindles and burns forth in the writings of Hortensius. The British may say of him what Philip of Macedon said of Demosthenes: "I do not fear the ranks of the Spartan foot, or the lines of the Trigalian horse, half so much as the lightning of that orator." [1] We shall be happy in the correspondence of Hortensius.

The Theban General Epaminondas has favored us with some very good pieces in a magazine published in Pennsylvania. His reflections on the marriage state were very well received, especially by

1. *The Philippics* (352 B.C.), orations by Demosthenes to arouse the Athenians to the threat of Philip II of Macedonia.

the ladies who are for the most part well pleased that the world is put in mind of that great duty incumbent on the members of society.

I do not know whether you have any acquaintance with some of the more modern statesmen and worthies; I speak of Hampden [2] and Sidney [3] and Harrington [4] and Russel [5] and others, who in their days were the great assertors of liberty. Some very good things have appeared from the pens of these gentlemen in our present great contest for the rights of human nature. Tell them therefore if you anywhere meet with them that we shall be glad to have the honor of their correspondence, subjoining this hint that typographical politics will not properly come within our plan, which being confined to no party civil or religious will not admit of party, much less of personal debate and altercation.

I shall from time to time communicate to you some information of the state of our affairs. This will counteract the false accounts carried down by the Tory ghosts, which accounts, I am informed, are published very regularly in the journals and gazettes of Tartarus. These publications, I am told, do sometimes find their way to Elysium and impose upon the unwary of that honest, and of consequence, unsuspicious country. By the present opportunity of a Whig shade going to Elysium, I have sent you down the last *Pennsylvania Packet,* and that containing the seventh number of the *Crisis,* [6] which paper is extremely well written. I am gentlemen, with great respect,

> Your most obedient
> and humble servant,
>
> One of the Moderns
>
> Philadelphia
> January 15, 1779

[*United States Magazine*
January 1779]

2. John Hampden.

3. Algernon Sidney (1622–1683) led a cavalry regiment in Fairfax's army under Cromwell and was devoted to the parliamentary cause. He was convicted for implication in the Rye House plot in 1683 and sent to the Tower on charges of high treason.

4. James Harrington (1611–1677), author of *Oceana,* follower of Cromwell.

5. Lord William Russel (1639–1683) joined Hampden and others in vehement antagonism to the court and in promotion of the Dissenters' cause. He was beheaded for implication in the Rye House plot.

6. *The Crisis Papers* of Thomas Paine.

The Cave of Vanhest

[*From January through July, the* United States Magazine *carried installments of a short story, the second piece of prose fiction from Brackenridge's pen. Although the last installment ends with a parenthetical "to be continued," the story of the narrator who discovers a new and compelling view of life is a complete one. The existing installments focus on the reactions of the narrator as he contrasts the blights of war with the blessed life of a hermit's family. The hermit is a cultured man who sustains an active interest in civilization but will not partake in it. He prefers to sow and reap his own plums. (The suggestion of even finer fruit to be reaped in the West indicates the author's contemplation of his own withdrawal from Philadelphia society.) The hermit has created a self-sustaining social unit which is not only cultured and beautiful but also protective of the weak, as symbolized by the care his daughter gives to a half-witted servant who suffers an injury.*

The hermit will not condemn civilization and postpones an explanation of his withdrawal from it. The explanation is rendered through the narrator's discovery of a new love—the ladies of the cave who represent the virtues of complete independence. He sees that he had confused his former loves—Miss Muse, Miss Theology, Miss Law—with his ambitions. The story presents the author's first painful realization that perhaps the muses had not favored him after all. Fundamentally Brackenridge is reflecting upon his own life in this story.]

In my younger years I had read much of that romantic kind of writing which fills every mountain with a hermitage so that you can scarcely miss your way in any part of the country, but you stumble in upon a residence of this kind and discover some old man who, when the usual civilities are over, tells you a long story of his conflicts with the evils and accidents of life until, sick of the world, he has retired from it to this cell in which alone he has found happiness. I have often wished it might, one day, be my special fortune to fall in with some such individual of the hill and to hear from his own mouth the tale of his disappointed love or ambition, and how it was that he could be happy in that solitude. Not unfrequently in my excursions to the country, I have missed my way through the bad information of the peasants directing me to go straight forward while the road, perhaps in the space of half a mile, was to bend into several angles and to send out paths to the thirty-two points of the compass. In this situation I have consoled myself with the hope that while I was wandering amongst the rocks I might have the good fortune to stumble in upon the cell of a hermit and be invited by him to partake of a mess of roots gathered from the soil or the milk which the wild goats of the mountain had afforded him. I have been a thousand times disappointed in my expectation and never had the pleasure to descry any mortal of this stamp until lately in a tour through the Jerseys in company with a young gentleman of Philadelphia.

We had rode out to see the field of Monmouth, and having made every observation to which our curiosity invited us, we proposed to return by the way of *Coryel's Ferry* so much spoken of while the two armies of the British and the Americans lay upon the Delaware. In this route we had traced the windings of the Raritan until we found ourselves upon the southwest branch of that river and amongst the mountains whence it takes its rise. We had missed the direct road and were endeavoring to regain it by a cross course through the country, shaded sometimes by the woods and sometimes by the projection of the precipice above us. The indistinctness of the path made it impossible to trace it, so that at last we wandered from it altogether and were at a loss which way to steer, when the glimmering of a taper through the disjointings of the rocky mountain gave us the hope of finding some hospitable dwelling where we might detain a few hours until the moon should be up to assist us in our journey. Approaching to the light we found a kind of gothic building in the bosom of the mountain. Knocking at the door through the crevices of which the light seemed to issue, a voice from within called to us, "Who is there?" We answered, "Friends." And immediately the door was opened to us by a man in a long white linen robe who desired us to walk in and be happy, if we could be happy in the cave of Vanhest.

We informed him in what manner we had lost our way, and added that we thought ourselves fortunate in falling in with the dwelling of a gentleman of his civility whom we hoped would be kind enough to give us some directions, [and] that as soon as the moon was up we might pursue our course to *Coryel's Ferry* on the Delaware. "My sons," said he, "you will detain with me tonight and tomorrow, if I cannot be able to prevail upon you to detain longer? You will better with the light of the day enter on your journey. You will find a bed in that apartment and you will oblige me by endeavoring to repose yourselves upon it until the morning shall arise to bless the mountains." We accepted very gracefully his hospitality and were lighted by him to a chamber where we found a very rich bed with the beautiful covering of a counterpane in which there were wrought many figures of the summer season of the year. Wishing us a good repose, he retired to his hall, which was but half divided from the apartment in which we lay, and gave us an opportunity to see him as he reclined on his sofa, a lamp burning by him, and a number of books strewed around him, in one of which he read in the intervals of his meditation.

We composed ourselves to sleep, not a little at a loss to account for the unusual appearance, language, and behavior of this person who had so courteously received us to what I now began to call his hermitage. His reply "Is it possible?" when we answered "Friends" was remarkable. It would seem, that disgusted with the world, he thought it a phenomenon to find a friend in it. (*to be continued*)

[*January 1779*]

The light began to dawn through a small window of the apartment in which we lay, when we proposed to arise and set out upon our journey. "My son," said the master of the cave, who in the meantime was awaked on the sofa and overheard our conversation, "this morning is unfavorable to the traveller. We shall have rain upon the earth; and as you are now sheltered by a friendly roof, be contented and wait a day of fair weather." "Sir," said I, "the sky appears somewhat cloudy, but we apprehend there will be but little rain." "Not so, my sons," said the master of the dwelling. "I perceive by the haziness that settles on the distant top of the mountain that we shall have a rain of some days continuance. Repose yourselves, my sons, and think not of leaving this retreat until fair weather with her dry breezes shall again come to visit us." Agreeable to his advice we composed ourselves to sleep, and the heavy air of the morning sealed up our eyes in a pleasing reverie of soft dreams and slumbers.

The day was considerably advanced when we were awaked by a soft voice penetrating to the room in which we lay in the following words, "All ye mortals who love food, come and taste of this repast. Here is water from the limpid rill wherewith to wash and prepare for breakfast." Having dressed ourselves with as much dispatch as possible, we advanced to the head of a staircase which communicated with our room; and beginning to descend, we were addressed from the lower floor at the bottom of the steps by the master of the dwelling, who had received us the evening before and now desired us to walk down to the lower apartment of the cave and partake of the repast prepared for us. We descended and were introduced by him to the mistress of the cave, a very amiable lady, who with two lovely daughters, just arriving to the years of women, bade us welcome, very welcome to the cave of Vanhest.

We cast our eyes around the subterranean apartment and were struck with the richness of the furniture. There stood a bed at one angle of the cave with a set of hangings of the finest chintz, variegated with a thousand flowers of the springing year. At another angle was placed a buffet replenished with china cups and bowls and with silver plates and vases of every shape and dimension. The floor was covered with a very rich carpet whose variety of figures resembled that which Themistocles alluded to in his conversation with the king of Persia. "Thought expressed in a foreign language and translated," said that great hero and philosopher, "is like a carpet rolled up; you see the bulk, but not the figures of it. But thought expressed in a native tongue is to those who hear it like the carpet of a king's hall unfolded, and discovering to the eye every spring, flower and fancy that the imagination of the artist has been able to inweave in its tapestried borders." Such was the carpet upon which we stepped in this subterranean residence. The neat but small mahogany table that stood upon it was that around which we sat down to breakfast and which supported a set of china cups depicted with the tops of the jonquil, also a silver tea urn of the most original construction. The lady handed each of us a dish of tea or coffee according to our choice, and this with a smile of complacency that gave us to see she thought herself happy in having it in her power to serve us. She was indeed a very amiable woman, above the middle stature, but finished in her person to the last degree of the most happy ease and elegance. Nevertheless my whole attention was soon diverted from her to a careful survey of her two lovely daughters. The eldest was of that class of beauties that are said to be more agreeable than handsome, that is with features not so regular but with an air and accomplishment of manner that engages the heart without giving warning that it is about to engage it. The younger of the two was all that the poets mean when they talk of Venus and the Graces. The plain of her forehead was beautifully rising; her eye-brow exquisitely painted; her eye itself vermilioned with blushes, and a small mole upon it was that on which the power of love seemed to erect his standard. The fine ringlets of her auburn hair flowed upon her shoulders and her bosom largely uncovered, as is the mode of these times, showed a skin that without touching it appeared as the down on the soft flower of the white rose.

We were waited on at breakfast by the dwarf of the cave, who was called Bernardus and in whose visage fortitude was painted like the shading of the twilight or the fog of a hazy eve. This we did not wonder at when we were informed that he had been born in the cave and had scarcely ever had the curiosity to go above ground. He had belonged to the man who built the cave, and who having died some years ago, left it to be inhabited by the present family on whom the boy continued to attend as on his former master.

A variety of conversation passed during breakfast. The gentleman himself did not speak a great deal, but what he did say discovered him a man of pious thought and attention to the ways of providence. "You observe," said he, "the Raritan is almost dried up, which bespeaks what we have experienced, a very dry summer; and yet, what must appear strange, we have never had more plenteous crops upon the fields than have been this season. We may readily explain the phenomenon by bringing into view that though in the course of this summer there have been no heavy rains to sink into the earth and fill the basins of the mountains, yet there have been a sufficiency of gentle showers to satisfy the soil and give vegetation to the fruits upon it. Hence it is that the crops are everywhere joyful, and in the meantime the channels of the rivers dry."

The day continued to be cloudy and to promise rain, which gave this pleasing family good ground of argument against our setting out upon our journey. We were indeed by this time so perfectly resigned to their pleasure that we sat down in a sweet and romantic disposition, ready to forget the world and all the hopes of eminence that we formed in it. (*to be continued*)

[*February 1779*]

"Sir," said I, addressing myself to the master of the cave, "this young gentleman who accompanies me and whom I have the pleasure to introduce to you is the son of a worthy citizen of Pennsylvania, who on a short excursion to the field of Monmouth famous for the battle lately fought between the American and British armies has done me the honor to put him under my care; and as his education has been considerably interrupted by the progress of the war in that state, I have endeavored in the meantime to be of some service to him by directing his attention to the study of the Latin language, in which he had made some proficiency before the frown of Mars had driven the Muses from our country. In the course of our small tour it has been useful for him at an early hour to recite to me a morning exercise in this language, and at noon, when we have withdrawn from the heat of the solar ray and have lain ourselves down by the margin of a brook, he has made it his amusement to translate a few passages from a classic author, which at our first setting out he had been careful to make the companion of his journey. I mention this circumstance as an apology for the request I am about to make, that you will permit me to suspend the happiness which I promise to myself from your agreeable conversation and to hear for a short time the young gentleman recite to me a page or two from this author."

"My son," said the master of the cave, "I am much pleased with your mode of travelling and instructing the youth at the same time, and it will be agreeable to me to hear him repeat to you his exercise in the Latin language which is of all others except Greek the noblest and most harmonious."

"Then," said I, "it only remains to apologize to the ladies and to enquire if it may be pardonable to obtrude on their ears, even for half an hour, the hard sounds of a foreign language which it is not to be supposed the sex are taught to understand."

"Sir," said the eldest of the two young ladies, "we have heard Papa read Latin, and though we do not understand the sounds, yet we think them not hard but musical; and were it not so, yet the politeness of your apology secures our complaisance, and whatsoever you are pleased to make the object of your attention will become our entertainment."

A page was recited, and the young ladies thought it a very odd language. The master of the cave commended very highly the docility and progress of the youth and made some observations on Salust, the author which was read, as an historian, who in one happy expression had oftentimes given us a character more clearly and fully than many others in a long delineation of the various passions, views, and interest of the person. From his observations on this author, he was led to speak of Thucydides whose conciseness he had copied, and of Livy and Tacitus, who had perhaps excelled him in judicious reflection upon men and things which became the subject of their story. From these he was drawn insensibly to speak of the orators and poets of antiquity, and in this excursion it was evident, from the great critical propriety with which he spoke of the character of every writer, that in his early years he had cropped the poppies of Arcadia and drank of the streams of Helicon, that he had visited the bower of Museus and conversed with Homer at the feast of Alcinous,[1] that in short he was acquainted with all the divine learning and genius of the ancients.

But recollecting himself, and returning from this classic ramble, "My son," said he, "you have made mention of the field of Monmouth which you have had the curiosity to visit, and were it not to give you the trouble of a tedious relation, I should be happy to hear from you some account of the action of that day, and what remarks you may have made upon the field where it was contended."

"Sir," said I, "it would be tedious to you to hear the whole account of the affairs of that day and impossible for me to relate them, as no regular account by those who were present had been yet published to the world; but I shall think myself happy in giving you any account of the smaller circumstances which I have collected from the inhabitants in the neighborhood of Monmouth, or any observation which I may have made of the traces of the battle on the plain where it was lately fought between the two armies.

"We arrived, Sir, in the evening at the church which stands at the northwest point of the plain at Monmouth. Here we were struck with the sight of six new graves, in which were interred a like number of American officers who had fallen in the battle. At the head of one of these graves was a board with a cross-bar on which was written, if I remember right, the name of Lieutenant Haymond of the Third Maryland Regiment. At this church it was that Captain Fant le Roy fell by a cannon ball which from the artillery of the enemy, at the distance of one and one-half mile, had made its way through an orchard of high trees, and as he was mounting his horse, passed level through his body. The orchard of which I speak had obscured the view of the enemy and from this circumstance, and the distance at which he was, this young gentleman, who I believe was only a spectator of the battle, had not apprehended that he was in any danger.

"From the church we proceeded to a farmer's house about one-half mile farther on the plain and just in the rear of that ground on which our army had been drawn up in three lines on the day of the engagement. Here we were received very hospitably, and the farmer, who was an intelligent and good-natured man, gave us a very particular account of what had happened in the neighborhood previous and subsequent to the battle. Amongst other things he related to us that on the approach of the two armies the inhabitants had

1. *The Odyssey,* vii.

carried out their household furniture, their beds, trunks, and other articles, to the woods, swamps, and hidden places of the country. Some they had buried under ground, or covered with the bramble bushes or the woodland leaves that lay upon the soil. These, whether found by the enemy or by our own army equally rapacious, were the greater part carried off. The enemy in many places had taken up the floors of the house, and for the purpose of searching places where they might suspect things to be buried, they had long pikes which they thrust under ground. From this circumstance a very odd incident had happened in the town of Monmouth. A gentleman had hastily buried on the approach of the enemy, his plate, papers, and a large sum of money in an earthen pot in his garden. In the hurry of his spirits he had left his spade on the very spot where he had deposited his wealth. The enemy, on advancing to the town, were led by this circumstance directly to explore it with their pikes and to dig up the soil to a considerable depth. The gentleman returning home, when the enemy had left the village the day succeeding that of the engagement, saw the earth removed in his garden and gave his treasure up for lost. He sat himself down resigned to the loss which was to be attributed more to the will of providence than to any want of care or industry on his part. His wife, however, could not so easily console herself but continued greatly distressed on seeing themselves reduced almost to poverty. In this agitation of her mind, she had a dream the succeeding night that the pot was still in that spot of the garden where it had been deposited. Her husband labored to drive it from her thoughts and reasoned with her on the great improbability that the enemy would dig up the soil and find the pot, as they must have found it, and yet not take it with them. Nevertheless no reasoning would satisfy her, but he must dig up the ground in the morning and try whether it might not be there still. Agreeably to her request the ground was dug up, and at a considerable less depth than the enemy had penetrated, the pot was found, split asunder by a pike which had struck it and passed transversely through its side.

"With these and the like circumstances our host entertained us for the evening, and this with much cheerfulness, as he himself had escaped the ravage of the enemy; for I find it in human nature that even when we commiserate the evils and distresses of others, we draw some consolation from it that we ourselves are not in the same situation."

"My son," said the master of the cave, "you draw an unfavorable picture of human nature; nevertheless I believe there is too much truth in it; but go on, if you please, for the small circumstances of your story are to me very entertaining."

"Sir," continued I, "early on the next morning our host became our guide, and we rode to take a view of the field of battle. To the east of the plain and on the left of our line of battle, Lord Stirling [2] had been posted near a graveyard, on a bold and commanding eminence, with a morass for several miles running at right angles to the line of his array and securing his left flank from any attempt of the enemy to turn it. From this eminence his artillery annoyed the enemy in a line diagonally drawn to a height occupied on their part at the distance of about a mile, and from whence he was answered for the space of two hours without intermission.

"On the right of his Lordship, and in front of the main line of battle, was our principal park of artillery, which played incessantly upon the enemy at nearly the same distance of one mile, and here we could perceive the shattered frames of the carriages of dismounted pieces, the deep beds wrought in the earth by the recoiling of the cannon, the furrows ploughed upon the hill, and the trenches cut by the balls which striking it had made their way for some distance, or again rebounded from the soil and sought a course through the lines or above the heads of the soldiery.

"On the northeast of the intermediate ground before the enemy was an old orchard to which they had penetrated, crossing a morass passable to light-armed troops only. In this orchard they were met by the artillery under Lord Stirling, whose right flank they had in view to gain and who on this occasion made a very great slaughter with his grape shot and obliged them to retire, leaving seventy-five dead upon the soil.

"In the front of our main battle, and just at the foot of the eminence possessed by the enemy, was a morass undetermined in length and about one hundred yards in breadth, passable but not easily to foot and horse but impassable to the artillery, save at one place slightly bridged by split pieces of timber, six or eight feet in length, laid across it. This bridge for a considerable time had been raked by one of our pieces under cover of a point of woods, which piece was afterwards dismounted, and we saw the broken splinters of the carriage scattered everywhere around the spot where it had been planted.

2. Lord William Alexander Stirling (1726–1783), Major General in the American Army.

"In this spot, by what had been told me, fell Lieutenant James M'Nair of the artillery, having his head taken off by a cannon ball. I was truly sorry for his death, having known the mild disposition and the merit of the man. From his less elevated rank as an officer, he will never be taken notice of by the historian, and yet he is no less deserving of renown than those in the band of brothers who have fallen at the head of a brigade or battalion.

"The bridge in front had been so raked that the enemy were cut down as they came upon it, but a body in the meantime had passed the morass to the right of the bridge and advanced in the front of our lines over some low ground a considerable distance, but beginning to ascend the hill they suffered much and were driven back by the artillery to which they were exposed. Here we saw a grave in which it would seem that just on their retreat they had buried hastily one of their number, and that so slightly in the earth that one foot of the poor fellow was still uncovered; and though he had been once our enemy, yet touched with humanity, we did him the small office of throwing the loose soil over him to a greater depth." (to be continued)

[March 1779]

. . . I had finished my narration, and the hermit of the cave was silent; but from the kindling lustre of his eyes, at every circumstance which in the course of the narration reflected honor on the arms of America, it was evident that he was in sentiment a Whig.

Nevertheless I was still greatly at a loss to know what could be the cause of his retirement to his present solitude. On my first acquaintance with him, I had thought it possible he might be disaffected with the present cause of America, and had withdrawn to this mountain that he might not be under the necessity of taking any part in the contest. But the visible benevolence and good sense of the man, and at the same time the pleasure discoverable in his countenance on every circumstance of advantage in our favor, placed it beyond a doubt that he was a friend to America. However, I had a desire to know his history, and for this reason, after some preface of smooth words, hinted to him that curiosity which had naturally been excited in my mind, and requested him, though in a manner distant, and with some degree of that delicacy which the circumstance required, that it would give me great pleasure to hear the life and travels of a man of his years and experience.

"My son," said he, "I will with great pleasure gratify your very natural and pardonable curiosity. But the story of my life is saddened with adversity and will accord better with the shadows of the evening. Until that time give me leave to defer the narrative. The day you see is become bright with the rays of the cloud-dispelling sun. It is time that we go upon the soil to collect fruits and vegetables for the short repast of the dinner hour. After which it will remain for the slow hours of the day that we try the river with the hook and return home to light up the cave with the twilight lamp, and while Bernardus dresses what we may have taken, it will [be] our amusement to recall former times, and repeat with a melancholy pleasure, the laborious toils of experience in the ways of men." (*to be continued*)

[*May 1779*]

Issuing from the cave in the bosom of the mountain, we walked upon the margin of the Raritan and found ourselves by a large plumb tree which, having shaken, we filled a basket with the fruit, which was luscious and refrigerating to the taste. We were led insensibly to speak of the nature of plumb trees.

"There is," said the hermit, "your great damask plumb. This is a pretty large plumb, inclining to an oval shape; the outside is of a dark blue covered with a violet bloom; the juice is richly sugared; the flesh is yellow and parts from the stone.

"There is your red imperial plumb. This is a large oval-shaped fruit of a deep red color, covered with a fine bloom. It is excellent for sweet meats.

"There is your myrobalan plumb. This is a middle-sized fruit of a round shape. It is ripe in August. But indeed there are a variety of plumbs; and amongst them all there is none of which I am fonder than the cherry plumb. It is round and is of a red color. The stalk is long like that of a cherry, which this fruit so much resembles as not to be distinguished at some distance. The blossoms of this tree come out very early in the spring, and being very tender, are oftentimes destroyed by cold; but it affords a very agreeable prospect in the spring, for these trees are generally covered with flowers which open about the same time with the almonds so that when they are intermixed therewith they make a beautiful appearance before many other sorts put out; but by their blossoming so early, there are few years that they have much fruit.

"Besides these," continued he, "there is the white pear plumb, which is a very good fruit. There is also the musele plumb and the Julian plumb and the Mogul plumb."

"There are," said I, "a great variety of plumbs in the different soils of America."

"Yes," replied the hermit, "and some of them very fine; equal, if not superior to any to be found in Europe or the more eastern countries. This plumb, which is of the red cherry kind, is excellent to be eaten from the tree and suits very well for sweet meats. I have been told there are fine plumbs on the creeks to the westward."

"I have seen some very good," said I, "on the creeks of Elk and Octorara; but in the state of Maryland, on Deer Creek, there are much better; though I am told that to the westward they are still in greater quantities and of better quality."

By this time we had filled our basket, and remeasuring back the margin of the Raritan, we found ourselves at the entrance of the cave, and were saluted by the younger of the two young ladies in a stream of tears. Beauty in distress is perhaps the most melting sight in nature. The cause was that Bernardus, having conceived a great affection for the young gentleman who had walked with us to the plumb tree, had been willing to follow and to be one of the company; but poor fellow, he had been so long accustomed to the cave that as soon as he had reached the head of the steps that led from it, in the rays of the sun he began to hallucinate, and turning to get in again he fell from the steps, and had hurt his ankle in the fall. The young lady was of the opinion that poor Nardy's foot was broke, and that it might be past all remedy.

I easily conceived that a very small hurt might give rise to Nardy's complaint and to the young lady's apprehensions, and therefore [I] was perfectly composed. Nevertheless, with as much condescension and appearance of humanity as possible, [I] told her, that having read many books in my early years and having spent some time in the army, where hurts were very frequent, I had acquired a considerable skill in the treatment of them, and made no doubt but that with the help of bandages and vinegar, I could restore him to his feet again in a very short time. The hermit smiled; for knowing well, I suppose, how great an alarm a small affair will give to a tender breast, he was easy with regard to the circumstance of Nardy's fall, and was disposed to be

diverted with the serious and grave manner in which I addressed myself to the young lady, entering into all her sympathies and mixing my
assuasives kindly with her griefs.

"Nardy," said I, "where is your ankle hurt?" "Here, Sir," said he,
pointing to it. "Yes, yes," said I, "I perceive the whole affair at one
single glance. It is not a dislocation or a fracture, nor indeed anything
but a small disprain that will be speedily relieved by a few simple
applications."

I saw the rays of returning pleasure begin to dart through the
crystal tear that now hestitated to descend from the young lady's eye.

"Miss," said I, "I shall be greatly honored by having presented to
me by your hand a small bit of linen for a bandage and at the same
time a little vinegar made warm to bathe the ankle, which remedy
of bathing, in a case of this nature, I have always found to be without
fail efficacious."

The bit of linen was presented to me, and at the same time the
vinegar, with which having washed the lad's ankle and having bound
it up, he himself, whose hurt was more in imagination than in feeling,
began to recover spirits; and the young lady who had shared particularly in sympathy with his misfortune and was attentive to him in
assisting me to bandage and to bathe his ankle, was cheered like a
vernal day after April flowers.

Bernardus was composed away in an angle of the cave, upon a bed
of green leaves, and we sat down to dinner. *(to be continued)*

[*June 1779*]

Plumbs shaken from the tree, peaches gathered from an orchard
on the brow of the hill above, apples at the same time, vegetables
from the garden, dried fish, milk, cheese, butter were upon the board;
and intermingling a variety of conversation on the nature of the
several fruits, and on other matters, we had now dined. "Sir," said
the lady of the cave, "I have heard your request to the gentleman,
whom with some propriety you will call a hermit, that he would be
pleased to relate a sample of his life and travels. This, as according
better with descending shades, he has deferred to the evening. But
in the meantime, may it not be possible to prevail with you, Sir, to
give some sketch of what you may have seen in life? It is true, not
more than one-third of yours can be yet past; but as some part even of

the story of an old man is the fortune of his early years, why may it not be proper in a young man to relate the history of that part of life which he has just passed over?"

"Madam," said I, "I am ready to obey you in this so very reasonable command, but you are not to expect in my story any great example of uncommon fortitude struggling with adversity, for the history of youth is rather that of follies than misfortunes. Nevertheless my life has had some varieties, and these have arisen chiefly, as is usual with young men, from the indulgence of one single passion, love.

"My father was a worthy good man, who wishing to see me step along the quiet vale of life, as he had done, had entertained the thought of matching me with a farmer's daughter of the neighborhood in which he lived. But I had heard of the Miss Muses, who were great beauties." "The Miss Maises, did you say, Sir?" said the lady. "No, Madam, the Miss Muses, of whom I had heard much and had long desired to see. At length having cultivated an acquaintance with a worthy clergyman in their neighborhood, I was introduced to them; for as the young ladies had no father living, and they were by themselves, nine sisters of them, they did not choose to be visited by every one. Miss Urany Muse, you must know, was my flame: The same lady that Milton talks of when he says,

> Descend from heaven, Urania, by that name,
> If rightly thou art called.[3]

"The old bard, kindling into rapture at the name of so great a beauty, could not help calling that ground heaven where this young lady with her sisters dwelt. And indeed from the pleasant situation of the hill on the bending river of Castalia, and from the laurel with which it was everywhere planted out, and from the poems of divine thought which these young ladies sung to harpsichords and violins, it was little short of heaven. I was in love, that is the truth of it, and every thing said was to me the speech of paradise.

"I shall not stop to tell you the many pleasant evening walks that I had on this hill, and the tender things that Miss Urany deigned to say to me, for I cannot yet be persuaded but that I possessed some share of her affection. Nevertheless, it has so come to pass that the hope I had entertained of making her one day my own has long since vanished. The circumstances of this small affair must remain a secret to the world. Perhaps when I die some hint of it may be found amongst my papers, and some friend may inscribe it on my tomb.

3. *Paradise Lost*, vii, 1.

"The next fair young lady for whom I conceived an affection was Miss Theology, a young lady of indeed great merit, and who had been sometimes mentioned to me by my friends. But whether it is because we are apt to dislike those who are too much pressed upon us, or whether it is that the will of heaven gave a new current to the affections of my heart, I cannot tell; but I had until this hour set light by her, and could see nothing handsome in her person or captivating in her air and manner. My affection for Miss Theology was a stream of love springing from a cold aversion.

"I have loved Miss Theology, and for five years I paid her a constant attention. But so it is that though with much condescension and many marks of tenderness she received my addresses, yet we both saw the necessity of ceasing to indulge any fond thought of a union. This has cost me many sighs; and it is my only consolation that we are hastening to a state where circumstances of a various nature will not intervene to divert us from the company of those persons whom we value highest and whose conversation will be no small ingredient in the happiness of that clime where the spirits of the just are made perfect.

"The present object of my soft attentions is a Miss Law, a grave and comely young lady, a little pitted with the small pox.

"Her steward, an old fellow of the name of Coke, is a dry queer genius, and with him I have almost every day a quarrel. However, upon the whole I am pleased with the old fellow, and tossing him about with a string of young fellows of a more cheerful vein, and who are likewise attached to the family of Miss Law, I make myself merry with him. This young lady is of a prudent industrious turn, and though she does not possess at present any very great fortune, yet what she has in expectancy is considerable. I have paid my addresses to her now about a year. But I begin to apprehend that the beauty of some persons not so far distant as the head of the gulf of California is in a confederacy to draw me away from her, and whereas I first set out with a warmth of affection for the young ladies of the hill [4] I shall this day fall a victim to the young ladies of the cave."

The young ladies smiled. But it was now time to try the river with the hook, and we advanced on the margin of the Raritan accordingly. (*to be continued*)

[*United States Magazine*
January–July 1779]

4. Parnassus.

Before the Battle of Brandywine

A publication containing six political discourses made its appearance last winter, which discourses the author had originally drawn up to be delivered in the army. He had written several others, which at that time he did not make public. These, with some additional performances of this kind, he now offers through the channel of the *United States Magazine.*

"Noah a Preacher of Righteousness." 2 Pet. ii, 5.

As a hill at a distance, or an old castle wrapt in fog, it is venerably pleasing to travel down through antiquity, and to call to mind the memory of great and good men who have lived before us. At the same time it is useful, as the part which they sustained on the stage of life and the character which they left behind them may serve to excite our emulation to attain to the same rememberance. With this view, suffer me to take back your attention to the age of venerable Noah, while with me you consider:

1. The state of the world in his time
2. His character, a preacher
3. His doctrine, righteousness
4. Apply the subject

1. The state of the world in his time. I do not mean to consider the state of society, or the political establishments at this early period. I do not know what may have been the population of the world or the progress of the human mind in the knowledge of arts, government, or science. It is possible that in the course of more than 1,500 years, the space of time elapsed from the creation to the deluge, the earth may have been pretty generally inhabited. It is possible the arts and sciences might have been carried to a very great perfection. It is possible that great states may have flourished, equal in policy and commerce to any on the earth at present. These things are possible, and a great deal might be said to illustrate the possibility.

But I shall confine myself to consider the religious and moral state of the world in the last centuries of this old and decayed period. This, we have full reason to believe, was by no means prosperous; for we read that the wickedness of man was very great: "All flesh had corrupted his way upon the earth." [1] Human nature lost its beauty and perfection in the melancholy lapse of our great progenitor; and

1. Genesis, vi, 12.

Cain his first-born soon gave an instance of that horrid enmity and murder which the human heart is capable to entertain and perpetrate. The family of Cain, early driven to the land of Nod, and deprived of the instruction of their father Adam, sunk down to the deepest ignorance, and by the bad examples of a parent became greatly immoral in their conduct; debauchery and every vice rioted and had its full dominion in their hearts. Not contented with the self-possession of their own wickedness, they labored to seduce the kindred family of Seth, which had been religiously educated and retained some degrees of moral purity and virtue. They attempted it by introducing to their tents loose but fair women with music and dancing which effeminate the soul. By this means they, in part, accomplished their purpose; for many of the family of Seth, by an intermarriage with the family of Cain, became infected with their manners and degenerated to the same degree of immorality. Milton has imaged the circumstance with great delicacy of description—

> They, on the plain, long had not walk'd,
> When from the tents, behold, a bevy of fair women,
> Richly gay, in gems and wanton dress; to the harp they sung
> Soft amorous ditties, and in dance came on.[2]

From this unhappy mixture, giants, it is said, were born. Providence set a mark of infamy upon it by causing the misshappen offspring to be of an unwieldy and monstrous bulk of body; hateful, and by their great strength, hurtful to society. From this connection sprang also men who were of old, men of renown. These were the conquerors and battle-men; the Howes, the Clintons, the Erskines, and the Greys [3] of that early period. These fought for war and waded to empire through a sea of blood. These wished to be the first upon the earth for having done some marvellous exploit, such as that of subduing two or three kingdoms. This is evident from that expression of scripture, "The earth was filled with violence." [4]

It is reasonable to suppose that it was against the unoffending of the line of Seth that the first tyranny made its horrid inroads. Many a man perished in opposing it; many a brave and patriotic Warren,[5] many an intrepid and virtuous Montgomery.[6] Tyranny pre-

2. *Paradise Lost*, xi, 581–84
3. Major General Sir William Howe, Major General Henry Clinton, Brigadier General Sir William Erskine, and Major General Charles Grey were British leaders at the Battle of Brandywine.
4. Genesis vi, 11.
5. Dr. Joseph Warren, killed at Bunker Hill, 1775.
6. General Richard Montgomery, killed at Quebec, 1775.

vailed; and in the age of Noah, every thing was put to death that had been good and great upon the earth.

2. Noah's character, a preacher. I shall not say that he was in orders regularly bred and appointed; for I do not know that any line of education for the church was as yet regularly established. Be this as it may, his blameless life was a constant sermon to his neighbors. His admonitions and instructions more especially gave him a title to the character of preacher. He bore an open and an honest testimony against the manners of the age in which he lived. He warned individuals and he warned publicly. The mountain on which he built the ark may have been principally his pulpit. Multitudes of persons, no doubt, had come to visit him upon this eminence. It was a new thing to build a vessel on the mountain top and so distant from the waters. The opportunity of multitudes convened upon the mountain, he frequently embraced to rouse them to a sense of anger and to call them to repentance. From the mountain, as a type of Christ, he preached every day to one or other party who, led by curiosity, had come to visit him. The seventh day, forgotten by the world as a Sabbath but kept by them as a day of recreation and amusement, may have been that on which he delivered them the most alarming discourses. On this day, he himself rested from his labor; and on this day, as a holy day, it may have been agreed upon to meet in one and another pleasant party to take a walk to see the old grey-headed preacher on the mountain. That we may conceive what he may have said to them, let us consider:

3. His doctrine, righteousness. The word rendered righteousness has its origin from the word which signifies law. By law we are to understand the relation of man to the Deity and the relation of man to his neighbor. Conformity of action to the first conceived line is religion, and conformity of action to the second is moral equity and justice. Both of these are included in the word righteousness. There is also implied in it that which is the sanction of the law, rewards and punishments.

"Sons and daughters of the fallen and unhappy Adam, you are struck with surprise to see me thus engaged on the mountain. You are not able to conceive what I mean by this ark which you see abuilding. It is far from the ocean and the rivers, and it is not in the usual course of nature that the water should forsake its bed and rise to a level with this eminence. Nevertheless the day is fast approaching when such shall be the great phenomenon of nature. Not long hence you shall behold the ocean swell. That ocean to the south shall forsake its bed and roll its billows on the summit of this mountain. The fountains of the great deep shall be broken up. They shall burst from their confinement and pour a deluge on the world. The storms shall descend and mingle from above. The water shall prevail upon the earth. Fifteen cubits higher than the summit of the highest mountain shall they rise. All flesh shall perish. Everything that hath in it the breath of life shall be destroyed. It is therefore high time that you arouse yourself and break off every wicked course of action. You have seen (many of you) Methuselah and have heard of the piety of Enoch. How far are you degenerated from the piety of such great originals? For this is the wrath of God about to come upon you; and vengeance, speedy vengeance is threatened to the world. Repent therefore of your crimes, that when the Mighty Judge shall overwhelm the world in the burial place of waters, he may extend mercy to your spirits."

4. I am, in the last place, to apply the subject. The state of the world, at least in this quarter of it, at the present time is not much unlike the state of the world at the time of Noah. The earth is filled with violence. Wicked men, if not the lineal descendants yet the spirit of the first-born Cain, have ravaged our globe. Brothers by language, by religion, by consanguinity (many of them) have sheathed their swords in a brother's breast. The famine of the jail, the fever of the camp, the sickness of the hospitals, and the death-bed wounds of the soldier on the field of battle have wasted many parts of our country. In the meantime the voice of many honest men, like the voice of Noah on the mountain, has been lifted up to dissuade from a course of action so hostile to others and so pernicious to themselves. The voice of a Burke,[7] a Price,[8] and a bishop of St. Asaph has been lifted up against the injustice of the claim of Britain, and the ruinous consequences of persisting in it. The voice of a noble and incorrupt minority of Lords and Commons has been lifted up to reclaim (if possible) the steps of those in power in their wild career of unchecked and unlimited ambition. The voice of many wise men amongst the neighboring nations on the continent of Europe has been lifted up in expressions of astonishment at the mad system that has been adopted by an infatuated ministry against the right of human nature. The voice of many thousand statesmen and patriots on the mountain tops

7. Edmund Burke supported the colonists' cause. His views are expressed in "Speech on American Taxation" (1774) and "Speech on Conciliation with Americans" (1775).

8. Richard Price, a friend of Benjamin Franklin and author of "Observations on Civil Rights and the Justice and Policy of the War with America" (1777) .

and the far-bending shores of America has been lifted up; and it is the declaration that they will enjoy freedom or die in the attempt to support it. It is the universal sound of the mighty voice: "Desist O Britain from the cruel thought of subjugating men whose birth-right is liberty; and let not the sharp edge of tyranny be rendered still more sharp, that like a machine of swift wheels and edges, when the food which supplied it amongst the others is exhausted, it may return and grind upon thy own substance. It is thy glory, O Britain, to be free; and it is even thy happiness that America be independent. Recall speedily thy troops from her long-scourged shores. Revoke thy bloody edicts, and give peace to a bleeding, but unconquered and still to be unconquered country."

This is the voice of nations; and my voice mixing with it, like a small current running to the ocean, would repeat the loud sound and pronounce a *Momento mori* [9] to Britain. Even though hostile, yet I feel myself interested in her fate. I call to mind the sweet remembrance of her once friendly plains, her white rocks, and her full-resounding shores. I travel in imagination on the banks of the Cam, the Isis, and the Avon, where the fair form of Shakespeare rises to my view. I am touched with the magic sound of a Milton's harp, and the lyre of a Gray modulating soft music to my ravished ear. I lift my thought to the noble strain of a Pope, and feel the enthusiasm of the bard rushing on my soul.[10] I walk with her philosophers—the Lockes, the Bacons, and the Newtons that she boasts. I mingle with her statesmen and patriots of every name—her Sir Thomas Mores, her William Temples, her Hampdens, her Sidneys, her Raleighs, her Harringtons, her Russels, and all the illustrious throng that adorns her chronology in every age. I feel a momentary impulse of concern for a country that gave these noble spirits birth. I could wish that, bounded in her empire, she were immortal in her date. But the will of Heaven has determined otherwise, and she is infatuated in her counsels. Her renown is declining from its summit. Her great names fade upon my sight. Her virtue, her patriotism disappears: her glory in commerce and in war is wholly gone. She is lost from the things that are, and the cold shades of oblivion are gathering on her isle.

[*United States Magazine*
March 1779]

9. Remember you die.
10. The quality of enthusiasm is seldom attributed to the work of Alexander Pope.

Establishment of These United States
An American Account

[*Growing up in York County, Pennsylvania, Brackenridge probably witnessed cruel Indian attacks which helped form his lifelong prejudices. To him the Indians were savage animals. He rejected the noble savage concept. In the "Establishment of These United States," he relies on biblical authority to sustain his rationale for denying the Indians any rights to the American soil. The land, he argues, belongs to men who will cultivate it, not to those who remain in the state of hunters. In terms of economy, an animal who lives by the hunt requires a vast extent of land. Through cultivation, however, a civilized man requires but little land, thereby allowing all men a share of God's bounty. A man has no mandate from God to occupy more land than he can use for his personal needs. To accommodate all men, the soil must be cultivated. This argument also denies the British any rights in America. Their claim is based on discovery, not on cultivation.*]

The right of Great Britain to the soil of North America, founded on the first discovery of the coast, however just in its nature, yet was limited in its extent by the right of the natives and the right of other nations. The right of the natives has been generally supposed not to limit but to exclude all others. For the law of nature vests the soil in the first occupant, and these from the earliest times had possessed the country. But shall a few tribes thinly scattered over an immense continent retain possession of it while other parts of the globe are overcharged with inhabitants?

I set this matter in a clear point of view. We shall revert to the origin of that right which all men have in common with each other, to the earth, the water, and the air; and this we shall find in that extensive grant to the first pair, and in them equally to all their descendants. This grant is recorded in the first chapter and the first book of the sacred law: "And God blessed them, and God said unto them, be fruitful and multiply and replenish the earth, and subdue it; and have dominion over the fish of the sea, and over the fowl of the air, and over every thing that moveth upon the earth." The words of this grant convey no right of primogeniture or any other right by which one man may occupy a larger portion of the soil than his neighbor; for rights of this kind are the establishments of civil policy, and can have no place between individuals in a state of nature, or between different nations who are in a state of nature with relation to each other. The unequal distribution of the soil would disappoint the manifest intention of the grant, which was to people and improve the earth; for it is unfavorable to population that societies or individuals should possess a greater quantity of soil than is necessary for their own subsistence.

To apply this to the aborigines or native Indians of America: shall these tribes, inferior in number to perhaps one-twentieth of the inhabitants of Europe, possess ten times the territory? It will be said that their manner of life makes a greater quantity of soil necessary. They live by hunting. And though their tribes are thinly scattered over this continent, yet the whole is not more than sufficient for a hunting ground; nay, with even this extent of country their subsistence is precarious, and they frequently experience the severest rage of famine when the wild animals that make their food are rendered scarce or have withdrawn to a different forest of the country. But do the laws of revelation or of nature leave every man at liberty to use what manner of life he pleases? This will deserve some consideration.

Before the fall the earth spontaneously brought forth every herb and every tree for the use of man, and we may reasonably presume that without cultivation it would then support a larger number of inhabitants than it can at present with the utmost labor we are able to bestow upon it. In this state of things it was not necessary to exercise the arts of industry; but when the curse attendant on the lapse of Adam "glanced aslope upon the ground" [1] and it became sterile, the cultivation of it was enjoined on man, not only as his punishment, but as now the only means by which he could support himself and comply with the conditions of the grant, "replenish the earth and subdue it. The Lord God sent (the first man) forth from the garden of Eden to till the ground." [2]

I acknowledge in the early times the cultivation of the earth was not so immediately enjoined as necessary; for the few inhabitants might live by pasturage; and for some space of time posterior to the general deluge, when the flesh of animals was given to the use of man, they might subsist by hunting; but on the closer settlement of families and nations, this manner of life became impossible to one without engrossing more territory than could be spared to another, and as all could not subsist in this manner, no one had a right to claim it as an exclusive privilege.

The law of nature, where the law of revelation is not known, sufficiently enjoins on every man that he contract his claim of soil to equal bounds, and pursue that manner of life which is most con-

1. *Paradise Lost*, x, 1054.
2. Genesis iii, 23.

sistent with the general population of the earth and the increase of happiness to mankind. And it will easily appear that the mode of life by pasturage or hunting requires a more extensive territory than by agriculture; and at the same time from the very circumstance of thin and scattered settlements in that state, the powers of genius are inactive, the arts and sciences remain unknown, and man continues to be an animal differing in nothing but in shape from the beasts of prey that roam upon the mountain. The life of these is therefore not human, for it is abhorrent from the way of life which God and nature points out as the life of man. "The Lord God sent him forth to till the ground," and common reason has discovered that from the goodness and benevolence apparent in the whole creation, and from that provision made abundantly for every creature, it must be most agreeable to the Creator that the earth be stored with inhabitants; and that in order to this end, a way of life be chosen in which individuals or particular nations may subsist with the least extent of territory.

The aborigines of this continent can therefore have but small pretense to a soil which they have never cultivated. The most they can with justice claim is a right to those spots of ground where their wigwams have been planted and to so much of the soil around them as may be necessary to produce grain to support them in their families or towns upon the coast or in the inland country where they have inhabited. Perhaps they may have some priority of rights to occupy a different tract of country, should it be their choice to change the situation where former circumstances may have placed them.

The continent of North America may therefore, on the first discovery of the coast by any civilized European nation, be considered as the greater part of it, a vacant country, and liable to become the property of those who should take the trouble to possess it. Nevertheless I do not mean to justify the waging an unnecessary war against the natives or the extirpation of them altogether; but yet I would justify encroachment on the territory claimed by them until they are reduced to smaller bounds and under the necessity of changing their unpolished and ferocious state of life for fixed habitations and the arts of agriculture. At the same time I think it still advisable to purchase from them, if it may be done conveniently, because it is a dictate of humanity to decline insisting on the full extent of any claim of property, if it may involve the shedding of the blood of those who though sunk beneath the dignity of human nature yet bear resemblance and are seen in the shape of men.

From the whole of this reasoning it will be evident that the right of Great Britain to the soil of this continent, in consequence of the first discovery of the coast, was limited by the rights of the aborigines or native Indians found upon it. But it was limited in small degree, and the greater part of this immense territory was then, in strict view of revealed and of natural law, without an owner or inhabitant. (*to be continued*)

[*April 1779*]

The right of Great Britain to the soil of North America, limited by the right of the natives, was also limited by the right of other nations. The terms of the grant made to Adam, and renewed to Noah, equally embraced the whole of their descendants. The earth lay in common, and the occupancy of a portion of the soil was that alone which gave to individuals an exclusive right to hold it. We must restrict the right of occupancy to a moderate portion of the soil, because it is inconsistent with the original condition and express purpose of the grant that an individual or nation should possess a more extensive tract of country than is necessary for their particular subsistence. I have no doubt but that a nation greatly populous, whose numbers overcharge the soil, have a right to demand territory from a nation in possession of a soil equally fertile and less abounding with inhabitants.

From the position which I have established, that it is the occupancy of a portion of the soil necessary for subsistence that alone gives a right to hold it, it will follow that the circumstance of having first visited a country cannot give a right to any greater portion of the territory than is necessary for subsistence; and not indeed to any portion of it, unless the visitant persons [are] to occupy and dwell upon it. Perhaps it may confer a priority of right to occupy the soil while it shall be unoccupied by any other visitant.

We shall be sensible of this, if adverting to the early emigrations we consider that it would have been absurd in Japheth the eldest son of Noah, wandering westwards from the mountains of Armenia,[3] where the ark rested, to have advanced a claim to two or three countries, because in his way of life by pasturage or hunting he had first passed their mountains or first visited their boundaries.

The right of discovery was unknown in term or idea to the early

3. Genesis x, 2, 5.

ages, and it came first into view on the modern improvements in the arts of navigation, when several of the sovereigns and states of Europe fitted out vessels to explore the seas and to make discoveries. The expense and labor of the enterprise would seem to give a right to the soil of that continent or island which they had discovered. But it may be said that an exclusive right of this kind would be unfavorable to the settlement of that country, and therefore could have no place even amongst the sovereigns and states of Europe, who by tacit and implied consent had submitted to it. Much less could it have a place amongst the claims of other nations of the world, who in no way by direct assent or implication had come to such agreement. In the meantime it will appear from history that the claim of right, founded on first discovery of the coast, was usurped by several of the sovereigns and states of Europe, rather than acknowledged by the others who had been equally adventurous or successful in expeditions of this nature. The Swedes and Dutch seem to have paid no regard to the claim of Britain, founded on the first discovery of Sebastian Cabot,[4] who coasted North America; for maugre [*in spite of*] this claim, the Dutch took possession of the country of New York and the Swedes of Pennsylvania. No state or individual ought to have regarded it; for no expense, enterprise, or labor of a nation or of an individual can give a right which in its operation would defeat the end in view by the Creator, which was that the earth be fully stocked with inhabitants. To this great end every claim and institution of a partial nature ought to be subordinate. The claim therefore of the first adventurers could with justice only be to so much of the soil as they themselves immediately should occupy and plant and settle with inhabitants. These things may be said plausibly; it is to be considered that from the (*to be continued*)

[*May 1779*]

heart of Asia where man was first planted, it was an easy thing to emigrate and discover new countries. Hence it is that a pretense of right, from the first discovery of a country, would in these early ages have been vain, and we hear nothing of it. But when the whole eastern continent and the islands of the coast had been visited and planted, it

4. The discovery of the North American coast in 1497 is attributed to John Cabot, the father of Sebastian.

became an object of the industry of man and required much sagacity, fortitude, and perseverance to explore the ocean and effect discoveries. It was at the same time an affair of no small expense to fit out vessels for the voyage.

For these reasons natural justice would seem to give to the adventurers not only a priority of right to occupy a new discovered country, but also a right to demand from others some consideration in services of money for admission to it.

The only reason to be urged against the claim from a discovery is that it is not favorable to the population of the earth that individuals, on any pretense whatsoever, should hold a greater portion of the soil than is necessary for their particular subsistence. But it is to be considered that it is favorable to population, because it is favorable to discovery of unknown regions of the earth that the individual who by much labor and expense hath effected the discovery shall nevertheless enjoy no advantage resulting from his ingenuity and enterprise. But [he shall hold] a priority of right to occupy an equal portion of the soil with him who, led by the information of the first navigator, shall come to settle on it. The best argument in favor of the right of a first discoverer will therefore be that, by giving due encouragement to men who shall search the globe by sea and land and discover new soil, the whole earth will become peopled. And it seems to be the will of the Creator that the whole earth be stocked with inhabitants.

[*United States Magazine*
April–June 1779]

Thoughts on the Enfranchisement of the Negroes

[*Later issues of the* United States Magazine *were filled with reprints of state constitutions and other documents. But the last issue contained a surprise—a public expression of disgust with black slavery and a proposal for abolishing it. The article forewarns the infant democracy that the institution of slavery not only offends the sensibilities of any humane person but also "casts a shade upon the face of this country." Attributing the causes of slavery to a dominant Calvinism, Brackenridge proposes a solution. If the white man cannot accept those of different color, let him not suffer the sight. Free the slave and give him the land beyond the Alleghenies for his livelihood.*]

It casts a shade upon the face of this country that some of those who cultivate her soil are slaves; slaves, not to Britain, but to men who are themselves free. I know that many things are said to justify or palliate the circumstance, for it is with great reluctance that men admit the truth in cases where their interest is in question. Some time ago it was told me by a Calvinist and, to my astonishment, a man of understanding above the common level, that as some had been pre-destined to pain and misery in the future world, so likewise some were fore-ordained to wretchedness and slavery in the present state.

I have met with others not so deeply read in casuistry, who have apologized by saying that the slaves of their families were not in a worse situation as to food and clothing than their masters. Yes, but they are in worse situation as to liberty, which is (a phrase common in our ears every day) a most valuable blessing.

Some have been so grossly stupid as to assign the color as a mark for servitude. This, if it could prove anything, would prove too much. It would establish it that all complexions but the fairest should be in some degree deprived of liberty. That all black persons should be slaves, says Montesquieu, is as ridiculous as that law of a certain country that all red-haired persons should be hanged.[1]

But not to dwell on these things, it remains to be considered in what manner it may be possible to enfranchise these people. Shall they be set immediately at liberty amongst ourselves? No; for my part I am for the plan to colonize them. In the words of the angel to Abraham, it is my vote, "Cast out the bond woman, and her son." [2] . . . I would have these black people led out by some generous mind and colonized, perhaps beyond the Ohio or the Mississippi river, in that country forfeited by the native Indians in consequence of their hostilities against us.

[*United States Magazine*
December 1779]

Conclusion of the First Volume of the Magazine

This number, which is for the last month in the year, will conclude the first volume of the magazine, a publication undertaken at a time

1. *Lettres Persanes* (1721).
2. Genesis xxi, 10.

when it was hoped the war would be of short continuance and the money, which had continued to depreciate, would become of proper value. But these evils having continued to exist through the whole year, it has been greatly difficult to carry on the publication; and we shall now be under the necessity of suspending it for some time, until an established peace and a fixed value of the money shall render it convenient or possible to take it up again.

The muses and the graces, on hearing this, will no doubt shed tears. In the course of this pleasant work they have entertained others and they have been entertained themselves. All that we can say to them is that it may again revive and they may be invited from their hills and their bowers on the mountain tops to sip the nectar of our verses.

There is one sort of people to whom the news of the suspension of this work will not be disagreeable: I mean those persons who are disaffected to the cause of America. These have been sorely pricked and buffeted with the sharp points of Whiggism, which, like arrows from the great machines of Archimedes, have been darted out from it. They have been sorely injured by these points, and will be ready to believe that in the suspension of this work is accomplished that prophecy of the Apocalypse, "And Satan shall be bound a thousand years." [1]

There is yet another class of men that will be sensible of some happiness now that the mouth of this publication is in a fair way to be at length closed; I mean the people who inhabit the region of stupidity and cannot bear to have the tranquility of their repose disturbed by the villainous jargon of a book. Reading is to them the worst of all torments. And I remember very well that at the commencement of the work it was their language, "Art thou come to torment us before the time." [2] We will now say to them, "Sleep on, and take your rest." [3]

No man of common philanthropy would choose to give pain to innocent though ignorant souls, when he has in his power to help it. It is but ceasing to blow our flutes for a while, and the beasts will retire to their coverts and be happy in the brown shades of their own hills.

Nevertheless there are some peasant swains to whom our flutes

---

1. "And he laid hold on the dragon, that old serpent, which is the Devil, and Satan, and bound him a thousand years." Revelation xx, 2.
2. Matthew viii, 29.
3. Matthew xxvi, 45.

were agreeable; and every month calling for a new song, they have given encouragement to prepare new music for their taste. We could wish it had been in our power to have drawn forth more dulcet sounds for the listening ears of these happy men and to have shown them by a rare touch of melody that we had it in our hearts to do them honor. Such as it has been they have received it, and it only remains for us to thank them for their condescension in hearing us and to love them for that degree of praise which they have vouchsafed to our performance, in which good will at all times to the commonwealth of letters has prevailed.

[*December 1779*]

II

The Early Frontier

from the *Pittsburgh Gazette*

Value of a Newspaper

One of the earliest things which I thought of on going to reside in the Western country was the encouragement of a public paper. An establishment of this nature was accomplished after some time [the *Pittsburgh Gazette*], and a good deal by my exertions. With a view to assist it I wrote some things serious, and some ludicrous. The following is of the last cast. I had an ambition, or rather I obeyed the impulse of my mind in being among the first to bring the press to the west of the mountains. . . .   [*Gazette Publications*]

Messieurs Scull and Hall,

I have heard it said that you are about to publish a *Gazette* in the town of Pittsburgh; this will be of great use, especially to our young people after they are taught the catechism and to read the scriptures, inasmuch as they will find in this all the hard names which they do not meet with in the tenth chapter of Nehemiah or the Chronicles. By reading the Old Testament they may have heard a great deal about Jerusalem and Nineveh, but in this we read of the modern cities, such as Paris, Constantinople, and Cork in Ireland, and other great capitals. In short, an almanac and a newspaper are almost all the profane books that a layman need read.

I suppose under the head of advertisements you will keep a good lookout after stray cattle and Negroes, or lands to be sold. It will be a great advantage to have such an opportunity of making public any grievance of this nature. But it is to be supposed that the principal object will be to collect occurrences from abroad and concentre those at home, especially such as are of a political nature. When I say abroad I mean in the eastern world, and by those at home I mean America. I had an uncle in Chester county who had been a long time a subscriber for the paper, and from a frequent perusal of the intelligence respecting different powers in the system of Europe, he had a perfect knowledge of them; like a man looking through a glass-beehive he could, as it were, see them all before his eyes and distinguish the workings and counter-workings of cabinets and councils. Who would not give half a guinea to know, exactly as he does his own calf pasture, what is going on everyday when he rises, at Smyrna and Amsterdam, and count as easily as he can the stripes of his waistcoat, the armies that are on foot in Europe, the state treaties that are relieving the inconvenience or changing the happiness of mankind, to be able to look up with the tail of his eye as far as Russia and down again with the same glance to the islands in the West Indies, and to see all the intermediate space swarming with men and things? Instead of half a guinea, this is worth an 100 half-joes to a man.

But we shall know something even of the upper world from the *Gazette;* I do not mean the account of the balloons, though it may be well enough to know what experiments are making in that way, but the discoveries of philosophers, who teach us at what distance the bulls, goats and rams depasture from each other in the firmament. I wonder how David Rittenhouse comes on in rubbing down the stars, since he was appointed astronomer to the Commonwealth. It is said he has considerably corrected the vapors of the moon's atmosphere, for though there are as many natural fools in the neighborhood of Philadelphia as formerly, there has not been one instance of a lunatic for several years past.

A principal advantage will be to know what is going on in our state, particularly what our representatives are doing. Heretofore, like boys creeping into a hay stack at such a remote distance, we could see only their heels, while their heads were hid away among the cabals of Philadelphia; when they returned home they had generally a great deal to tell us of their contests with ———— ———— and other over-grown men; but as to the merit or demerit of their opposition, we could know it only from themselves.

On all these considerations I think your understanding will be of a public benefit and ought to be encouraged. The farmers can read it on all wet days, Sundays excepted, and become informed without losing time.

Your humble servant,

William Donachy

[*Pittsburgh*
July 1786]

Observations on the Country at the
Head of the Ohio River

[After promoting the establishment of the first newspaper west of the Alleghenies, Brackenridge became its most prolific contributor. Through the Pittsburgh Gazette he attracted attention to the need for cultural, religious, and commercial development in the western country. And by means of these appeals he hoped to gain popular favor as a candidate for the State Assembly.

In "Observations on the Country at the Head of the Ohio River" he explains the civic and moral contributions of churches to the community welfare, the necessity of a court in the immediate area which can insure justice for those not able to travel great distances at great expense, and most significantly, the urgent need for an academy of learning. "We well know," he tells the settlers, "the strength of a state greatly consists in the superior mental powers of the inhabitants." Satisfying development of the West would depend upon the education of its people.]

I

A clergyman is settled in this town of the Calvinist church. Some of the inhabitants are of the Lutheran or Episcopal church; but the distinction is brought little into view, the younger people scarcely knowing that there is a distinction in the mode of government of the two churches, for in doctrine there is none and the more advanced in life not thinking it of sufficient moment to take notice of it. The passions which agitated our fathers are subsided and the minds of men are gradually clarifying on these subjects, so that in America, or at least in this part of it, there is the most perfect liberality of sentiment.

The establishment of a clergyman in this town, to carry the idea no further, is a high political good. The black cloth, the sedate and grave presence of a divine, the idea of dignity and reverence from common opinion annexed to his character, restrains the disorderly in the streets where he walks or in the neighborhood where he lives. His visits and private admonitions at the houses of such give impressions favorable to good behavior. His sermons lay down rules of life and manners which form the good citizen. Even the convening to church teaches the lower class of people to attend to dress and cleanliness and to set a value of their personal appearance. The sitting down among those of more refinement of behavior kindles in their minds a love of what is elegant. They pay interest to their own manners and are ambitious that their children should behave in such a manner as to deserve respect in life. Human nature is insensibly actuated by these secret springs and touches, and we see a people where a church is established, even where there is not great devotion evident, nevertheless more orderly, temperate, and industrious than elsewhere. The idea moreover of a future existence and retribution according to acts in life cannot fail in some degree to govern the conscience and enforce morality. I say nothing of those more energetic principles which every preacher of Christianity will teach those under his care to desire and cultivate and which constitute true religion, but in a moral and political point of view I would consider the institution of such public orator to convene the people on that day established as a day of rest and to impress sentiments of virtue, a highly useful, under whatever name and by whatever mode it may be thought, expedient. Were I in faith a Mohammedan, pagan, or Jew, I would nevertheless, as a good citizen, contribute to the support of such and carefully assemble with others to hear the discourses.

A clergyman in the German Calvinist church also occasionally preaches in this town, and it is expected from the increase of German inhabitants that a clergyman who can deliver himself in this language will in a short time be supported here altogether.

In laying out the town of Pittsburgh, five lots have been assignated for churches and for burying grounds. These comprehend the former burying ground, and which is adjoining the ancient cemetery of the natives, being one of those mounds before mentioned and which, from the height of earth in this place, would seem to have been a place of sepulture for ages. These lots are about the center of the town, as it is laid out, and at an intermediate distance between the two rivers. A church is on the way to be built of squared timber and moderate dimensions, which may accommodate the people until a larger building can be erected.

In this town we have also two gentlemen of the medical faculty, one a native of South Britain, the other a native of America. But though health may be accounted a birthright of this place, nevertheless we account those gentlemen a great acquisition. The accidents of life are numerous; feeble youth and failing age require assistance, and there are complaints from which no climate, however favorable to health and long life, can wholly exempt the constitution. I will not take the liberty of saying anything with respect to the . . . merit or professional abilities of these gentlemen; but I will answer for it that if individuals or families at any time should think it advisable to cross the mountains and spend a few months at Pittsburgh for the sake of health, they will find it in their power to receive the best advice the science can afford and the most judicious treatment.

There are also two of the profession of the law resident in this town.

"Quae regio in terris, nostri non plena laboris." [1]

The bulk of the inhabitants are traders, mechanics, and laborers. Of mechanics and laborers there is still a great want. Masons and carpenters are especially wanted; indeed from this circumstance, the improvement of the town in buildings is greatly retarded.

This town must in future time be a place of great manufactory. Indeed the greatest on the continent, or perhaps in the world. The present carriage from Philadelphia is six-pence for each pound weight, and however improved the conveyance may be and by whatever channel, yet such is our distance from either of the oceans, that the importation of heavy articles will still be expensive. The manufacturing them will therefore become more an object here than elsewhere. It is a prospect of this, with men of reflection, which renders the soil of this place so valuable.

With all the advantages of natural situation and the settlement of inhabitants, this town still labors under the inconvenience of the want of a court held within it. The seat of justice for the county of Westmoreland, within which the town lies, is at the distance of more than thirty miles, with a rugged road and a stream for a great part of the year difficult to pass. The greater part of the inhabitants, as is the case in all towns, cannot afford to keep horses, so that as jurymen, witnesses, or suitors of the court they are under great inconvenience in attending. Even women and aged persons are oftentimes under the necessity of travelling on foot. As this town is a great thoroughfare from the neighboring country and from all the states, many persons avoiding justice are found to pass this way; and when they are apprehended, as many of them are in this town, it is not a little inconvenient to send them under a guard to so great a distance. In the meantime greater opportunity for making their escape, there not being a place of confinement into which they can be immediately put, is given to them.

In another point of view a seat of justice ought long ago to have been established here. The holding a court brings money to a town, retains a number of officers, and brings inhabitants and contributes

1. "What place on earth is there which is not full of our labor." Virgil, *Aeneid,* i, 460.

to its improvement. If the town of Pittsburgh is a principal market of this country, as doubtless it is, it ought to be cherished; for every house that is built in it increases the value of every tract of land in the country adjoining. This is an object which the mind of every man cannot comprehend, and therefore it is that the people of this country adjoining do not all seem sensible of it.

When first the county of Westmoreland was laid out, commissioners were appointed to fix the county town.[2] They are said to have fixed on Pittsburgh as the place, but the governor at the instance [insistence] of George Groghan[3] did not confirm the report. This gentleman, conceiving Pittsburgh to be within a grant of boundary to him from the natives, is said to have been unwilling that the jurisdiction of Pennsylvania should extend to it. There is no kind of doubt that if the seat of justice had been then established at this place, the contest with Virginia[4] which has given us so much trouble would never have existed. The strength of civil authority which would have been fixed in this quarter would have baffled at once all the efforts of Lord Dunmore[5] to have engaged adherents.

We have presented petitions from one session of our Assembly to another, since the Revolution, to have a county laid off comprehending the town of Pittsburgh; for in the present extended settlement of the country it would not be convenient to make this town the seat of justice for the county of Westmoreland. Our petitions have not been regarded, whether it has been that our representatives have not attended to this object or that other members, from mistaken ideas of our situation, have opposed it. We are regardless of the line of boundary which shall divide us from the adjoining counties. It is the convenience of the people of the town and those immediately adjoin-

2. Pittsburgh was in Westmoreland County until September 14, 1787, when the State Assembly established the new County of Allegheny, with its seat at Pittsburgh. This legislation was advanced by Assemblyman Brackenridge.

3. Colonel George Groghan had purchased vast tracts of land from the Indians and later sold much of it to George Washington, who then attempted to eject thirteen squatters from his newly acquired property. Brackenridge defended the squatters in court, arguing that Indian land purchases were not legal and that therefore Groghan had never possessed the land he sold. Brackenridge lost the case.

4. In a boundary settlement of 1779 an area that had been Virginia became Pennsylvania. The former Virginians started a secessionist movement, declaring independence from both states.

5. John Murray, Earl of Dunmore (1732–1809), became Governor of Virginia in 1771. He dissolved the Virginia Assembly because of its revolutionary sentiments. Early in 1775 he removed gunpowder from the magazine at Williamsburg and thereby occasioned the first armed uprising in Virginia.

ing that we have in view. It may be ten or fifteen miles, as it shall seem good to the House.

It ought to be a great object with the state of Pennsylvania to encourage and cultivate the town of Pittsburgh. It will be a means which will bind the two extremes of the state together. The greater part of those who settle here are from that city or the counties within the state and below the mountains. These have connections in trade or manufactures with those whom they have left behind. A town of note at the confluence of these rivers must for ages secure the trade of the Western country to Pennsylvania. It is an observation of Baron Montesquieu, founded in reason and the nature of circumstances, that the extremes of a despotism are most happy because farthest removed from oppression, and on the other hand the extremes of a republic least happy because farthest removed from redress of grievances. This abstract observation of that great writer I have found verified. Insomuch that though it would be an easy thing for me to represent those things which ought in sound policy to be done for this country, having resided many years in it and having a perfect knowledge of it, yet I have been discouraged at all times from attempting it, knowing this country and the circumstances of it lying at a great distance, it would be greatly difficult to bring anyone to attend to me. However, in the present instance, I have made a trial, and if this representation should find its way to eyes of any of our assembly, it may have some effect to induce the House to think of our situation.

[*Pittsburgh Gazette*
August 26, 1786]

II

The situation of the town of Pittsburgh is greatly to be chosen for a seat of learning: the fine air, the excellent water, the plenty and cheapness of provisions tender it highly favorable.

The inhabitants have entertained the idea of instituting an academy, but have it not in their power all at once to accomplish every wish. Public spirit is not more apparent among any people, but it is impossible to answer every demand which a thousand wants of those settling a new country require. The first efforts have been made to accommodate themselves with lots of ground, with buildings and common means of life; next, to establish and support a Christian church. In a short time, more conveniently, they may be able to attend to that great object, the education of youth. One or two schools are established to teach the first elements, but it is greatly desirable that there be such which can conduct to more advancement in science.

It is provided by our constitution, "That public schools be erected in every county." Agreeable to this provision it may be expedient that the legislature establish schools in each county, either by an appropriation of something from the public funds for that purpose or by a special county tax. Nevertheless I am disposed to be of opinion that it will better answer the object that a few schools, well endowed, be established throughout the state, where men of superior academic knowledge may find it advisable to remain for a number of years or for life.

I do not know that the legislature could do a more acceptable service to the Commonwealth than by endowing a school at this place. It will introduce money to Pennsylvania, for a series of years, from the whole Western country. It will institute knowledge and ability in this extreme of the government. We well know the strength of a state greatly consists in the superior mental powers of the inhabitants. "When I have resolved," says the historian,* "the Roman history, I have been led to consider what it is that has given this people so great a superiority over its neighbors in peace and war, and I have found that it has been owing to a few great men that happened to arise in it."

It is certain that a few eminent men in any period have usually given the tone, so to speak, to a whole nation, nay, sometimes to a whole age. They have been the authors of that superiority which one age has obtained over another. To give examples from our own country: a few men at the beginning of this Revolution discovered the limits of the authority of Britain and pointed out our just rights. The cultivated genius of these men, through the darkness of a night which might otherwise have involved the continent, flashed fires and gave the flame of Aeneas.[6] What then must be the strength and dignity of a government where eminent genius is everywhere called forth by education? Academies are the furnaces which melt the natural ore to real metal, the shops where the thunderbolts of the orator are forged. Cultivated genius has the force of electric fire. "I value not," said Philip of Macedon, speaking of Demosthenes, "the Illysian foot or Treballian horse, so much as the lightning of that orator."

---

* Sallust. [H.H.B.]

6. Hero of Virgil's *Aeneid*, who wandered to Latium. It is believed he carried Greek culture to the Romans.

The eloquence of our writers and orators at the beginning of this contest was universally felt; it roused like the storm of desert; it hurried to resistance like the sound of a trumpet. Britain fell back with astonishment not more at the power of our oratory in the senate than at the gleam of our bayonets in the field.

The glory of each state was in proportion to the heroes, in the deliberative assembly or in the field, which it produced. From a partiality to Pennsylvania natural to a citizen, I envied Virginia her Henry and her Lee; New Jersey her Livingston, and Massachusetts her immortal Adams.[7]

The door of Janus has been long open, presenting battle axes and all the armory of war. The literary education of our youth has been in the meantime neglected. It becomes us to reinstitute the arts of peace and keep an equal pace with our sister states. I should rejoice to see Pennsylvania at all times able to produce mathematicians, philosophers, poets, historians, and statesmen equal to any in the confederacy. With a view to this object it will become her to provide for the cultivation of genius in every part of the government. Who knows what portions of the elementary fire may rest in this country? Seminaries of learning will [spring] forth and kindle it to a blaze.

The state of Pennsylvania has not been wholly inattentive to the interests of learning since the late war. [It] has added to the funds of the university of Philadelphia, and set apart some lands for the endowment of the college at Carlisle. It remains that a seminary of learning be established in this western part of the government. For it cannot be expected that the university of Philadelphia can be of the least service to [about] five hundred of the inhabitants in this country, [whose] but moderate [circumstances] will not enable them to support their children even for a short time in that city. The college at Carlisle is at the distance of near two hundred miles from the greater part of this country, and admitting that the expenses of education are not greater there than they would be at a seminary here, yet the inconvenience must be obvious of sending to so great a distance and providing for the usual wants of those abroad. But why shall this country be under the necessity of remitting money to the county of Cumberland for the advantages of education?

The country west of the mountain certainly deserves a particular attention from the Commonwealth. It has been a barrier of the war against the savages and has greatly suffered from the depredations.

7. Patrick Henry, Francis Lightfoot Lee, Governor William Livingston of New Jersey, Samuel Adams.

To the inhabitants the whole war has been a tour of duty. Since the war, money has been drawn from the country in obtaining rights for the lands which they have defended. In the meantime the country on the west of the Ohio has been sold at a distance, and scarcely an individual of this country has had it in his power to make any purchase. Inasmuch as there are lands still remaining, might it not be wise in the government to discover a disposition of doing equal justice to all parts of the Commonwealth, to appropriate some of them for the use of an academy at Pittsburgh? The three thousand acres that are opposite the town sold in lots would establish a handsome fund for that purpose. There is certainly no better use to which the wisdom of the state could apply it. It will be well that the representatives, especially of the three western counties, press this point. It will be for the interest of this county in particular and for the credit and interest of the whole Commonwealth.

I have thrown out these ideas carelessly as to style and method, for to do service and not to acquire fame is my object. I write only when it suits me, to unbend my mind from severer studies, and I cannot make a task of it. For this reason I am the more alarmed at the appearance of a critic,* an animal which has always impressed on my mind the image of a spider, for it can attack the filaments of the richest tapestry but can itself weave nothing beyond the texture of a cobweb. The common people, by a mistake of the term, call it a cricket, but I take it to be a kind of brown spider.

This animal I perceive begins to come already. The correspondent who makes his question in the last *Gazette* is a metaphysical spider. I have read over *Tristram Shandy* and several other books to be able to answer him but dare not venture it. It gives me pain because I would be willing to keep on good terms with this formidable species. It is usual with me sometimes in a summer evening to recline in the shade of a spreading tree, and should I offend one of these, it might in that situation be easy to creep up my back and give a bite that might be dangerous. I knew a young man that was bit one day as he sat at dinner, just above the haunch bone; the lad was growing stiff,

---

* The critic referred to wrote in August 26:

To the Printers

A correspondent would be happy to know how the author of the Remarks or Observations on the Country at the Head of the Ohio River obtained such an intimacy with the doctrine of spirits as to assert that material objects or images were impressed upon the mind which is immaterial.

[H.H.B.]

and had not oils and other antidotes been applied speedily, he must have perished from the poison.

An apprehension of danger of this nature induces me to break off my writings for the present. Perhaps I may resume them when the frost comes and the critics retire to their holes or die with the cold weather.

[*Pittsburgh Gazette*
September 2, 1786]

Letter from Angus MacMore

[*To his frontier setting, Brackenridge adapted the eastern custom of writing letters under signatures taken from ancient authors. Assuming various characters of actual settlers, he criticized the actions of Congress and of the western representatives to the State Assembly. More significant than the criticisms are the images in which they are rendered. The "Letter from Angus MacMore" contains invaluable local color glimpses of real life and its conditions on the frontier.*]

Messieurs Scull and Hall,

I have been a subscriber from the list, and sent in a dollar the other day by William Guy when he went to the contractor's store to buy an ounce of snuff for his wife. Our neighbors think a great deal of the paper, and I have as many of them about me between sermons on a Sunday to hear the news, as Mathew M'Connel has on his justice days when come about the law business.

I see the Congress have appointed a superintendent of the Indians, to give them presents and to keep them in peace. I am persuaded it is meant well and the men may be capable that are nominated to this station, but I am apprehensive the task is beyond their ability to restrain the savages for any length of time. In my opinion it would be better to let them run in the woods and live at their own purchase; for when they can get meat and drink without hunting, they get a habit of idleness and must be supplied by presents or by going to war. It is with them as with our cattle in the fall of the year. There is a great deal of good grass in the woods and they might live very well till near Christmas, but if you begin to winter them too soon, they stay about the house and have their heads in every pot and pail; and when a good day comes, if you refuse to give them anything, instead of going to the woods they get into the turnip patch and are the greatest break-fences about the whole plantation. It would be for the good of the country, if, when the blankets and leggins come, the superintendent would give them to some of the poor women and children whose husbands and fathers have been murdered in the war, or if that proposition will not go down, drink them out among yourselves in the town there.

We have read over the extracts of the debates in the house of assembly. I would wish to see a great deal less said and more done. The vanity of talking appears to be visible in many of them. There are two or three of them that are up and down every minute like the elbow of a man playing on the fiddle. It makes my heart ache to hear the members from our own country jangling about small points, while land jobbers are running away with our property by laying warrants on improvements. Honest Thomas Macmurrochy has lost his plantation, unless a law is made to exclude these rights.

I have several more things to say, but my neighbor Robert Richey, who takes this to you, says he is in a hurry, and I do not know who I can send it by if I miss this opportunity.

Angus MacMore

Washington County
September 20

[*Pittsburgh Gazette
September 20, 1786*]

Defense of the Church Bill

[*Elected to the State Assembly in 1786, Brackenridge devoted his energies to the cultural development of his constituency. His major triumphs were a new road bill, a new county with its seat at Pittsburgh (Allegheny), and a grant of land for an academy (now the University of Pittsburgh). He also introduced a bill for the incorporation of a non-sectarian church in Pittsburgh. A Presbyterian minister, however, maneuvered a change. When the bill was passed, it established a Presbyterian church, and Brackenridge observed: "The people of that town were all well disposed to remain under one roof; but whenever priests come they make trouble."*

Brackenridge defended his community church concept in the Pittsburgh Gazette. *The "Defense" reveals his role in bringing the first minister to the town and arousing public desire for a house of worship. It defines the kind of church necessary to fulfill the community functions which he described earlier in "Observations on the Country at the Head of the Ohio River." The church was not to be associated with a synod, but the minister might attend the synod if he wished and if his absence would not detract from his duties. Any person of ecclesiastical character would be permitted to preach. The form of worship would be of no consequence. Presbyterianism would do if not called by that name. Only the name Christian would be suitable for a church of Christians.*

The roots of the argument are democratic and economic. The town did not have enough people to support more than one church. But a Presbyterian church would be discriminatory because it would ignore the other denominations.]

There is one transaction of mine, as a member of the legislative body, of which I did not take notice in my general address, because it was local and respected the inhabitants of Pittsburgh only; but as it has been misunderstood by some and misrepresented by others, it may be allowable in me to give my relation of it, more especially as the clergyman of Pittsburgh in the paper of last week had introduced it to the public view, and in my opinion has not done himself or me perfect justice.[1]

That the transaction may be the more clearly understood, I will take the liberty of stating some preliminary circumstances.

When the clergyman first presented himself in Pittsburgh, it was by introduction to me. I stated to him minutely and precisely the prospect of support from this town. That the people united might have it in their power to make up an adequate salary, not otherwise. That they were of different denominations but liberal, and with prudent conduct towards them might be brought together and preserved under one roof in assembling for divine service.

This representation seemed pleasing to the clergyman, and accordingly a subscription paper was made out with a promissory obligation to pay to him etc. as pastor of the *church of Pittsburgh*. A short time afterwards, the clergyman expressed a wish that we should send what he called a "call" to the presbytery [whence] he came. I recollect to have made objections to the word as savoring

---

1. Rev. S. Barr had written in the *Gazette* of June 16, 1787: "But we were incorporated, or rather designed to be incorporated under the denomination of Presbyterian; how this came to pass seems now a mystery to Mr. Brackenridge, he pretends to be ignorant how the assembly of Pennsylvania gave our society that epithet more than any other; and to get clear of the difficulty, basely insinuates that I must have altered the petition or suppressed it altogether. But what are his reasons for such insinuations? We were not denominated Presbyterian in our petition and therefore he concludes, I must have altered it. . . . 'Let us only style ourselves the church of Pittsburgh,' said he, under Mr. Barr's pastoral care, and Mr. Woods. . . .'"

of the conventicle, and to the measure as unnecessary. We cared nothing about his presbytery. It was himself with whom we had to deal. However as it was a matter of small moment, if my memory serves me, the measure was adopted but the word was changed to "invitation." Both in the subscription paper and in the invitation, the phrase "Presbyterian congregation" was avoided. Public notice was given, and at a meeting of the people, though not very general, a committee was chosen to transact the business of the church. It was stipulated expressly with the clergyman that he should baptize and admit to privilege generally, at the recommendation of the committee, without inquiry as to what denomination they might belong. It was stipulated expressly that any other gentleman of an ecclesiastical character, occasionally present, should be admitted to preach in the church at the approbation of the committee.

A short time after the clergyman had his residence among us, it was proposed to petition the legislature to incorporate our church in order to take from the Messrs. Penns a conveyance of a lot or two of ground in the town of Pittsburgh for the site of a church or churches and for a graveyard. I had the honor to be appointed with the clergyman to draw the petition. I drew the first draft and submitted it to the clergyman. He made a fresh draft of it without any alteration save the insertion of the words "Presbyterian congregation." To these I objected, as contrary to the liberal principle on which the church was instituted and as what would give an instant alarm and produce a dismemberment of it. Nay, as the people were too few to support a clergyman divided, it would put an end to the church altogether. This reasoning prevailed, and the words were struck out. If my memory serves me, I signed the petition with others, and it was put into the hands of the clergyman to be carried by him or transmitted to Philadelphia.

When I took my seat in the House of Assembly, I made inquiry for the petition. The clerk could not find it. I observed in the minutes that a member of the preceding house had presented a bill for the incorporating the *Presbyterian Congregation of Pittsburgh.* The bill was found upon the files. It had been once read and no more. I called it up for a second time, which was granted. In reading I moved to strike out the words "Presbyterian congregation" and insert the general term of "Christian Society" * in their place. The words were struck out, and the general term inserted. In this state the bill

* The word "religious" was added by a member. I thought it a tautology, and meant to have it struck out. [H.H.B.]

was published for consideration, and in this state remains at this hour.

It may be said I was not instructed by the society to take up this business in the house, very true; but I had conceived they would think themselves under obligation to me for this attention to the local interests of Pittsburgh. If I have [been] unfortunate in giving myself trouble, I hope it is pardonable, more especially as the copying and reading of the bill by the clerk, the publishing for consideration, etc.; the bill being of a private nature cost me money and it will be punishment enough to have been at this expense without thanks for it.

It may be said I was not warranted in bringing forward a bill under the general term of "Christian Society." This will depend upon the facts already stated. I did not recollect the term in our petition, but I thought this was it. However, it appears to have been of the same import, viz., the "Church of Pittsburgh." It was not my intention to have had the bill passed into a law until I had returned to Pittsburgh and laid what was done before the committee. In that case they might have given me what instructions they thought proper, and I should have obeyed them.

I was early informed in Philadelphia that the inhabitants of Pittsburgh had entered into an agreement to be incorporated under the denomination of Presbyterian. I said it was well, the bill should be altered to that style. I wrote a paragraph to that effect to the *Pittsburgh Gazette*. On the return of James Barr, my colleague, to the House, I was informed by him that this agreement and representation to the House was in the hands of Mr. Findley.[2] I said it was well, all things should be done as desired. A short time before the close of the session, Findley presented me with the agreement and the representation; I was struck with some words which held me up in an unfavorable point of view with the House. I told Findley that I should not present that paper, and that if he did I would consider it as an additional insult to those I had already received from him. That there was another session in which the business could be done, and I was well persuaded that when I returned to Pittsburgh and represented to the people the damage it would [do] to themselves and me to have the memorial in which my name was used laid before the House, so far as respected me, they would change it.

I was informed in Philadelphia that it had been represented by the clergyman in Pittsburgh that in assigning the reasons for using the

2. William Findley, Brackenridge's political enemy and object of his Hudibrastic satire.

general term "Christian Society" in the bill, I had held up the inhabitants as "not capable of determining between one denomination and another." To give the words that I used, my memory serves me not, but I will venture to say that I used not an expression which any man of candor could interpret as placing the people in an unfavorable point of view. Am I known to possess so little address in the management of causes in the course of my profession as to say anything to hurt the client I mean to serve? *

I am informed since I returned by George Wallace and Robert Galbraith, Esquires, that the clergyman assured them the assembly had refused to incorporate unless under the name of "Episcopal" or "Presbyterian." †

So far of my conduct in the House with respect to the church. I regret that I meddled with it at all. But it was from a wish to carry into effect every object for the people of Pittsburgh; and though my conduct may not have given satisfaction, I am well persuaded there is not an individual save the clergyman who will not excuse it.

My object from the commencement has been well known to the people of this town. It was to keep them united that we might be able to support a church. Moreover, in a small village especially it must be painful to see families with whom we converse every day assembling together in every amusement and yet separating in receiving good advice for the conduct of life and manners. I should suppose it must be particularly so to a clergyman who had considered a number of people as his flock to see them depart from him merely

---

* The foundation the clergyman pretends to have had for this assertion are the notes taken by the shorthand writer without the bar. From the noise in the gallery and other causes, these are often inaccurately taken; but I have looked over them, and though the language and some of the ideas are very different from those expressed by me, yet I can see nothing in these notes which could warrant him in his deduction. The truth is he did not believe it himself, but made use of this artifice at my expense to inflame the people and induce them to show that they were capable of distinguishing denominations by praying to be incorporated under that of "Presbyterian." [H.H.B.]

† The only foundation the clergy had for this was an observation of a member, Wynkoop of Bucks, "that before we were incorporated we ought to choose our religion"; this was laughable enough, as if the Christian religion was none. It produced a general smile in the house. Mr. Wynkoop is a very modest man. He blushed and sat down.

This was not so; they will incorporate under any term. I believe it gave the most sensible of them pleasure to [find] that we had so much liberality to the westwards as to throw off the distinction of sect and be contented with the general name of Christian. However, certain it is that every man being informed of our peculiar and local circumstances in this town must have approved of it. [H.H.B.]

for the sake of a term, which he ought to be above considering as of any consequence.

Archbishop Tillotson [3] earnestly endeavored in England to unite the dissenting and Episcopal churches, but was disappointed. It was the hope of some great men, with whom I have had the honor to converse since the Revolution, that in these states we might be able, by yielding on both sides, to constitute an "American Church."

A laudable advance has been made towards it by the Episcopal denomination, the controverted articles being retrenched and the liturgy amended. I had been sanguine in the idea that in this town, from a variety of circumstances, all distinction might have been for a long time kept out of view.

It was often my language to the clergyman that he might be Presbyterian, attend the synod, provided he did not stray too long away, and no one would make inquiries about it. The people habituated by degrees to the Presbyterian mode of worship would cease to have a prejudice against it, the younger part of the society especially, and he might have them what he pleased. The prejudice was not against the substance so much as the name, and that ought to be kept out of view. Caesar declined the name of king because the memory of the Tarquins was odious to the Roman people. Cromwell declined it because a part of the nation were opposed to it on a like principle. They both had the same authority and all advantages without the odium of the term.

What is obtained by the incorporation of a Presbyterian congregation? Surely the lots could have been vested for the same use, and in the same persons as the trustees of the "Christian Society" or the "Church of Pittsburgh." Experience will convince the clergyman that his industry to have the term Presbyterian brought into view has made an unfavorable impression on the minds of the many and will abridge his power of doing service.

It will abridge his salary. This consideration may affect his feelings; the other will not.

[*Pittsburgh Gazette*
June 23, 1787]

---

3. Archbishop John Tillotson (1630–1694), a low church latitudinarian favoring an understanding of non-conformists. He attacked popery but not dissent within Protestantism.

Cursory Remarks on the Federal Constitution

The following is a sample, perhaps a caricature, of the objections to the adopting the Federal Constitution as they appeared in the publications of the time. Ridicule is not the test of truth, but it may be employed to expose error; and on this occasion it seemed not to be amiss to use it a little, as a great object was at stake and much prejudice or willful misrepresentation to be encountered. It will show also that on our part, though in a remote quarter, we were willing to be assisting and contributed a little to consolidate the government of the union, which after all the pains taken was with great difficulty brought about.

[*Gazette Publications*]

It is not my intention to enter largely into a consideration of this plan of government but [to] suggest some ideas in addition and of the same nature with those already made, showing the imperfections and the danger of it.

The first thing that strikes a diligent observer is the want of precaution with respect to the sex of the president. Is it provided that he shall be of the male gender? The Salii, a tribe of the Burgundians in the eleventh century, excluded females from the sovereignty.[1] Without a similar exclusion what shall we think if in progress of time we should come to have an old woman at the head of our affairs? But what security have we that he shall be a white man? What would be the national disgrace if he should be elected from one of the southern states, and a vile Negro should come to rule over us? Treaties would then be formed with the tribes of Congo and Loango instead of the civilized countries of Europe. But is there any security that he shall be a freeman? Who knows but the electors at a future period in days of corruption may pick up a man's servant, a convict perhaps, and give him the dominion? Is any care taken that he shall be a man of perfect parts? Moses, the legislator of the Jews, precluded those laboring under any incapacity from entering the congregation of the Lord. Shall we in affairs of a civil nature leave a door open to bastards, eunuchs, and the devil knows what?

A senate is the next great constituent part of the government,

---

1. Brackenridge is following a common error here which alleges that the Salii law forbid females from succeeding to the throne. It is believed that the Salii law was invoked in 1316 and 1322 to deny the throne to the daughters of Louis X and Philip V. Actually the Salii law is a penal code handed on by the Salian Franks. It sets the amount of fines for various offenses and declares that daughters cannot inherit land.

and yet there is not a word said with regard to the ancestry of any of them, whether they should be altogether Irish or only Scotch-Irish. If any of them have been in the war of the White Boys, Hearts of Oak, or the like,[2] they may overturn all authority and make the shillelah the supreme law of the land.

The House of Representatives is so large that it never can be built. They may begin it, but it never can be finished. Ten miles square! Babylon itself, unless the suburbs were taken into view, was not of greater extent.

But what avails it to dwell on these things? The want of a bill of rights is the great evil. There was no occasion for a bill of wrongs, for there will be wrongs enough. But oh, a bill of rights. What is the nature of a bill of rights? It is a schedule of inventory of those powers which the Congress do not possess. But if it is clearly ascertained what powers they have, what need of a catalogue of those powers which they have not? Ah! there is the mistake. A minister preaching, undertook first to show what was in his text, second what was not in it. When it is specified what powers are given, why not also what powers are not given?[3] A bill of rights is wanting and all those things which are usually secured under it:

1. The *rights of conscience* are swept away. The *Confession of Faith,* the *Shorter Catechism,* and the *Pilgrims Progress* are to go. The Psalms of Watts, I am told, is the only thing of this kind that is to have any quarter at all.

2. The *liberty of the press;* that is gone at the first stroke. Not so much as an advertisement for a stray horse or runaway Negro can be put in any of the *Gazettes.*

3. The *trial by jury;* that is knocked in the head. And all that worthy class of men, the lawyers who live by haranguing and bending the juries, are demolished.

I would submit it to any candid man if in this constitution there is the least provision for the privilege of shaving the beard? Or is there any mode laid down to take the measure of a pair of breeches?

2. In 1793, England and Ireland had some 7000 mutual-interest societies and associations. The two Brackenridge mentions were agrarian associations formed among Irish peasants to redress grievances against landlords. They went on night raids, destroying property. The White Boys wore white shirts.

3. Brackenridge is taking literally Locke's concept of the social contract in which people consent to be governed. Thus, powers not given remain with the people and a bill of rights becomes a redundancy.

Whence then is it that men of learning seem so much to approve while the ignorant are against it? [4] The cause is perfectly apparent, viz., that reason is an erring guide, while instinct, which is the governing principle of the untaught, is certain. Put a pig in a poke, carry it half a day's journey through woods and byways, let it out, and it will run home without deviation. Could old Franklin do this? What reason then have we to suppose that his judgment, or that of General Washington, could be equal to that of ———— [5] in state affairs.

Were it not on this principle that we are able to account for it, it might be thought strange that old Livingston [6] of the Jerseys could be so hoodwinked as to give his sanction to such a diabolical scheme of tyranny among men—a constitution which may well be called hell-born. For if all the devils in Pandemonium had been employed about it, they could not have made a worse.

Neil MacLaughlin, a neighbor of mine, who has been talking with ————,[7] says that under this constitution all weavers are to be put to death.[8] What have these innocent manufacturers done that they should be so proscribed?

Let other states think what they will of it, there is one reason why every Pennsylvanian should execrate this imposition upon mankind. It will make his state most probably the seat of government [9] and bring all the officers and cause a great part of the revenue to be expended there. This must make the people rich, enable them to pay their debts and corrupt their morals. Any citizen, therefore, on the Delaware or Susquehanna waters ought to be hanged and cursed that would give it countenance.

I shall content myself at present with these strictures, but shall continue them from time to time as occasion may require.

[*Pittsburgh Gazette*
March 1, 1778]

4. The reference is to the new Constitution, not to the Bill of Rights which was proposed by Anti-Constitutionalists. In the opinion of the Federalists, the proposal was aimed at stalling ratification. Brackenridge explains his position in "Sermons in Favor of the Federal Constitution" below.
5. William Findley, an Anti-Constitutionalist.
6. Governor William Livingston, advocate of the new Constitution.
7. William Findley.
8. Findley was a weaver before his election to the State Assembly.
9. In 1790 Philadelphia became the capital of the nation.

To the Dissenting Assemblyman by an
Assenting Constituent

[*In October 1787, the Pennsylvania House of Representatives voted to call a convention to ratify or reject the new Federal Constitution. Nineteen western members voted against the measure, and immediately after their defeat they took leave in order to avoid a quorum and thus obstruct the transaction of business. The sergeant-at-arms and an assistant clerk pursued them through the streets of Philadelphia and managed to corner two of them. Forcibly returned to their places in the House, these representatives tried devious means of escape but were successfully restrained until the vital business of establishing the time, place, and procedure of the convention was transacted.*

Brackenridge, the only western representative to favor the new Constitution, satirized the farcical occurrences in the following letter, in which he assumes the role of a constituent who ironically reduces the actions of William Findley, the leader of the western representatives, to the absurd.]

You have great merit in answering an objection which has been made to the constitution . . . the want of an efficient check on the enacting laws hastily. There is not an upper but there be an outer house, the dissenting members absconding or receding when the vote is about to be taken. The many can enact laws, but the few may prevent. It is in fact putting the government into the hands of the minority, for without them cannot anything be done that is done. But this is analogous to things in nature. The tail is small part of the fish, and yet it directs the whole body. The rudder of a ship is small, compared with the hull and rigging, and yet it moves it anyway. What wonder then that the minority by turning tail should govern the legislature?

I acknowledge this will considerably affect the system of education, alertness and speed of foot becoming the necessary qualification of a legislator, for if a member is not swift in running off, the check may be lost, the vote being taken before he fairly disappears. There will hence be two kinds of motions in the House, that to the speaker and the other to the door.

It may be well to study wrestling. A scuffle may ensue, the minority endeavoring to get out, the majority to keep them in. There is a kind of wrestle called Cornish hug, which is taking each other by the waistband of the breeches with the arms crossed. This I would much recommend. Trips will be of great use. There is the back lock and the cross buttock, but masters in each branch must be employed to teach the art. I knew one Archy Dysart in Ostorara,[1] when I was a boy, who understood what is called the inside lift. He would have made an excellent tutor in an academy of this nature.

On the principle of strength of body, skill in jostling, and agility of heels, it will be improper to send old and weak men to the House, because they will be unable to exercise this check to advantage.

A doctor must be paid to attend the House, with plasters for the broken shins of the members, over benches in running off; a boy also to pick up wigs, hats, and the like.

But to avoid any kind of disorder and confusion it would be advisable in all cases where the vote does not come too quick upon them to withdraw insensibly by slipping out one by one under pretense of making water, for instance, until they are all gone.

Great is the excellence of this check, and the inventor of it deserves as great a premium as the discoverer of the longitude. Nevertheless it will be proper to exercise it modestly, and not be retrograding always on every negative lest they make a farce of the business. For it may look a little odd to see them running out hurry-scurry every moment, like boys at a baring when the master gets it at the chimney.[2]

On the same principles that I justify the minority, which is the mob of the House, in withdrawing, I would apologize for the mob out of doors in bringing them back; viz., this is a secondary check in the Constitution and marks the glory of it, giving perfect safety, which no other government on earth has. That they have the right to bring them back on the principles of the Constitution there be no doubt. Each member is the representative, not of his particular county only but of the whole state. Every constituent has therefore an interest in the attendance of each member. On his departure may he not take him up and bring him back to his duty?

Indeed, had the mob no right, yet it would be impossible to hinder them from exercising this check; for when they see men running and others after them how can they tell but that they have stolen money from some of their colleagues, who may wish to have them back in order to be searched? At the last time this check was exercised, which was about the calling a convention, when the sergeant-at-arms with the clerk, the door-keeper, and one or two more were sent after Findley, they running and he running, what could the mob think but that he had been guilty of some misdemeanor? No

---

1. In the "Barrens" of York County, Pennsylvania.

2. Exposing the skin for a whipping, which apparently took place in front of the chimney stack.

wonder therefore that before he could turn the corner of the second square there were about a thousand at his heels.

There is only one thing against this check, and that is the indignity done to the members and the consequent indecency of chasing them like men escaped from the wheel-barrow and ferreting them out of garrets and cellars in order to retake and bring them back to their places. Another thing is that breaking up the House, unless they can be retaken, the work they leave undone is all lost, which may often cost the state great sums of money; but this might be laid as a tax upon their own estates and for this excellent check still preserved.

Having thus acknowledged the use of this negative and shown the right of the minority of the constituents, viz., a mob, to countercheck this, the Constitution of Pennsylvania, like a double-geared mill, will be allowed by all good judges to be the best that the wit of man can devise.

                                                    An Assenting Constituent

[*Pittsburgh Gazette*
May 10, 1788]

Sermons in Favor of the Federal Constitution

[*Defeated for re-election to the State Assembly in 1788, Brackenridge came home, where he continued his campaign to popularize the Federal Constitution. He appealed to the settlers, who were set against the new instrument of government, through a series of sermons in which republicanism approached a religion and the Federal Constitution its bible. Having nothing to gain personally, Brackenridge spoke out of sheer altruism. These sermons are less fiery than the* Political Discourses *but are similar in tone and intent. The evils of American demagoguery replace those of British tyranny. If the people were informed and were led by men who placed the national good above their selfish ambitions, they could not possibly oppose the new Constitution. But the sermons are self-defeating. They offer evidence that all through history the people have been uninformed and they have rejected the leadership of the educated and dedicated for that of the demagogues.*]

                              I

              "Oh, my people, they which lead thee cause thee
                to err, and destroy the way of thy paths."
                                        Isaiah iii, 12.

Living on the west of the mountain, I consider this country as particularly mine. My interest is interwoven with that of the inhabitants, and I may with propriety call them "my people."

Hence it is that I am led to consider on all occasions of moment the public affairs of this country and to give my opinion with respect to the measures which ought to be pursued.

No people ever were more mistaken than we are at the present time with respect to the new Constitution of the federal government. I have been led to consider whence it is that we so disgrace ourselves with sentiments unfavorable to a system which a convention of the greatest and best men in any age or nation have devised and which the good sense of America seems disposed to approve.

The answer is easy: a few men who have obtained a fortuitous and temporary influence among us are the cause of this. The people have naturally as much good sense as those of any other country; but honest and unsuspecting, they are imposed on by individuals who by attention and flattery have engaged their favor. It is well known who it is about the center of Westmoreland that carries up from below palpable falsehoods and disseminates ideas unfavorable to this government.[1] It is well known who it is in Fayette county that in open harangue has enveighed against a Washington and proposed the bayonet in opposition to those councils in which he has had a great share.[2] These and some others of the same spirit are those who "lead the people" of the country "and cause them to err."

But will it not naturally be inquired what pretensions have those men to lead? Are they of great natural abilities? Or have the advantage of much improvement? By no means; in pursuing their own trades, in managing their farms, in the common concerns of life, they have not more understanding than their neighbors. Why then shall they set up to "lead"?

It would be well if they were capable of leading in the right course. But this is not the case; they cause the people of this country to err by their vain babblings. The consequence is not only disgrace but injury. While we become the object of ridicule abroad, we obstruct our happiness at home. What man who had great household affairs to adjust, extensive mercantile or even farming concerns to manage would entrust them with those persons? Yet you entrust the management of the Commonwealth to them, and when they act contrary to the wisdom of men of real understanding in these affairs you permit your senses to be deceived by the vile nonsense which

1. William Findley, Assemblyman from Westmoreland County.
2. John Smiley, Assemblyman from Fayette County, adhered to Findley's policies.

they utter to excuse their conduct. By these means the "way of your paths" or your path way is disturbed; that is, you are impeded or altogether thrown out of the proper course in your progress to wealth and happiness.

But is this any prodigy or wonderful thing? Far from it. It has always been and will always be the case in some degree while human nature remains the same. On this head examples are brought every day from the Greek and Roman history. But that of the Jews is sufficiently fraught with such. Isaiah, the author of the words prefixed to this discourse, was a man of a noble mind, educated in the schools of the prophets, and possessing great understanding. It would naturally be imagined that such a man would be heard with attention and that his advice would be received. Not so. It appears that there were persons who had the ear of the populace, demagogues, who could do with them as they pleased.

It is his language, "Oh, my people, they which lead thee cause thee to err, and destroy the way of thy paths."

[*Pittsburgh Gazette*
March 22, 1788]

II

"My people are destroyed for lack of knowledge."
Hosea iv, 12.

I again address the inhabitants of the Western country under the appellation of "my people." From my residence among them, I conceive myself most naturally to belong to them and they to me. This will not only justify me in speaking my sentiments on affairs which concern them but [this] has made it my duty. I ask then why is it that so many of the inhabitants of this country are opposed to the new Federal Constitution? It is from the want of knowledge. I do not mean to say that they are less capable of judging than their neighbors. On the contrary, from the experience which I have had of their understanding in the capacity of magistrates, jury men, or in the common concerns of life, I have conceived as highly of them in this respect as of any other people. But they are distant from the means of information and are at the mercy of vague reports and the judgments of others. How else could they be led to oppose a government which must so greatly advance their own interest? For without the energy of such a constitution, how can we expect the opening of the Mississippi river,[3] the surrender of the posts on the lakes,[4] the support of troops on the frontier, and the protection of settlements about to be made on Muskingum?[5]

It is true this Constitution will be adopted, let the voice of this country be what it may; but it must greatly affect the character of the inhabitants to have been a drawback. On this very account a man is made to blush when he travels to other parts and is obliged to acknowledge that he is from these settlements.

The simplicity of those whom we send to represent us in the public bodies is at the bottom of this misfortune. There is a knot in Philadelphia consisting of a few persons whom I could name, who, under pretense of great affection for the western country members, associate with them at the sign of the Black Bear[6] and play them off, sometimes to revenge themselves on the richer merchants or for purposes of private advantages, by obtaining local laws, etc. This is the origin of the funding system, the attacks upon the bank, the breaking up the Assembly, etc.

Our representatives coming home communicate the same impressions to their countrymen, and we become the laughing stock of the Commonwealth.

"My people are destroyed for lack of knowledge."

Ignorance has done more mischief in the world than villainy. For if men were intelligent, rogues could not deceive them. All the prophets from Moses to Malachi constantly complain of the want of understanding in the people. They do not so much arraign their bad intention as their mistakes. If prejudices could be removed, and they [the people] would hearken to those who have it in their power to inform them, it would be well; but on the contrary they give their ear only to those who are less informed than themselves. "My people ask counsel of their flocks, and their staff declareth unto them."[7]

[*Pittsburgh Gazette*
March 29, 1788]

3. Spain held navigation rights on the Mississippi.
4. British posts on the Great Lakes.
5. Government troops for protection against the Indians.
6. Black Bear Inn, Philadelphia.
7. Hosea iv, 12.

III

> "Say ye not a confederacy, to all to whom this
> people shall say a confederacy." Isaiah viii, 12.

Under pretense of pointing out defects and mischiefs in the new Constitution, it is the object of many to prevent any confederation whatever. Men of influence in the several states, who owe it more to local favor than to extensive abilities, may apprehend that on the large scale they cannot be considerable and will therefore wish to have the small wheel within which they move distinct from any larger one. A snail may work the shell which it inhabits, but let the same body be put into a marine conch and it will not be able to give it motion.

I found my opinion on the very reasoning of our adversaries, because things are advanced by them which are calculated merely to take the populace and which I am convinced they do not themselves believe, viz., the necessity of a bill of rights.[8]

It is private interest that governs them. Some who possess offices may apprehend that those will be abridged, others that they will not be able to obtain by the aid of party, local, partial, and ex post facto laws for their private emolument. A third class may have their eyes upon honorary and lucrative deputations. If each state becomes independent, it must have its foreign ministers residing abroad or negotiating with the neighboring commonwealths, and in this case the little demagogues within their respective sovereignties will be thrown up into splendid political existence. The loyal [. . .] weaver[9] may come to be a negotiator of treaties.

There is a class of demagogues superior to these, who would not object to a consideration of two or three states comprehending that in which they live, because even then they might hope to be considerable. It is on this principle that three confederacies have been suggested, a northern, a southern, and a middle. There would in that case be three sets of legislative, judiciary, and executive men, and all the train of officers which would be competent for a greater republic.

But let these be the views of the adversaries or not, all their conduct leads to this object. For if we do not adopt the present schedule of confederation, it is not probable that we shall ever agree upon any other. To defeat this will be the same as to determine that we shall have no confederation at all. Those who oppose it might

8. See "Cursory Remarks on the Federal Constitution," pp. 126–28.
9. The original text is blurred. The reference is to William Findley.

just as well speak out and "say not a confederacy to all to whom this people shall say a confederacy."

[*Pittsburgh Gazette*
April 5, 1788]

An Address in Opposition to the Election of ——— ———[1]

Every one is disposed not only to choose his own part but assign to others what part they shall act. It was perhaps in this spirit of being the manager of the drama that the following was written in opposition to the pretensions of one who was a candidate for the Congress of the United States. **[*Gazette Publications*]**

> "All the world's a stage,/And all the men and women merely players."

Previous to the late election for a senator for this district,[2] I had thoughts of offering myself, but I had found an opposition springing up and especially from a professional character who had an eye to that place himself. I was far from being sanguine that either he or I could be elected, from the prejudice, however unreasonable, that exists against the profession of the law; but declining all pretensions on my part, I gave way and he succeeded. What must be my surprise then to hear that this gentleman talks of abandoning his trust at the expiration of one-fourth of the time for which he was elected? It will be said that he has done one year's work, and let another person go and do more. But he undertook a job of four years and let him go through with it. It is not every day that we can get a lawyer elected, and it is betraying the interests of the profession and of the country to put it to the risk of a second trial. But he must attend to his professional pursuits. Is that the case? Or is it that, being appointed to a general of militia and having had no military reading or experience, he finds it necessary to withdraw from the council chamber and apply

1. William Findley.
2. State Senator.

himself to the study of tactics and maneuvers in the field? If it is, it is commendable, and I will excuse him.

But it is whispered that he purposes to stand at poll at the ensuing election for a member of Congress for this district.

Is it that in so short a time he has made such progress in political studies that he has outrun the standing of the senate of an individual state? Has his education been so perfect and his subsequent application so great that he has no room for improvement after one year of public service in a state legislature before he must remove into that of the general government? Perhaps if he would inquire diligently he might still find something to learn in finance, in the law of nations, even in history or geography, in order to qualify himself for a more conspicuous and extensive field of deliberation and of eloquence. It would seem to me that the three remaining years might be spent to good advantage in attending to state objects and occasionally enlarging his general reading so that if after that time he should come forward we may derive credit from a representative that is not deficient in a single point of literature or information.

But should he persist, will the public countenance this "overstepping the modesty of nature" in a rise to public offices and honors? Will it not offend the pride and self-love of every mind? Or is he of such rare endowments that what would be arrogance in others is justifiable in him?

But can it be avoided? Are there no means of supplying the vacancy or combating this adversary but by filching from our Senate the member of which they have possession? I flatter myself there are and that we may find a tolerable substitute for two years at least, until his term expires. And we can enjoy the advantage of his talents without outraging principle and violating every rule of decorum.

But will it not be doing the world wrong to keep him three years, as it were in a dungeon, in a vile state senate while he might be the brightest gem in the forehead of the union? Why? It will make his head a dungeon of knowledge, if I may indulge a pun. Did not Demosthenes sink himself a long time to a cellar and shave his head to keep himself from coming out while he formed that style which afterwards commanded Greece and gave immortality to his orations?

But as he never reads, he has no occasion for acquired knowledge. His academic education was extremely limited and his literary application since none, but it is genius—his native powers—that make amends for all. I give it up then. I admit he has no occasion for improvement. But as to occupying place, there might be a propriety in letting older though weaker lights be carried to the upper chamber and go out first, or at least in letting some other lights exist at the same time.

To avoid offense, I do not deny, as I have already said, that he is a prodigy. What is more, I admit he is far from being ignorant of this himself. It might be a query whether the lion knows that he is the king of the beasts or the jack-daw that it has variegated feathers; but there can be no question but that ———— ————[3] knows all his pre-eminences, and perhaps adds to them in his own imagination. He is none of your people that is not acquainted with himself. The Gnothi Seauton of the Greeks [4] is his motto, not just in the sense the philosophers intended but in the meaning that he thinks more of himself than of anything else. Some are troubled with what is called absence of mind; this is not his defect. He has continual presence of mind, a rare qualification. His thoughts are never abroad, no more than if there was not an animal in the creation but himself. His ideas center where they first arise. He feels no blush at precedence of others because they are never the subject of his thoughts.

No. Let him reduce his mind within a reasonable compass, let him wait till he is called upon for his services, and then they may be valued. Dropping irony, let him occupy the present interval to improve himself in books; for most assuredly he is not without the need of this. I am now in the fiftieth year of my age, and have been forty-five a severe student; and yet because I know something, I should tremble, were I to think of a seat in the legislature of the union, at not knowing more. Perhaps from what we have heard of that House last year, he may think it is but a game of cudgel-playing to act a part there. Indeed from the half of their speeches, it is pretty evident that a bare garden would suit some better than a hall of philosophers; but ought we not to labor a reform? If there are a number of harsh, haughty, and intolerant young men in that assembly, why carry coals to Newcastle and increase the store from our stock? Suggesting these things to your consideration, citizens, I leave the matter. . . .

[*Pittsburgh, 1789*]

3. William Findley.
4. The maxim inscribed on Apollo's temple at Delphi, "Know thyself."

A Sermon on Village Slander

I find the following in the *Pittsburgh Gazette* of March 28, 1789. The usual draw-back on the happiness of a village society (scandal) had begun to show itself, and as no regular clergyman was settled in the town who could make a stand by moral or theological lecture against its advances, it was thought not amiss, in the guise of a sermon, for even a layman to suggest a word or two of doctrine; and which had a good effect, perhaps from the novelty of the manner, coming forward in a newspaper, more than from the weight of the observations.

[*Gazette Publications*]

"I know thy works, and where thou dwellest, even where Satan's seat is." Rev. ii, 13.

There seems to be little or no mention made of a devil in the books of Moses unless you suppose the book of Job to be his writings, for there it is said that when "the sons of God came to present themselves, Satan came also amongst them." [1] Nevertheless the doctrine seems to be well established in the subsequent parts of the sacred scriptures. Nor is it only in divine revelation that we find this idea but also in the opinions and religious systems of heathen sects and people. The Manicheans,[2] a school of pagan philosophy among the Oriental nations, talk of "good principle and a bad"; the savages of North America tell us of the "good and bad man," meaning the author of happiness and the author of evil.

But there need be little said on this great point, seeing it is a principle so well established and believed insomuch that it has become a mode of speech by which we assert truth, for we say commonly, "If I do not do this or that, there is no devil." It evinces the firmness of our belief of this doctrine, that when we express our anger against anyone we say, "The devil take him." For whatever insincerity there may be in our professions of esteem, there is none in our declarations of resentment; so that the man who wishes his worst enemy at the devil entertains, doubtless, a persuasion that there is a devil to receive him.

That the devil has some fixed habitation on the face of this earth appears from the expression in the text, "where Satan's seat is," but

1. Job ii, 1.
2. Manicheans, the followers of Manes (216–276?), believed that man's soul springs from the kingdom of light and that it seeks escape from the kingdom of darkness which is the body.

our consolation is that it cannot be in this town, for in that case he would be too great a distance from the center of his vast dominions, being on the very verge of the settled globe, I mean of close settlement and population. Some of the great cities in the heart of Europe or Asia must be more convenient for his operations.

But it will be asked, "How then comes it to pass, that we find traces of his acting here? Can he reach his magic wand to us? Or does he make excursions now and then?" In this case it would behoove him to be perpetually on foot, running to and from the outskirts to influence the thoughts and prompt the conduct of men. No. I take it he is not such a laborious busy devil but consults his ease and is not always on the pad. "How then," it will be asked, "can he manage his concerns?" Doubtless by the intervention of subordinate devils, and in this point, as in all others, the Christian system is consistent with reason, for though the Manichean doctrine and the ideas of barbarous nations admit a devil, yet they do not supply us with a plurality and enable us to account for the ubiquity of diabolicism.

It may there be set down as certain that though this town cannot be the seat or Pandemonium of Satan himself, yet it may be the residence of some intendant or sub-devil.

This has been always my private opinion, and I have taken great pains by repeated observations to examine the kind of devil he is. For knowing what manner of spirit he was of, I could the more successfully apply myself to counteract him. No astronomer ever held his tube more constantly to the heavens to ascertain the movements of the heavenly bodies than I have applied my eyes and ears to determine the particular powers of this demon; and this I do not say out of spiritual pride and vanity of religious zeal, but to found the probability and truth of what I shall assert on the subject.

The way I have taken was to ascertain that vice which is particularly predominant among us, whether it is of a generous and bold nature or mean and sneaking in its quality, for the offspring usually bears the features of the parent, the workmanship bespeaks the artificer. I have found this vice to be tale bearing.

This is a vice which shows no genius and requires no wit. It is a low, vulgar, and cowardly iniquity, and designates the devil that inspires it to be of the most inferior species. Some little insignificant cur that could find no employment at the court of Pandemonium of the great devil or the more important parts of the empire, but was dispatched to this quarter as a remote situation.

It will be said that all vices are equally infernal, and therefore all equally magnificent. No, for among the infernalia there are the majora and minora peccata, the greater and the lesser sins, and a noble devil will naturally choose to exhibit his talents in some splendid way. But ours is a mean creature; he attempts nothing great; we hear of no robberies. Are there any rapes? And yet I believe we have as handsome women as any in the world. No, the rascal exercises himself solely in the lowest acts of mischief, this of tale bearing particularly.

It is incident to this vice that it is only the most worthless and meanest persons that are capable of it and with whom none but a little dirty devil would choose to have anything to do. As an ass' hoof from its coldness is said to be the receptacle of poison, so the most ignorant and low-thoughted mortals are most proper for the entrance and impulse of a creeping reptile of a devil that could not agitate a more excellent machine.

But what the devil wants in talents he makes up in assiduity. He is as busy as a bee in a tar barrel. Not a word is said by one of another but it is taken up, carried around like the brand in the play of Jack's alive and alive like to be; [thus] the tale-bearer, afraid it [the tale] will die in his possession. If the word is of no account, it is changed; the inference substituted for itself, the construction of the word applied in the place of the original expression. If the manner would qualify or explain, it is suppressed. The incident that gave rise to it left out. Their own words that introduced the conversation omitted. The question made by the tale-bearer, "Did you hear this? And do you know that?", wholly passed by. This is a demon who, where he has no ground at all, will invent. This shows him to be artful and ingenious as all devils are; for when I undervalue his capacity, I mean only the extent of his nature and not the sublety of it.

You will ask me what principle it is of human nature that the demon takes hold of to instigate persons to this vice. Doubtless the love of self. It is the interest of the animals with whom this devil has to do that there should be a difference amongst neighbors, because by this discord they may gain. It is the policy of such individuals that all others should be at war but themselves. If they envy a neighbor the conversation and company of another, a variance between them is their object. If they hate the neighbor, an indirect war is the safest by prompting another whom they do not hate to undertake it. It is the conduct of a low servant in the family, complaining of another, "He used me ill; and, madam, he called you names too."

The tale bearer, says the wise man, "separateth very friends." Persons who have the highest respect and the most cordial regard for each other and who would have lived and died in amity are excited to suspicion, hatred, and revenge by this base incendiary. There is no mind which feels not at some moment irritation at those they most prize, and words are used at this time which spring like the spark of fire and are extinguished as soon, but they are carefully picked up and kept alive by the tale-bearer. The passions of men, the anger of the mind, the resentments of the moment, the saliency of temper, the sudden gusts of vexation, and the correspondent ideas and language would be lost and perish like the April showers, but the tale-bearer bottles them up, and by his decoctions and composition, they become drops of poison to infect the vitals of all concord in society.

It is a master stroke of a tale-bearer when in a village like this—where we are stowed away like persons in a jail or on board a man of war and know the words, the transactions, the manners, the incidents, and almost the thoughts of each other, and when something with regard to an individual has become the subject of general conversation and the tale-bearer wishes to injure a particular person—to fix on this one as having taken a principal hand in the business, because as the conversation has doubtless come his way and he may have passed it on, there is some truth in the case, and from the intermixture of a thousand discourses, it is difficult to ascertain what was the special property of any one. It is also the policy of the tale-bearer to fix on some person whose sentiment is of weight and opinion regarded, to play off this artfully against the object hated; and while this creature is blowing the pestiferous breath of flattery in the face of one and telling them what has been said of them or done to them by another, it is the very persons addressed that are chiefly the objects whom they mean to wound, by leading them to entertain passion against a third person, which will produce passion and lead them to entertain hate to one another, the fair offspring of the succubus that carried the first tidings. Like the snakes winding round Laocoön in the fable,[3] they embrace closely, hiss with a serpentine siffilation, but they bite mortally and breathe poison in the veins. It will remain to be considered in what manner [we] shall

---

3. The Trojan priest of the Thymbraean Apollo. As he was preparing to sacrifice a bull to Poseidon, two serpents came out of the sea, coiled around his body, and destroyed him. An ancient sculpture found in 1506, now in the Vatican, freezes the terror in his face the moment before his death.

best provide against the bad effects of this. On this head I shall lay down a few rules.

1st. When the tale-bearer comes to you and tells you anything of what another has said of you, consider whether, besides the general interest which he has in making everybody enemies, there is not some particular interest in making you an enemy to the person mentioned; weigh this well, and if you cannot determine immediately, wait some time until events may elucidate the circumstance. Say nothing, feel nothing, do nothing rashly; and set it down as a certain fact that, let it be as it may, the tale-bearer is a most worthless character, and is impregnated with the worst of all evils, for either he invents what he says, or if he does not, he had by some means induced the confidence of the person of whom he speaks and which confidence he now violates.

2nd. But if from circumstances or even perfect proof you find that there is some foundation of the account communicated, reflect with yourselves whether you have not given the person who has expressed himself unfavorably some provocation to this undervaluing. If so, you are to take it all upon yourself and pass it by, for it is a maxim that the trespasser is accountable for the consequences. Consider also that if true, it is the tenor of your life that must rebut the calumny and that the resenting argues some soreness and consciousness of deserving it. But what is still more Christian and philosophic—for Christianity and philosophy, however they may differ in speculative points, in morals are the same—oppose a breast of forgiveness and of love. "Be not overcome with evil," says the Apostle Paul, "but overcome evil with good." [4] The woolpack on the outside of an armed vessel receives the winged ball, and by yielding, though the swiftest and fiercest of all things, it instantly reduces it to rest.

It is difficult to say, when you are in the habits of friendship with anyone and you are told that disrespectful things are said of you by him, whether instantly you ought to acquaint him with it and have an explanation, or disregard it wholly and trust to your own eyes and ears for the fact. I think the last is best, provided you have resolution to hinder it making an impression on your mind. For the calling on a person to answer to reports argues a distrust of his honor, which to a delicate mind is a species of insult, and I will venture to say will not be easily forgiven. Perhaps to communicate it as the villainy of the informant, and as what you do not believe, may be the just medium. This will bring the author to be understood, and the truth will be

4. Romans xii, 21.

known. For I say it again, the general rule is [that] the tale-bearer is a worthless person; and this ought to be presumed until the contrary appears. To conclude: the writer of this sermon declares that in these strictures he has no particular person in view, and if any application is made it will be the act of him who makes the application and not of me. He only thought to give a little seasonable doctrine.

[*Pittsburgh Gazette*
March 28, 1789]

Sermon on the Duel

Mr. Scull,

The age of chivalry is not over, and challenges . . . have been given even in the midst of a yellow fever, which one would think was killing people fast enough already. The fear of God or the law are usual and just grounds of refusing; but I will give you a sample of the way in which I got off with some of my challenges, in the following letter and answer on a late occasion, but omitting the name of the challenger, as I have no inclination to trouble him with a prosecution.

Sir,

I will thank you to take a walk with a friend and meet me at the back of the graveyard about sunrise tomorrow morning. After what has happened, you know what I mean.

Your humble servant, etc.

Sir,

I know what you mean very well; you want to have a shot at me, but I have no inclination to hit you, and I am afraid you would hit me. I pray thee therefore have me excused.

[*Gazette Publications*]

"And the king lamented over Abner, and said,
'Died Abner as a fool dieth.' " 2 Sam. iii, 33.

It was not in a duel that Abner fell, but the words may be applied to those that fall in this way. They die certainly as a fool dieth; that is, without necessity or a sufficient reason to justify the voluntary risk. This evil, like the venereal complaint or the small pox, was unknown to the ancients. It is the offspring of modern barbarism, and in vain have the sage, the politician, or the divine endeavored to extirpate it. I have traced the evil with minute investigation in order to determine the principle on which it rests, and I find it to be that which is least supposed, a want of fortitude.

This indeed has been generally concededed by wise men. We are told, and with great truth, that it requires more spirit to sustain the shock of prevailing opinion than to risk life itself. There is not one in five hundred that is capable of it. It requires a soul illumined by reason, firm in itself, and balanced on the center of his own judgment.

Again, it is the fear of being brought to this kind of combat that induces many to affect to approve of it. They well know that should it be supposed they will decline it, who wishes to establish what he calls a character will call upon them to it.

A combat of this kind is wholly unreasonable because it is unequal. Shall a man of six feet present himself for a mark to a dwarf of five? Or a man of a square body to a thing that would almost cut the ball which it takes? It places the fool and the wise man on the same ground—the fool who robs himself and the world of a piece of earth only, the wise man who subtracts the light of thought and the intelligence of mind. It is unequal because character may be borrowed on the one side, while the other does not wish to spare. I have known a person wish to bring me to this kind of combat merely to have his name matched with mine; and I have fled from the association, with more dread of it than of all other evils.

On the principle of cowardice or passion, a man may be somewhat excusable who submits to this evil. But what shall we say of those who under no impulse of this nature act as seconds? His courage is not impeached who declines it; he is under the influence of no passion, and yet without such a person it is not probable a duel would be fought. It strikes me with horror that human nature could degenerate so far that in any instance a person could be found to undertake such an office. That instead of the noble duty of reconciling men and promoting peace and saving life there could be found those who would coolly assist to bring about the contest and stand by and see the issue, probably mortal to one or to both. If we had not such among ourselves and were told that they existed in some other planet, we should set that down to be hell and the inhabitants devils.

I am confident that no man ever rendered himself agreeable to another by being a second for him. It might pass for the moment, but he must look back upon it as an act of enmity, not of good will. It borders on the office but is much more odious than that of a hangman;

for the one helps away the culprit, with whom he has probably no acquaintance and for whom he professes no esteem, who is convicted of some offense and sentenced by the law of the land; the other [helps away] the very man who puts confidence in him, or the person with whom this friend of his has some occasional or unfortunate difference.

What shall we think of those who by countenance, language, or act prompt the duel; who take upon them to censure the conduct of others; who when injured have thought proper to take revenge in this way, or to carry it to this extreme? Doubtless we ought to look upon them as murderers in heart. Such behavior and sentiment have their foundations in meanness and malevolence; envy of another and a wish to take him out of the way, or hatred which leads to delight in the misery of the species. . . . By this means they make it necessary for him to act the part of the fool or the madman. Make it necessary? Why is it then men of sense do not unite and stand by each other in this case? They might form a phalanx against the brigade of fools; but they basely desert their colors, give up their opinion, and like slaves in the hall of a despot dare not speak their minds.

Surely a man dies the death of a fool who falls in this way: will those who promoted him to incur the risk shed a tear at his death? Will they contribute a mite to assist his widow or his orphans, or mix their griefs to console his relations? They will rather rejoice, and the very novelty of the incident will be more pleasing to them than the reviviscence of the deceased, were it possible. Shall a man then succumb to this false sentiment for the sake of those who care nothing about him, or rather triumph in his fall?

The question is, what will you do with a man who invites you to this kind of combat? Humor and play with him as a bear, or other beast, until you have got quit of him. What with a man who insults you with his language? Make your strictures with equal freedom upon him. What shall be done with one who abuses you personally and whose strength is superior? Add the assistance of art and aid yourself with a club or a cutlass. If in all these you fail, there is the law at hand. If those who administer it are so unfaithful to their trust as not to do you adequate justice by the severity of the penalty, set it down as one of those imperfections in the affairs of men which cannot be avoided. Is this theory only? Did not the Romans and the Greeks, the Jews, the Assyrians, and all the ancients act on this principle?

But though of recent date this evil has sprung up, yet the labor of sages and philosophers against it has been tried in vain. Let us make our last appeal to the fair sex, the beauty of nature and the solace of human life. Do you think that the persons of this description are the most likely to protect you? You will find a more determined, faithful, and successful support from those who have the nobleness of mind to be above it. What an honor it would be to your sex to lend the invincible force of your charms to extirpate this vice by the force of your opinion. You would secure the esteem of those who are more capable of knowing your merit than all the fools of the world put together.

I do not mean to insult the memory of anyone who falls in this way. David did not mean to insult the memory of Abner, whom he greatly respected when he uses the words of the text. A particular act may be branded as folly independent of the persons and the general character they deserve.

[*Pittsburgh Gazette*
June 13, 1789]

Oration on the Celebration of the Anniversary of Independence, July 4th, 1793

[*As late as 1793 Brackenridge called upon his early style of fiery images and sudden, staccato questions between balanced sentences. It was the style for his most direct appeal to the people. He wished to move them with the spirit that had moved him, a political spirit approaching the religious. Speaking in this manner at the celebration of Independence Day, he responded to the neutrality proclamation of the Federalists with a call to arms in defense of France. But he carefully inserted a safeguard. The American will to aid France would probably be sufficient. It would serve to comfort the newest republic in their war with monarchy. Casting aside treaty obligations requiring intervention on the side of France, Brackenridge bases his appeal on the higher principle of humanity, on the cause of republicanism itself.*

He was aware of his ultimate effect on the frontier audience. The settler would tend to ignore the qualifications and take the speech as an actual call to arms against the British. Then the government would be forced to send troops west to fight the Indians who were allies of the British and who were harassing the settlers.]

The celebration of the day introduces the idea of the principle that gave it birth: the wisdom of the king of Great Britain who saw the growing greatness of the provinces, that they were now of age to act for themselves and bade them be independent? No. The wisdom of the parliament of Great Britain, that seeing the inconvenience or impossibility of our being represented in the legislature and sensible of the being bound by laws without being represented, saw the expediency of a separation from them and said to us, "be independent and become an allied power?" No, nothing of all this. The king and parliament of Great Britain were of opinion that without representation we were bound by their laws and, though descendants of their isle, had no right to freedom in a great forest.

Whence then our independence? It was the offspring of the understanding and the virtue of the people of America themselves. The eloquent advised, the brave fought, and we succeeded. The day on which we assumed our rights became a festival, and every future year shall remember it.

The celebration of the day introduces the idea of the effect of it beyond the sphere of these states. The light kindled here has been reflected to Britain, and a reform in the representation of the commons is expected. The light kindled here has been reflected to France, and a new order of things has arisen. Shall we blame the intemperature of the exertions? Was there ever enthusiasm without intemperance? And was there ever a great effect without enthusiasm? Thy principles, O! Liberty, are not violent or cruel; but in the desperation of thy efforts against tyranny, it is not always possible to keep within the limit of the vengeance necessary to defense. Do we accuse the air or the bastille of the mountain when the rock is burst and the town engulfed? The air of itself is mild and scarcely wafts a feather from its place. But restrained and imprisoned, the yielding and placid element becomes indignant and tears the globe before it. Do we accuse the hurricane when the mariner is tossed with the tempest and is an incidental sufferer in the storm? The naturalist does not. He tells you that the equilibrium of the atmosphere has been disturbed; and if man has suffered more than the demerit of his transgressions, it is in a struggle of nature to restore itself.

Is it the duty of these states to assist France? That we are bound by treaty, and how far, I will not say because it is not necessary. We are bound by a higher principle, if our assistance could avail; the great law of humanity.

We might, it is true, allege the stipulations of a treaty and the guarantee of her possessions to France. But as the world would know and we ought to avow . . . it is the cause of republicanism which would induce our efforts. The tyrant of Great Britain alleged the stipulations of a treaty relative to the opening of the Scheldt [1] and waited for requisition on the part of Holland to observe the guarantee. But all the world knew and he might have avowed it, that it was not the opening of the Scheldt but the attack upon monarchy that prompted his interposition. Shall kings combine, and shall republics not unite? We have united. The heart of America feels the cause of France. She takes a part in all her councils, approves her wisdom, blames her excesses. She is moved, impelled, elevated, and depressed with all the changes of her good and bad fortune. She feels the same fury in her veins. She is tossed and shaken with all the variety of hopes and fears attending her situation. Why not? Can we be indifferent? Is not our fate interlaced with hers? For, O! France, if thy Republic perish, where is the honor due to ours? From whom respect to our flag upon the seas? Not from France restored to a monarch and indignant at those very feelings which are now our glory: not from the despots that are against her. These will easily recollect that the cause of their evils took their rise here.

Can we assist France by arming in her favor? I will not say that we can. But could we, and should France say, "United States, your neutrality is not sufficient; I expect the junction of your arms with mine, your heroes on the soil and your privateers on the ocean to distress the foe," who is there would not say, "It shall be so. You shall have them. Our citizens shall arm; they shall attack; our oaks shall descend from the mountains; our vessels be launched upon the stream; and the voice of our war, however weak, shall be heard with yours."

If we ourselves should judge that our arms could assist France, even though the generous Republic required it not, yet who would hestitate to interfere, not only at the risk of property but of life itself? Is it illusion, or do I hear France say, "My daughter America, I know the dutifulness of thy heart towards me, and that thou are disposed to show it by taking part in this war. But I wish thee not to provoke hostilities for my sake. If I perish, I perish; but let not a mother draw in a hapless child to suffer with herself." Is it illusion, or do I hear America reply? I do, and it is in the language of the Moabitish Ruth to her mother-in-law, the Jewish Naomi, "Intreat me not to leave thee, or return from following thee; for whither thou

1. At the Treaty of Munster in 1648 the Dutch obtained the right to close the Scheldt River to navigation, thus sacrificing the prosperity of Belgium for that of Holland. When the Belgians wanted to break the treaty and open the Scheldt to navigation, the British monarch objected.

goest, I will go; and where thou lodgest, I will lodge; thy people shall be my people, and thy God, my God; where thou diest, I will die; and there I will be buried. God do so to me, and more also if ought but death shall part thee and me." [2]

But whether we assist or not, thy cause, O! France, will be triumphant. Did the enthusiasm of a small Roman people repell their invaders until Rome became the protectoress of nations? Did the enthusiasm of a few Greeks repell the millions of Asia and afterwards overrun her kingdoms? Did the enthusiasm of the Saracens in a few years spread to Spain on the one hand and the Indus [3] on the other? Did the enthusiasm of a few mad Crusaders burst upon the Saracen and establish the kingdom of Jerusalem in the center of his empire? And shall the enthusiasm of a brave people more numerous than the early Roman republic—the Greeks under Alexander, the Saracens of Arabia, or the Crusaders of Europe—be subdued by all that are against them? The weight will condense resistance, and as the materials of explosion in the ordnance acquire a spring by confinement, so in proportion to the attack of this people will their voice be terrible, their blow irresistible.

France will be independent also and celebrate her anniversaries, and in doing so will recollect that our independence had preceded hers and made the example. The anniversary of the independence of America will be a great epoch of liberty throughout the world. Proceed we then to celebrate the day; advance to the festive board; pour out libations to sentiments of liberty; and let the loud-mouthed artillery be heard on the hill.

[*Pittsburgh Gazette*
July 5, 1793]

2. Ruth i, 16.
3. One of the great rivers of Northern India; but no doubt Brackenridge is referring to India itself.

from *Modern Chivalry*

[*The reputation of Hugh Henry Brackenridge has rested upon* Modern Chivalry. *Its picaresque structure is borrowed from Cervantes'* Don Quixote. *But its representations and mood are original, arising from the impact of frontier life upon the mind of a trained classicist. The satirical mood approaches the geniality of Horace rather than the severity of Juvenal. Brackenridge ridicules the foibles and follies of frontier life in order to show the new democrats their shortcomings, their needs for education, refinement, and self-knowledge. Ambition and ignorance are the targets of the satire. Success of the democratic experiment depends upon the people learning their lessons.*

Captain John Farrago, a gentleman at leisure whose ideas are "drawn from the old school, the Greek and Roman way of looking at things," administers the lessons while his servant, Teague O'Regan, illustrates them. As the Captain and Teague travel to Philadelphia and back, the characters, events, and customs they encounter stimulate the bog-trotter's ambition to rise in the new democracy though he cannot read nor write. With this narrative scheme Brackenridge was able to present a panorama of life in the burgeoning democracy and to demonstrate his critical judgments, many of them still pertinent and stimulating. Pomposity of the erudite, boorishness of the backwoodsman, and effete avarice of the eastern politician are all pilloried in the embracing portrait of early United States society.

A major motif—"let the cobbler stick to his last"—runs through all the author's previous work from "Father Bombo's Pilgrimage" to his Hudibrastic verse from which the novel evolved. But this motif implies no aristocratic concept of fixed stations in life. Through education and application of talents, the cobbler may become more than a cobbler and thus qualify for the broader responsibilities of a statesman. For Brackenridge, education meant a thorough knowledge and understanding of the Roman and Greek worlds.

To keep Teague in line, the Captain invents tales as tall as any of his bog-trotter's. Both characters are developments of Father Bombo. Much of the humor resides in their deceitful tales.

Composed over the last twenty-five years of the author's life, Modern Chivalry *contains many inconsistencies in thought and structure. Part II, written after Brackenridge had returned to the East, is critical of the Jeffersonian party which he had led while in the West. And its narrative elements are slight compared to those of Part I. Reviewing the second part, Brackenridge regretted his loss of imaginative powers and apologized, "There is some attempt at humor, but seldom have I been able to reach it." The following excerpts comprise most of the narrative elements of Part I, all completed by 1797.*]

[1]

John Farrago was a man of about fifty-three years of age, of good natural sense and considerable reading, but in some things whimsical, owing perhaps to his greater knowledge of books than of the world but in some degree also to his having never married, being what they call an old bachelor, a characteristic of which is usually singularity and whim. He had the advantage of having had in early life an academic education, but having never applied himself to any of the learned professions he had lived the greater part of his life on a small farm, which he cultivated with servants or hired hands as he could conveniently supply himself with either. The servant that he had at this time was an Irishman whose name was Teague O'Regan. I shall say nothing of the character of this man because the very name imports what he was.

A strange idea came into the head of Captain Farrago about this time; for by the bye, I had forgot to mention that having been chosen captain of a company of militia in the neighborhood, he had gone by the name of Captain ever since, for the rule is, once a captain and always a captain. But, as I was observing, the idea had come into his head to saddle an old horse that he had and ride about the world a little, with his man Teague at his heels, to see how things were going on here and there and to observe human nature. For it is a mistake to suppose that a man cannot learn man by reading him in a corner as well as on the widest space of transaction. At any rate it may yield amusement.

It was about a score of miles from his own house that he fell in with what we call races. The jockeys seeing him advance, with Teague by his side, whom they took for his groom, conceived him to be some person who had brought his horse to enter for the purse. Coming up and accosting him, said they, "You seem to be for the races, sir, and have a horse to enter." "Not at all," said the Captain. "This is but a common palfrey, and by no means remarkable for speed or bottom; he is a common plough horse which I have used on my farm for several years and can scarce go beyond a trot, much less match himself with your blooded horses that are going to take the field on this occasion."

The jockeys were of opinion, from the speech, that the horse was what they call a bite, and that under the appearance of leanness and stiffness there was concealed some hidden quality of swiftness uncommon. For they had heard of instances where the most knowing had been taken in by mean-looking horses; so that having laid two or more to one, they were nevertheless bit by the bet and the mean-looking nags proved to be horses of a more than common speed and bottom. So that there is no trusting appearances. Such was the reasoning of the jockeys. For they could have no idea that a man could come there in so singular a manner, with a groom at his foot, unless he had some great object of making money by the adventure. Under this idea they began to interrogate him with respect to the blood and pedigree of his horse: whether he was of the dove or the bay mare that took the purse and was imported by such a one at such a time? Whether his sire was Tamerlane or Bajazet?

The Captain was irritated at the questions and could not avoid answering. "Gentlemen," said he, "it is a strange thing that you should suppose that it is of any consequence what may be the pedigree of a horse. For even in men it is of no avail. Do we not find that sages have had blockheads for their sons and that blockheads have had sages? It is remarkable that as estates have seldom lasted three generations, so understanding and ability have seldom been transmitted to the second. There never was a greater man, take him as an orator and philosopher, than Cicero; and never was there a person who had greater opportunities than his son Marcus, and yet he proved of no account or reputation. This is an old instance but there are a thousand others. Chesterfield and his son are mentioned. It is true, Philip and Alexander may be said to be exceptions: Philip of the strongest possible mind, capable of almost everything we can conceive, the deepest policy and the most determined valor; his son Alexander not deficient in the first and before him in the last, if it is possible to be before a man than whom you can suppose nothing greater. It is possible in modern times that Tippo Sahib may be equal to his father Hyder Ali.[1] Some talk of the two Pitts. I have no idea that the son is in any respect equal to old Sir William. The one is a labored artificial minister, the other spoke with the thunder and acted with the lightning of the gods. I will venture to say that when the present John Adamses and Lees and Jeffersons and Jays and Henrys and other great men who figure upon the stage at this time have gone to sleep with their fathers, it is an hundred to one if there is any of their descendants who can fill their places. [Were] I to lay a bet for a great man

---

1. Hyder Ali (1722–1782) was the most formidable Asiatic rival the British encountered in India. Upon succeeding his father as Sultan of Mysore, Tippo Sahib (1753–1799) subjugated the people of Malabar, thereby provoking the British, who defeated him in 1792.

I would sooner pick up the brat of a tinker than go into the great houses to choose a piece of stuff for a man of genius. Even with respect to personal appearance, which is more in the power of natural production, we do not see that beauty always produces beauty; but on the contrary, the homeliest persons have oftentimes the best-favored offspring, so that there is no rule or reason in these things. With respect to this horse therefore it can be of no moment whether he is blooded or studded, or what he is. He is a good old horse, used to the plough, and carries my weight very well; and I have never yet made inquiry with respect to his ancestors or affronted him so much as to cast up to him the defect of parentage. I bought him some years ago from Neil Thomas, who had him from a colt. As far as I can understand, he was of a brown mare that John M'Neis had but of what horse I know no more than the horse himself. His gaits are good enough as to riding a short journey of seven or eight miles or the like; but he is rather a pacer than a trotter; and though his bottom may be good enough in carrying a bag to the mill or going in the plough or the sled or the harrow, etc., yet his wind is not so good, nor his speed, as to be fit for the heats."

The jockeys thought the man a fool and gave themselves no more trouble about him.

The horses were now entered, about to start for the purse. There was Black and All Black, and Snip, John Duncan's Barbary Slim, and several others. The riders had been weighed, and when mounted the word was given. It is needless to describe a race; everybody knows the circumstances of it. It is sufficient to say that from the bets that were laid there was much anxiety and some passion in the minds of those concerned; so that as two of the horses, Black and All Black and Slim, came out near together, there was dispute and confusion. It came to kicking and cuffing in some places. The Captain was a good deal hurt with such indecency among gentlemen, and advancing, addressed them in the following manner: "Gentlemen, this is an unequal and unfair proceeding. It is unbecoming modern manners or even the ancient. For at the Olympic games of Greece, where were celebrated horse and chariot races, there was no such hurry scurry as this; and in times of chivalry itself, where men ate, drank, and slept on horseback, though there was a great deal of pellmelling, yet no such disorderly work as this. If men had a difference they couched their lances and ran full tilt at one another, but no such indecent expressions as villain, scoundrel, liar ever came out of their mouths. There was the most perfect courtesy in those days of heroism and honor, and this your horse-racing, which is a germ of the amusement of those times, ought to be conducted on the same principles of decorum and good breeding."

As he was speaking he was jostled by someone in the crowd and thrown from his horse; and had it not been for Teague, who was at hand and helped him on again, he would have suffered damage. As it was he received a contusion in his head, of which he complained much, and having left the race-ground and coming to a small cottage, he stopped a little to alight and dress the wound. An old woman who was there thought they ought to take a little of his water and see how it was with him; but the Captain, having no faith in telling disorders by the urine, thought proper to send for a surgeon who was hard by to examine the bruise and apply bandages. The surgeon attended and, examining the part, pronounced it a contusion of the cerebrum. But as there appeared but little laceration and no fracture, simple or compound, the pia mater could not be injured; nor even could there be more than a slight impression on the dura mater. So that trepaning did not at all appear necessary. A most fortunate circumstance; for a wound in the head is of all places the most dangerous, because there can be no amputation to save life. There being but one head to a man and that being the residence of the five senses, it is impossible to live without it. Nevertheless as the present case was highly dangerous, as it might lead to a subsultus tendinum or lockjaw, it was necessary to apply cataplasms in order to reduce inflammation and bring about a sanative disposition of the parts. Perhaps it might not be amiss to take an anodyne as a refrigerant. Many patients had been lost by the ignorance of empirics prescribing bracers; whereas, in the first stage of a contusion, relaxing and antifebrile medicines are proper. A little phlebotomy was no doubt necessary to prevent the bursting of the blood vessels.

The Captain hearing so many hard words and bad accounts of this case was much alarmed. Nevertheless he did not think it could be absolutely so dangerous. For it seemed to him that he was not sick at heart or under any mortal pain. The surgeon observed that in this case he could not himself be a judge, for the very part was affected by which he was to judge, viz., the head; that it was no uncommon thing for men in the extremest cases to imagine themselves out of danger, whereas in reality they were in the greatest possible; that notwithstanding the symptoms were mild, yet from the contusion a mortification might ensue. Hippocrates, who might be styled an elementary physician and has a treatise on this very subject, is of opinion that the most dangerous symptom is a topical insensibility; but among the moderns, Sydenham considers it in another point of view, and thinks that where there is no pain there is as great reason to suppose that there is no hurt as that there is a mortal one. Be this as it may, antiseptic medicines might be very proper.

The Captain, hearing so much jargon and conscious to himself that he was by no means in so bad a state as this son of Aesculapius [2] would represent, broke out into some passion. "It is," said he, "the craft of your profession to make the case worse than it is in order to increase the perquisites. But if there is any faith in you, make the same demand and let me know your real judgment." The surgeon was irritated with his distrust and took it into his head to fix some apprehension in the mind of his patient, if possible, that his case was not without danger. Looking steadfastly at him for some time and feeling his pulse, "There is," said he, "an evident delirium approaching. This argues an affection of the brain but it will be necessary, after some soporiferous drafts to put the patient to sleep." Said the Captain, "If you will give me about a pint of whiskey and water, I will try to go to sleep myself." "A deleterious mixture in this case," said the surgeon, "cannot be proper, especially a distillation of that quality." The Captain would hear no more, but requesting the man of the cabin to let him have the spirits proposed, drank a pint or two of grog, and having bound up his head with a handkerchief, went to bed.

[2]

The Captain, rising early next morning and setting out on his way, had now arrived at a place where a number of people were convened for the purpose of electing persons to represent them in the legislature of the state. There was a weaver who was a candidate for this appointment and seemed to have a good deal of interest among the people. But another, who was a man of education, was his competitor. Relying on some talent of speaking which he thought he possessed, he addressed the multitude.

Said he, "Fellow citizens, I pretend not to any great abilities but am conscious to myself that I have the best good will to serve you. But it is very astonishing to me that this weaver should conceive himself qualified for the trust. For though my acquirements are not great, yet his are still less. The mechanical business which he pursues must

2. God of medical arts who could call the dead to life.

necessarily take up so much of his time that he cannot apply himself to political studies. I should therefore think it would be more answerable to your dignity and conducive to your interest to be represented by a man at least of some letters than by an illiterate handicraftsman like this. It will be more honorable for himself to remain at his loom and knot threads than to come forward in a legislative capacity, because in the one case he is in the sphere where God and nature has placed him, in the other he is like a fish out of water and must struggle for breath in a new element.

"Is it possible he can understand the affairs of government, whose mind has been concentered to the small object of weaving webs, to the price by the yard, the grist of the thread, and such like matters as concern a manufacturer of cloths? The feet of him who weaves are more occupied than the head or at least as much, and therefore the whole man must be, at least, but in half accustomed to exercise his mental powers. For these reasons, all other things set aside, the chance is in my favor with respect to information. However, you will decide, and give your suffrages to him or to me as you shall judge expedient."

The Captain hearing these observations and looking at the weaver could not help advancing and undertaking to subjoin something in support of what had been just said. Said he, "I have no prejudice against a weaver more than another man. Nor do I know any harm in the trade save that from the sedentary life in a damp place there is usually a paleness of the countenance, but this is a physical, not a moral, evil. Such usually occupy subterranean apartments, not for the purpose like Demosthenes of shaving their heads and writing over eight times the history of Thucydides and perfecting a style of oratory, but rather to keep the thread moist; or because this is considered but as an inglorious sort of trade, and is frequently thrust away into cellars and damp outhouses which are not occupied for a better use.

"But to rise from the cellar to the senate house would be an unnatural hoist. To come from counting threads and adjusting them to the splits of a reed to regulate the finances of a government would be preposterous, there being no congruity in the case. There is no analogy between knotting threads and framing laws. It would be a reversion of the order of things. Not that a manufacturer of linen or woolen or other stuff is an inferior character, but a different one from that which ought to be employed in affairs of state. It is unnecessary to enlarge on this subject, for you must all be convinced of the truth and propriety of what I say. But if you will give me leave to take the manufacturer aside a little, I think I can explain to him my ideas on the subject and very probably prevail with him to withdraw his pretensions." The people seeming to acquiesce and beckoning to the weaver, they drew aside; and the Captain addressed him in the following words:

"Mr. Traddle," said he, for that was the name of the manufacturer, "I have not the smallest idea of wounding your sensibility, but it would seem to me it would be more your interest to pursue your occupation than to launch out into that of which you have no knowledge. When you go to the senate house, the application to you will not be to warp a web but to make laws for the commonwealth. Now suppose that the making these laws requires a knowledge of commerce or of the interests of agriculture or those principles upon which the different manufactures depend, what service could you render? It is possible you might think justly enough, but could you speak? You are not in the habit of public speaking. You are not furnished with those commonplace ideas with which even very ignorant men can pass for knowing something. There is nothing makes a man so ridiculous as to attempt what is above his sphere. You are no tumbler for instance; yet should you give out that you could vault upon a man's back or turn head over heels like the wheels of a cart, the stiffness of your joints would encumber you and you would fall upon your backside to the ground. Such a squash as that would do you damage. The getting up to ride of the state is an unsafe thing to those who are not accustomed to such horsemanship. It is a disagreeable thing for a man to be laughed at, and there is no way of keeping one's self from it but by avoiding all affectation."

While they were thus discoursing, a bustle had taken place among the crowd. Teague, hearing so much about elections and serving the government, took it into his head that he could be a legislator himself. The thing was not displeasing to the people, who seemed to favor his pretensions, owing in some degree to there being several of his countrymen among the crowd but more especially to the fluctuation of the popular mind and a disposition to what is new and ignoble. For though the weaver was not the most elevated object of choice, yet he was still preferable to this tatter-demalion, who was but a menial servant and had so much of what is called the brogue on his tongue as to fall far short of an elegant speaker.

The Captain coming up and finding what was on the carpet was greatly chagrined at not having been able to give the multitude a better idea of the importance of a legislative trust, alarmed also from an apprehension of the loss of his servant. Under these impressions he resumed his address to the multitude. Said he, "This is making the matter still worse, gentlemen. This servant of mine is but a bog-trotter who can scarcely speak the dialect in which your laws ought to be written, but certainly has never read a single treatise on any political subject; for the truth is, he cannot read at all. The young people of the lower class in Ireland have seldom the advantage of a good education, especially the descendants of the ancient Irish, who have most of them a great assurance of countenance but little information or literature. This young man, whose family name is O'Regan, has been my servant for several years. And except [for] a too great fondness for women, which now and then brings him into scrapes, he has demeaned himself in a manner tolerable enough. But he is totally ignorant of the great principles of legislation and more especially the particular interests of the government. A free government is a noble possession to a people and this freedom consists in an equal right to make laws and to have the benefit of the laws when made. Though doubtless in such a government the lowest citizen may become chief magistrate, yet it is sufficient to possess the right, not absolutely necessary to exercise it. Or even if you should think proper, now and then, to show your privilege and exert in a signal manner the democratic prerogative, yet is it not descending too low to filch away from me a hireling which I cannot well spare, to serve your purpose? You are surely carrying the matter too far in thinking to make a senator of this hostler, to take him away from an employment to which he has been bred and put him to another to which he has served no apprenticeship, to set those hands which have been lately employed in currying my horse to the drafting bills and preparing business for the house."

The people were tenacious of their choice and insisted on giving Teague their suffrages, and by the frown upon their brows seemed to indicate resentment at what had been said, as indirectly charging them with want of judgment or calling in question their privilege to do what they thought proper. "It is a very strange thing," said one of them, who was a speaker for the rest, "that after having conquered Burgoyne and Cornwallis and got a government of our own, we cannot put in it whom we please. This young man may be your servant or another man's servant, but if we choose to make him a delegate what is that to you? He may not be yet skilled in the matter, but there is a good day a-coming. We will impower him, and it is better to trust a plain man like him than one of your high flyers that will make laws to suit their own purposes."

Said the Captain, "I had much rather you would send the weaver, though I thought that improper, than to invade my household and thus detract from me the very person that I have about me to brush my boots and clean my spurs." The prolocutor of the people gave him to understand that his surmises were useless, for the people had determined on the choice and Teague they would have for a representative.

Finding it answered no end to expostulate with the multitude, he requested to speak a word with Teague by himself. Stepping aside, he said to him, composing his voice and addressing him in a soft manner, "Teague, you are quite wrong in this matter they have put into your head. Do you know what it is to be a member of a deliberative body? What qualifications are necessary? Do you understand anything of geography? If a question should be to make a law to dig a canal in some part of the state, can you describe the bearing of the mountains and the course of the rivers? Or if commerce is to be pushed to some new quarter by the force of regulations, are you competent to decide in such a case? There will be questions of law and astronomy on the carpet. How you must gape and stare like a fool when you come to be asked your opinion on these subjects? Are you acquainted with the abstract principles of finance, with the funding public securities, the ways and means of raising the revenue, providing for the discharge of the public debts, and all other things which respect the economy of the government? Even if you had knowledge, have you a facility of speaking? I would suppose you would have too much pride to go to the house just to say 'Ay' or 'No.' This is not the fault of your nature but of your education, having been accustomed to dig turf in your early years rather than instructing yourself in the classics or common school books.

"When a man becomes a member of a public body, he is like a racoon or other beast that climbs up the fork of a tree, the boys pushing at him with pitch-forks or throwing stones or shooting at him with an arrow, the dogs barking in the meantime. One will find fault with your not speaking, another with your speaking if you speak at all. They will have you in the newspapers and ridicule you as a perfect beast. There is what they call the caricatura, that is, representing you with a dog's head or a cat's claw. As you have a red head, they will very probably make a fox of you or a sorrel horse or a brindled cow. It is the devil in hell to be exposed to the squibs and crackers of the gazette wits and publications. You know no more about these matters than a goose; and yet you would undertake rashly, without advice, to

enter on the office, nay, contrary to advice. For I would not for a
thousand guineas, though I have not the half of it to spare, that the
breed of the O'Regans should come to this, bringing on them a worse
stain than stealing sheep, to which they are addicted. You have nothing but your character, Teague, in a new country to depend upon.
Let it never be said that you quitted an honest livelihood, the taking
care of my horse, to follow the new-fangled whims of the times and
to be a statesman."

Teague was moved chiefly with the last part of the address and
consented to give up the object.

The Captain, glad of this, took him back to the people and announced his disposition to decline the honor which they had intended
him.

Teague acknowledged that he had changed his mind and was
willing to remain in a private station.

The people did not seem well pleased with the Captain; but as
nothing more could be said about the matter, they turned their attention to the weaver and gave him their suffrages.

[3]

Captain Farrago, leaving this place, proceeded on his way; and at
the distance of a mile or two met a man with a bridle in his hand who
had lost a horse and had been at a conjurer's to make inquiry and
recover his property.

It struck the mind of the Captain to go to this conjuring person
and make a demand of him, what was the cause that the multitude
were so disposed to elevate the low to the highest station? He had
rode but about a mile when the habitation of the conjurer, by the
direction and description of the man who had lost the horse had
given, began to be in view. Coming up to the door and inquiring if
that was not where conjurer Kolt lived, they were answered, "Yes."
Accordingly alighting and entering the domicile, all those things took
place which usually happen or are described in cases of this nature,
viz., there was the conjurer's assistant, who gave the Captain to understand that master had withdrawn a little but would be in shortly.

In the meantime the assistant endeavored to draw from him some
account of the occasion of his journey, which the other readily communicated and the conjurer, who was listening through a crack in
the partition, overheard. Finding it was not a horse or a cow or a
piece of linen that was lost but an abstract question of philosophy

which was to be put, he came from his lurking place and entered as if not knowing that any person had been waiting for him.

After mutual salutations the Captain gave him to understand the object which he had in view by calling on him.

Said the conjurer, "This lies not at all in my way. If it had been a dozen of spoons or a stolen watch that you had to look for, I could very readily, by the assistance of my art, have assisted you in the recovery; but as to this matter of man's imaginations and attachments in political affairs, I have no more understanding than another man."

"It is very strange," said the Captain, "that you who can tell by what means a thing is stolen and the place where it is deposited, though at a thousand miles distance, should know so little of what is going on in the breast of man as not to be able to develop his secret thoughts and the motives of his actions."

"It is not of our business," said the other, "but should we undertake it, I do not see that it would be very difficult to explain all that puzzles you at present. There is no need of a conjurer to tell why it is that the common people are more disposed to trust one of their own class than those who may affect to be superior. Besides, there is a certain pride in man which leads him to elevate the low and pull down the high. There is a kind of creating power exerted in making a senator of an unqualified person, which when the author has done he exults over the work and like the Creator himself when he made the world sees that 'it is very good.' Morever there is in every government a patrician class against whom the spirit of the multitude naturally militates, and hence a perpetual war, the aristocrats endeavoring to detrude the people and the people contending to obtrude themselves. And it is right it should be so, for by this fermentation the spirit of democracy is kept alive."

The Captain, thanking him for his information, asked him what was to pay, at the same time pulling out half a crown from a green silk purse which he had in his breeches pocket. The conjurer gave him to understand that as the solution of these difficulties was not within his province, he took nothing for it. The Captain, expressing his sense of his disinterested service, bade him adieu.

[4]

There was in a certain great city a society who called themselves Philosophers.[3] They had published books they called Transactions.

3. The American Philosophical Society of Philadelphia.

These contained dissertations on the nature and causes of things, from the stars of the heaven to the fire-flies of the earth and from the sea-crab to the woodland buffalo. Such disquisitions are doubtless useful and entertaining to an inquisitive mind.

There is no question but there were in this body some very great men whose investigations of the arcana of nature deserve attention. But so it was, there had been introduced by some means many individuals who were no philosophers at all. This is no unusual thing with institutions of this nature, though, by the bye, it is a very great fault. For it lessens the incentives of honor to have the access made so easy that everyone may obtain admission. It has been a reproach to some colleges that a diploma could be purchased for half a crown. This society [was] still more moderate, for the bare scratching the backside of a member has been known to procure a fellowship. At least, there have been those admitted who appeared capable of nothing else.

Nevertheless, it was necessary even in these cases for the candidates to procure some token of a philosophical turn of mind, such as the skin of a dead cat or some odd kind of a mouse-trap or the like, or have some phrases in their mouths about minerals and petrifactions so as just to support some idea of natural knowledge and pass muster. There was one who had got in by finding, accidentally, the tail of a rabbit which had been taken off in a boy's trap. Another by means of a squirrel's scalp which he had taken care to stretch and dry on a bit of osier bended in the form of a hoop. The beard of an old fox, taken off and dried in the sun, was the means of introducing one whom I knew very well. Or rather, as I have already hinted, it was beforehand intended he should be introduced, and these exuviae, or spoils of the animal kingdom, were but the tokens and apologies for admission.

It happened, as the Captain was riding this day and Teague trotting after him, he saw a large owl that had been shot by somebody and was placed in the crotch of a tree about the height of a man's head from the ground for those that passed by to look at. The Captain being struck with it, as somewhat larger than such birds usually are, desired Teague to reach it to him, and tying it to the hinder part of his saddle, rode along.

Passing by the house of one who belonged to the society, the bird was noticed at the saddle-skirts; and the philosopher, coming out, made inquiry with regard to the genus and nature of the fowl. Said the Captain, "I know nothing more about it than it is nearly as large as a turkey buzzard." "It is doubtless," said the other, "the great

Canada owl that comes from the Lakes, and if your honor will give
me leave, I will take it and submit it to the society and have yourself
made a member." As to the first, the Captain consented; but as to the
last, the being a member, he chose rather to decline it, conceiving
himself unqualified for a place in such a body. The other assured him
that he was under a very great mistake, for there were persons there
who scarcely knew a B from a bull's foot. "That may be," said the
Captain, but if others chose to degrade themselves by suffering their
names to be used in so preposterous a way it was no reason he should.

The other gave him to understand that the society would certainly
wish to express their sense of his merit and show themselves not inattentive to a virtuoso, that as he declined the honor himself, he probably might not be averse to let his servant take a seat among them.

Said the Captain, "He is but a simple Irishman and of a low education, his language being that spoken by the aborigines of his country.
And if he speaks a little English, it is with the brogue on his tongue,
which would be unbecoming in a member of your body. It would
seem to me that a philosopher ought to know how to write or at least
to read. But Teague can neither write nor read. He can sing a song
or whistle an Irish tune but is totally illiterate in all things else. I
question much if he could tell you how many new moons there are
in the year, or any [of] the most common things you could ask him.
He is a long-legged fellow, it is true, and might be of service in
clambering over rocks or going to the shores of rivers to gather
curiosities. But could you not get persons to do this without making
them members? I have more respect for science than to suffer this
bog-trotter to be so advanced at its expense.

"In these American states there is a wide field for philosophic
search, and these researches may be of great use in agriculture,
mechanics, and astronomy. There is but little immediate profit attending these pursuits, but if there can be inducements of honor,
these may supply the place. What more alluring to a young man than
the prospect of being one day received into the society of men truly
learned, the admission being a test and a proof of distinguished
knowledge. But the fountain of honor thus contaminated by a sedi-
ment foreign from its nature, who would wish to drink of it?"

Said the philosopher, "At the first institution of the society by Dr.
[*Benjamin*] Franklin and others, it was put upon a narrow basis and
only men of science were considered proper to compose it; and this
might be a necessary policy at that time when the institution was in
its infancy and could not bear much drawback of ignorance. But it

has not been judged so necessary of late years. The matter stands now on a broad and catholic bottom; and like the gospel itself, it is our orders to go out into the highways and hedges and compel them to come in. There are hundreds whose names you may see on our list who are not more instructed than this lad of yours."

"They must be a sad set indeed then," said the Captain. "Sad or no sad," said the other, "it is the case, and if you will let Teague go, I will engage him a membership."

"I take it very ill of you, Mr. Philosopher," said the Captain, "to put this nonsense in his head. If you knew what trouble I have lately had with a parcel of people that were for sending him to Congress, you would be unwilling to draw him from me for the purpose of making him a philosopher. It is not an easy matter to get hirelings now-a-days; and when you do get one, it is a mere chance whether he is faithful and will suit your purpose. It would be a very great loss to me to have him taken off at this time, when I have equipped myself for a journey."

Teague was a good deal incensed at this refusal of his master, and insisted that he would be a philosopher. "You are an ignoramus," said the Captain. "It is not the being among philosophers will make you one."

Teague insisted that he had a right to make the best of his fortune, and as there was a door open to his advancement he did not see why he might not make use of it.

The Captain, finding that it answered no end to dispute the matter with him, but [with] words of sense and reason, took a contrary way to manage him.

"Teague," said he, "I have a regard for you and would wish to see you do well. But before you take this step, I would wish to speak a word or two in private. If you will go, I may perhaps suggest some things that may be of service to you for your future conduct in that body."

Teague consenting, they stepped aside, and the Captain addressed him in the following manner:

"Teague," said he, "do you know what you are about? It is a fine thing at first sight to be a philosopher and get into this body. And indeed, if you are a real philosopher, it might be some honor and also safe to take that leap. But do you think it is to make a philosopher of you that they want you? Far from it. It is their great study to find curiosities; and because this man saw you coming after me with a red head, trotting like an Eskimo Indian, it has struck his mind to pick you up and pass you for one. Nay, it is possible they may intend worse; and when they have examined you awhile, [they may] take the skin off you and pass you for an over-grown otter or a muskrat or some outlandish animal for which they will themselves invent a name. If you were at the museum of one of these societies to observe the quantity of skins and skeletons they have, you might be well assured they did not come by them honestly. I know so much of these people that I am well persuaded they would think no more of throwing you into a kettle of boiling water than they would a terrapin; and having scraped you out to a shell, present you as the relics of an animal they had procured at an immense price from some Guinea merchant. Or if they should not at once turn you to this use, how in the meantime will they dispose of you? They will have you away through the bogs and marshes, catching flies and mire-snipes, or send you to the woods for a polecat, or oblige you to descend into drawwells for fog and phlogistic air and the Lord knows what. You must go into wolves' dens, and catch bears by the tail, run over mountains like an opossum, and dig the earth like a ground hog. You will have to climb upon trees and get yourself bit by flying squirrels. There will be no end to the mosquitoes you will have to dissect. What is all this to diving into mill-dams and rivers to catch crawfish? Or if you go to the ocean there are alligators to devour you like a catfish. Who knows but it may come your turn in a windy night to go aloft to the heavens to rub down the stars and give the goats and rams that are there fodder. The keeping the stars clean is a laborious work, a great deal worse than scouring andirons or brass kettles. There is a bull there would think no more of tossing you on his horns than he would a puppy dog. If the crab should get you into his claws he would squeeze you like a lobster. But what is all that to your having no place to stand on? How would you like to be up at the moon and to fall down when you had missed your hold, like a boy from the topmast of a ship, and have your brains beat out upon the top of some great mountain where the devil might take your skeleton and give it to the turkey-buzzards?

"Or if they should in the meantime excuse you from such out of door services, they will rack and torture you with hard questions. You must tell them how long the rays of light are coming from the sun, how many drops of rain fall in a thunder gust, what makes the grasshopper chirp when the sun is hot, how muscle shells get up to the top of the mountains, how the Indians got over to America. You will have to prove absolutely that the Negroes were once white, and that their flat noses came by some cause in the compass of human means to produce. These are puzzling questions, and yet you must solve them all. Take my advice and stay where you are. Many men have ruined themselves by their ambition and made bad worse. There is another kind of philosophy which lies more within your sphere, that is moral philosophy. Every hostler or hireling can study this, and you have the most excellent opportunity of acquiring this knowledge in our traverses through the country or communications at the different taverns or villages where we may happen to sojourn."

Teague had long ago given up all thoughts of the society and would not for the world have any more to do with it; therefore, without bidding the philosopher adieu, they pursued their route as usual.

[5]

It was somewhat late when the Captain arrived at an inn this evening. There was there before him a young clergyman who had been preaching that day to a neighboring congregation but had not as usual gone home with an elder, but had come thus far on his way towards another place where he was to preach the next day.

The Captain, entering into conversation with the clergyman, sat up pretty late. The subject was what might be expected, viz., the affairs of religion and the church. The clergyman was a good young man but with a leaning to fanaticism and being righteous over much. The Captain, on the other hand, [was] somewhat skeptical in his notions of religion. Hence, a considerable opposition of sentiment [existed] between the two. But at length, drowsiness seizing both, candles were called for and they went to bed.

It was about an hour or two after when an uproar was heard in a small chamber to the left of the staircase which led to the floor on which they slept. It was Teague, who had got to bed to the girl of the house. For as they would neither let him go to Congress nor be a philosopher, he must be doing something. The girl, not being apprised or not choosing his embraces, made a great outcry and lamentation. The clergyman, who slept in an adjoining chamber and hearing this, out of the zeal of his benevolence and humanity, leaped out of bed in his shirt and ran in to see what was the cause of the disturbance. The Captain, also jumping up, followed soon after and was scarcely in the chamber before the landlord, coming up with a candle, found them all together.

The maid gave this account of the matter, viz., that between sleeping and waking she felt a man's hand lifting up the bed-clothes, upon which she called out murder. But whether it was anybody there present or someone else, she could not tell.

Teague, whose natural parts were not bad and presence of mind considerable, instantly took the resolution to throw the matter on the clergyman. "By shaint Patrick," said he, "I was aslape in my own bed, as sound as the shates that were about me, when I heard the sound of this young crature's voice crying out like a shape in a pasture; and when after I had heard, aslape as I was, and came here, I found this praste, who was so wholy, and praching all night, upon the top of the bed with his arms round this young crature's neck; and if I had not given him a twitch by the nose and bid him ly over, dear honey, he would have ravished her virginity, and murdered her, save her soul, and the paple of the house not the wiser for it."

The clergyman stared with his mouth open, for the palpable nature of the falsehood had shocked him beyond the power of speech.

But the landlady, who in the meantime was come up and had heard what Teague had said, was enraged and could supply speech for them both. "Hey," said she, "this comes of your preaching and praying, Mr. Minister. I have lodged many a gentleman but never had such doings here before. It is a pretty story that a minister of the gospel should be the first to bring a scandal upon the house."

The Captain interrupted her and told her there was no harm done. The maid was not actually ravished; and if there was no noise made about it, all matters might be set right.

The clergyman had by this time recovered himself so much as to have the use of his tongue and began by protesting his innocence and that it was no more him that made the attack upon the maid than the angel Gabriel.

The Captain, interrupting him and wishing to save his feelings, began by excusing or extenuating the offense. "It is no great affair," said he, "after all that is said or done. The love of women is a natural sin, and the holiest men in all ages have been propense to this indulgence. There was Abraham that got to bed to his maid Hagar and had a bastard by her whom he named Ishmael. Joshua, who took Jericho by the sound of ram's horns, saved a likely slut of the name of Rahab under a pretense that she had been civil to the spies he had sent out, but in reality because he himself took a fancy for her. I need say nothing about David, who wrote the Psalms and set them to music, and yet in his old days had a girl to sleep with him. Human nature is human nature still, and it is not all the preaching and praying on earth can extinguish it."

The clergyman averred his innocence and that it was that red-headed gentleman himself, meaning Teague, who was in the room first and had been guilty of the outrage. Teague was beginning to make the sign of the cross and to put himself into an attitude of swearing, when the Captain, thinking it of no consequence who was the person, put an end to the matter by ordering Teague to bed and himself bidding the company good night.

The clergyman, finding no better could be made of it, took the advice of the landlord and retired also. The landlady seemed disposed to hush the matter up, and the maid went to sleep as usual.

[6]

It is not the nature of the female tongue to be silent. The landlady could not avoid informing her gossips and even some of her guests of what had happened the preceding evening in her house. The report, so unfavorable to the clergyman, had therefore got out and, coming to the ears of the consistory, was the occasion of calling him before them to answer to the accusation. The clergyman, much alarmed though conscious of innocence, bethought himself of applying to the Captain to extort from his waiting man a confession of the truth and relieve his character. Accordingly having set out on a bay horse that he had, he found the Captain and addressed him in the following manner:

"Captain," said he, "the affair of that night at the tavern is like to be of serious consequence to me. For though I am innocent as the child unborn, yet the presumption is against me, and I am likely to fall under church censure. It may be sport to you, but it is a matter of moment to me. Now, as sure as God is in heaven, I am innocent; and it must have been the devil or that red-headed Irishman of yours that made the disturbance."

The Captain gave him the comfort of assuring him that he might make himself easy; for be the matter as it might, he would take care that Teague should assume it and bear the blame. The clergyman thanked him, declaring at the same time that he would not forget him in his prayers, Sunday or Saturday, while he had an hour to live. The Captain, not so much from any mercenary motive of benefit by his spiritual solicitations as from a real love of humanity and justice, had determined to do him essential service in this affair. Accordingly, when the clergyman had retired, calling Teague before him, he began in this manner: "Teague," said he, "from what I know of your disposition, I have no more doubt than I have of my existence that it was yourself who made that uproar with the girl at the tavern where we lodged, though I could not but give you credit for your presence of mind in throwing it upon the clergyman. But whether the matter lies with you or him is of no consequence. You can take it upon you and lay up treasure in heaven. It will be doing a good work; and these people, you may be assured, have a considerable influence in the other world. This clergyman can speak a good word for you when you come there and let you into half the benefit of all the prayers he has said on earth. It will be no harm to you, for your character in this respect is as bad as it can well be."

Teague said he did not care much but thought the priest ought to pay a little smart money, for it was a thankless matter to do these things for nothing. Said the Captain, "These people are not the most plenty of money, but I will advance half a crown towards the accommodation." Teague was satisfied and ready to acknowledge whatever was demanded of him.

Accordingly having come before the presbytery on the day appointed for the trial, Teague made confession of the truth, viz., that being in the kitchen with the girl and observing her to be a good-looking hussy—

But suppose we give the speech in his own dialect. "Master prastes," said he, "I persave you are all prastes of the gospel and can prach as asily as I can take a chaw of tobacco. Now de trut of de story is dis: I was slaping in my bed, and I tought vid myself it was a shame amongst christian paple that a young crature should slape by herself and have no one to take care of her. So I tought vid myself to go and slape vid her. But as she was aslape, she made exclamation, and dis praste that is here before you came in to save her shoul from the devil; and as the Captain my master might take offense, and the devil—I am shartain that it was no better person—put it into my head to lay it on the praste. This is the trut, master prastes, as I hope for shalvation in the kingdom of purgatory, shentlemen."

On this confession the clergyman was absolved, to the great joy of the presbytery, who considered it as a particular providence that the truth was brought to light.

[7]

The presbytery sat a day or two at this place on church affairs, and the Captain, delaying with them, lodged at the same house,

Teague in the meantime having an opportunity of ingratiating himself with the clergymen by rubbing down their horses and other menial services. For it is the national character of the aboriginal Irish to give fair words, and Teague was not deficient in this address. What with master prasting and giving a great deal of what is called blarney, he insinuated himself into their good graces; and by affecting, now and then, to be seen at prayers by himself and to have a sorrowful countenance, he induced them to believe that he was in the first stage of conviction and likely to become a pious man. Having made this progress in their good opinion, he ventured to suggest what was the ultimate object of his ambition, viz., the being a candidate for holy orders. The presbytery, to whom the matter was represented by the individuals more particularly acquainted with him, thought favorably of the proposition. For though his common attainments might not be great, yet if the grace of God had wrought upon him, he might become a valuable man.

The Captain, having got a hint of this, took the first opportunity of addressing the presbytery. "Gentlemen," said he, "you are deceived in this ragamuffin. For, notwithstanding all the pretensions he may lately have to religion, you may be well assured that it is all hypocrisy and that he has no more religion than my horse."

The presbytery, suspecting the Captain to be a carnal man and regardless of the ministry, gave little heed to what he said and seemed disposed to take Teague upon trials.

The Captain, finding the case to stand thus and that in spite of all he could do he was likely to lose his servant, took his usual method of addressing the hopes and fears of Teague himself.

Taking him aside, he began with all possible art to impress such fears and apprehensions as the nature of the case suggested. "Teague," said he, "do you know what you are about? You have got into your vagaries once more. You want to preach, do you? Are you apprised of the difficulty of this work? The first thing you will have to do is to take a text; and when that is done, you will have to split it into parts. There are what are called heads; and these you must divide into firstlys and secondlys and thirdlys and fourthlys and so on, till you come to twentiethlys perhaps. Are you furnished with a concordance? Or do you know what a concordance is? Can you find a text to suit your purpose when you want it? Can you explain the scriptures, the meaning of Daniel's ram and the he-goat, or the seven trumpets in the Revelations? You are mistaken if you think your Irish will pass for Hebrew.

"You think it a great honor to preach now-a-days. It was an honor once, but the thing is now become so common that it is of little consequence to preach or not.

"But do you know how it will behoove you to conduct yourself if you take this office upon you? You will have to compose the muscles of your face to greater seriousness than your disposition can afford. You must quit whoring. How will you like that, Teague? It would look very ill after sermon to be catched in bed with a girl at a tavern.

"But do you know why these men are so anxious to have you of their mess? The truth of the matter is they carry on a war with the devil and they wish to recruit you for the service. Do they give you any bounty-money? Take my word, there will be but little of this going. Take my advice then and let them settle their own quarrels. It is a silly thing to be drawn into a party when there is but little to be got by it; nay, worse than little, for it will be all on the other side. Think you the devil will forget the mischief you do him in this world and not resent it when he comes across you in a future state? When you are preaching and praying do you think he will not hear all that you throw out against him? You may rely upon it, there will be enough to give him information; and as a story never loses in the telling, it is ten to one they will make the matter worse than it was. Take my advice, therefore, and make no enemies while you can help it. Steer through life as smoothly as possible. Keep a good tongue in your mouth and let those who choose to dispute with Beelzebub dispute. I never knew any good come of broils and quarrels, especially with low characters. And, to say the truth of it, this Satan, as they call him, is very little of the gentleman. Even where he is well disposed, he will do but little good to one, but a most dangerous creature where he takes a dislike. When you go to hell as one day you must, you can expect but little quarter after abusing him in this world. He will make you squeal like a pig, take you by the throat, and kick you like a cat. His very scullions will piss upon you, and give you no better life than a dog among their feet, while these very clergymen that put you forward to blackguard for them will stand by laughing in their sleeves that you could be such a fool."

The representation had the desired effect upon Teague, and he thought no more of the matter.

[8]

Not long after this, being at a certain place, the Captain was accosted by a stranger in the following manner: "Captain Farrago," said he, "I have heard of a young man in your service who talks Irish. Now sir, my business is that of an Indian treaty-maker; and [I] am on my way with a party of kings and half kings to the commissioners to hold a treaty. My king of the Kickapoos, who was a Welsh blacksmith, took sick by the way and is dead. I have heard of this lad of yours and could wish to have him a while to supply his place. The treaty will not last longer than a couple of weeks; and as the government will probably allow three or four thousand dollars for the treaty, it will be in our power to make it worth your while to spare him for that time." "Your king of the Kickapoos," said the Captain, "what does that mean?" Said the stranger, "It is just this: you have heard of the Indian nations to the westward that occasionally make war upon the frontier settlements. It has been a policy of government to treat with these and distribute goods. Commissioners are appointed for that purpose. Now you are not to suppose that it is an easy matter to catch a real chief and bring him from the woods, or if at some expense one was brought, the goods would go to his use; whereas, it is much more profitable to hire substitutes and make chiefs of our own. And as some unknown gibberish is necessary to pass for an Indian language, we generally make use of Welsh or Low Dutch or Irish, or pick up an ingenious fellow here and there who can imitate a language by sounds of his own in his mouth and throat. But we prefer one who can speak a real tongue, and give more for him. We cannot afford you a great deal at this time for the use of your man because it is not a general treaty where 20,000 or 30,000 dollars are appropriated for the purpose of holding it, but an occasional, or what we call a running treaty, by way of brightening the chain and holding fast friendship. The commissioners will doubtless be glad to see us and procure from government an allowance for the treaty. For the more treaties, the more use for commissioners. The business must be kept up and treaties made if there are none of themselves. My Pianksha and Choctaw chiefs are very good fellows; the one of them a Scotch peddler that talks the Erse;[4] the other has been some time in Canada and has been of great service in assisting to teach the rest some Indian custom and manners. I have had the whole of them for a fortnight past under my tuition, teaching them war songs and dances and to make responses at the treaty. If your man is tractable, I can make him a Kickapoo in about nine days. A breech-clout and leggins that I took off the blacksmith that died, I have ready to put on him. He must have part of

4. Scottish or Irish Gaelic.

his head shaved and painted with feathers on his crown; but the paint will rub off, and the hair grow in a short time, so that he can go about with you again."

"It is a very strange affair," said the Captain. "Is it possible that such deception can be practiced in a new country? It astonishes me that the government does not detect such imposition." "The government," said the Indian treatyman, "is at a great distance. It knows no more of Indians than a cow does of Greek. The legislature hears of wars and rumors of wars and supports the executive in forming treaties. How is it possible for men who live remote from the scene of action to have adequate ideas of the nature of Indians or the transactions that are carried on in their behalf? Do you think the one half of those savages that come to treaty are real representatives of the nation? Many of them are not savages at all but weavers and peddlers, as I have told you, picked up to make kings and chiefs. I speak of those particularly that come trading down to inland towns or the metropolis. I would not communicate these mysteries of our trade were it not that I confide in your good sense and have occasion for your servant."

"It is a mystery of iniquity," said the Captain. "Do you suppose that I would countenance such a fraud upon the public?" "I do not know," said the other. "It is a very common thing for men to speculate, now-a-days. If you will not, another will. A hundred dollars might as well be in your pocket as another man's. I will give you that for the use of your servant for a week or two and say no more about it." "It is an idea new to me entirely," said the Captain, "that Indian princes, whom I have seen escorted down as such, were no more than trumpery, disguised, as you mention, that such should be introduced to polite assemblies and have the honor to salute the fair ladies with a kiss, the greatest beauties thinking themselves honored by having the salutation of a sovereign." "It is so," said the other. "I had a red-headed bricklayer once whom I passed for a Chippewa and who has dined with clubs and sat next the President. He was blind of an eye and was called Blind Sam by the traders. I had given it out that he was a great warrior and had lost his eye by an arrow in a contest with a rival nation. These things are now reduced to a system, and it is so well known to those who are engaged in the traffic that we think nothing of it."

"How the devil," said the Captain, "do you get speeches made and interpret them so as to pass for truth?" "That is an easy matter," said the other. "Indian speeches are nearly all alike. You have only to talk of burying hatchets under large trees, kindling fires, brightening chains; with a demand at the latter end of blankets for the backside and rum to get drunk with."

"I much doubt," said the Captain, "whether treaties that are carried on in earnest are of any great use." "Of none at all," said the other. "Especially as the practice of giving goods prevails, because this is an inducement to a fresh war. This being the case, it can be no harm to make a farce of the whole matter, or rather a profit of it by such means as I propose to you and have pursued myself."

"After all," said the Captain, "I cannot but consider it as a kind of contraband and illicit traffic, and I must be excused from having any hand in it. I shall not betray your secret, but I shall not favor it. It would ill become me, whose object in riding about in this manner is to give just ideas on subjects, to take part in such ill-gotten gain."

The Indian treaty-man, finding it in vain to say more, withdrew.

[9]

The Captain, apprehending that he might not yet drop his designs upon the Irishman but be tampering with him out of doors should he come across him, sent for Teague. For he well knew that should the Indian treaty-man get the first word of him, the idea of making him a king would turn his head and it would be impossible to prevent his going with him.

Teague coming in, said the Captain to him, "Teague, I have discovered in you for some time past a great spirit of ambition, which is doubtless commendable in a young person; and I have checked it only in cases where there was real danger or apparent mischief. There is now an opportunity of advancing yourself, not so much in the way of honor as profit. But profit brings honor and is, indeed, the most substantial support of it. There has been a man here with me that carries on a trade with the Indians, and tells me that red-headed scalps are in great demand with them. If you could spare yours, he would give a good price for it. I do not well know what use they make of this article; but so it is the traders find their account in it. Probably they dress it with the hairy side out and make tobacco pouches for the chiefs when they meet in council. It saves dyeing, and besides, the natural red hair of a man may in their estimation be superior to any color they can give by art. The taking off the scalp will not give much pain, it is so dexterously done by them with a crooked knife they have for that purpose. The mode of taking off the scalp is this: you lie down upon your back; a warrior puts his feet upon your shoulders, collects your hair in his left hand, and drawing a circle with the knife in his right, makes the incision, and with a sudden pull separates it from the head, giving in the meantime what is called the scalp yell. The thing is done in such an instant that the pain is scarcely felt. He offered me a hundred dollars, if I would have it taken off for his use, giving me directions in the meantime how to stretch it and dry it on a hoop. I told him no; it was a perequisite of your own, and you might dispose of it as you thought proper. If you chose to dispose of it, I had no objections; but the bargain should be of your own making, and the price such as should please yourself. I have sent for you to give you a hint of this chapman that you may have a knowledge of his wish to possess the property and ask accordingly. It is probable you may bring him up to a half Johannes [5] more by holding out a little. But I do not think it would be advisable to lose the bargain. A hundred dollars for a little hairy flesh is a great deal. You will trot a long time before you make that with me. He will be with you probably to propose the purchase. You will know when you see him. He is a tall-looking man with leggins on and has several Indians with him going on a treaty. He talked to me something of making you a king of the Kickapoos after the scalp is off; but I would not count on that so much, because words are but wind and promises are easily broken. I would advise you to make sure of the money in the first place and take chance for the rest."

I have seen among the prints of Hogarth some such expression of countenance as that of Teague at this instant, who, as soon as he could speak, but with a double brogue on his tongue, began to intimate his disinclination to the traffic. The hair of his scalp itself, in the meantime, had risen in opposition to it. "Dear master, vid you trow me into ridicule and de blessed shalvation of my life and all dat I have in de vorld, to be trown like a dog to de savages and have my flesh torn of my head to give to dese vild bastes to make a napsack to carry deir parates and tings in for a hundred dollars or the like? It shall never be said that the hair of de O'Regans made mackeseens [6] for a vild Indian to trat upon. I would sooner trow my own head, hair and all, in de fire dan give it to dese paple to smoke wid out of deir long pipes."

"If this be your determination," said the Captain, "it will behoove you to keep yourself somewhat close and while we remain at this

---

5. Captain Farrago probably means a half-joe, which is equivalent to one Johannes, a Portuguese coin worth about $8.80.
6. Moccasins.

public house avoid any conversation with the chapman or his agents, should they come to tamper with you. For it is not improbable, while they are keeping you in talk proposing to make you a Kickapoo chief and the like, they may snatch the scalp off your head and you not be the wiser for it."

Teague thought the caution good, and resolving to abide by it, retired to the kitchen. The maid at this time, happening to want a log of wood, requested Teague to cut it for her. Taking the axe accordingly and going out, he was busy chopping with his head down, while in the meantime the Indian treaty-man had returned with one in Indian dress who was the chief of the Killinoos or at least passed for such and whom he brought as having some recruiting talents and might prevail with Teague to elope and join the company. "I presume," said the Indian treaty-man, "you are the waiter of the Captain who lodges here at present." Teague, hearing a man speak and lifting up his head, saw the leggins on the one and the Indian dress on the other, and with a kind of involuntary effort threw the axe directly from him at the Killinoo. It missed him but about an inch, and fell behind. Teague, in the meantime raising a shout of desperation, was fixed on the spot and his locomotive faculties suspended, so that he could neither retreat nor advance but stood still like one enchained or enchanted for a moment, the king of the Killinoos in the meantime drawing his tomahawk and preparing for battle.

The Captain, who was reading at a front window, hearing the shout, looked about and saw what was going on at the wood-pile. "Stop villain," said he to the king of the Killinoos, "you are not to take that scalp yet, however much you may value it. He will not take a hundred dollars for it, nor five hundred, though you make him king of the Kickapoos or anything else. It is no trifling matter to have the ears slit in tatters and the nose run through with a bodkin and a goose quill stuck across; so that you may go about your business. You will get no king of the Kickapoos here." Under cover of this address of the Captain, Teague had retired to the kitchen and ensconced himself behind the rampart of the maid. The Indian treaty-man and the Killinoo chief, finding the measure hopeless, withdrew and turned their attention, it is to be supposed, to some other quarter to find a king of the Kickapoos.

[10]

Meaning to remain some time in a certain town to which he came, the Captain had his horse put out to pasture and took private lodgings. The first day at dinner he was struck with the appearance of a young man who sat at table but could not be said to dine with them; for except a little water and a bit of bread, he ate or drank nothing, and though sometimes addressed he made no answer. There was a settled melancholy in his countenance, and he often sighed deeply. He had been in this house six weeks and had behaved uniformly in the same manner. In the evening he would walk by himself till midnight. Whence he came or what was his object, no one knew. He had bespoke a back room and wished to have one where there was but little light, also that a little water and a bit of bread might be sent when he should require it. The landlady, not choosing to have a person in the house who was unwilling to be seen, declined the circumstance of sending in provisions to his room but thought it proper he should come to table. He did so but entered into no conversation though much pain was taken to engage him. He had paid his boarding regularly and did not seem to be in want of money. This was the account given by the family when the young man retired from dinner.

The Captain's curiosity was much excited, for being a philanthropic man he found himself interested in the history of this person. Taking an opportunity that very evening when the young man was walking in the back porch, he joined him and with the bluntness of a plain man insisted to converse with him. "Sir," said he, "it is from no motive of vain curiosity that I thus solicit you. It is from a disposition to know and alleviate your griefs. For it is evident to me that something hangs heavy on your mind. I am a man, as you see, advanced in life and have had some experience. It is possible it might be in my power to say or do something that may serve you; at least it is my disposition to soothe your melancholy. If it should be an unfortunate murder, the guilt of which lies upon your mind, you will find no accuser in me; I shall preserve a secret obtained in this manner. Probably it might have been a duel, and with such alleviating circumstances that though the law would take hold of it humanity will excuse."

The young man finding the charge of murder, or suspicion of it, ready to be fixed upon him, spoke. Said he, "I am no murderer but a murdered man myself. I am in love with a young woman of the most celestial beauty but of a cruel heart."

"The beauty may be more in your brain than in her face," said the Captain, "for, as the poet says, 'There are three, the children of imagination: the madman, the lover, and the poet. The madman sees more devils than vast hell can hold; the lover, all as frantic, sees Helen's beauty in a brow of Egypt.' [7] I am not unacquainted with the nature of this passion, and I have seen a gypsy myself in my time that has had dominion over me. Perhaps I may have been carried to as much extravagance as other people, and therefore am a proper person to advise against it. A principal source of my extravagance was an opinion that the jade who had hold of my affections at the time would pity me when she heard of the pain which her beauty gave me, that she would be afraid I would hang myself for her sake, that she would come to soothe and caress me in order to prevent it. Far from it. My uneasiness was the proof of her power to wound; and the more distress I felt, the greater credit to her beauty. She would not have lost a sigh which she caused me for any consideration. My lamentations were as agreeable to her as the groans of the damned are to the devil. And so it must be with every woman, because self-love induces it. Hanging is the last thing they would be at. If they could get the lover brought to this, they are then at the height of fame. It falls but to the lot of one here and there to have a man drown himself for her, and when it does happen it makes such a noise that all covet it.

"I would venture to say that this female whom you fast and pray about so much would be very unwilling to breathe the soul into you were it once out. Instead of fasting, she is eating; and while you sigh in the night, she snores.

"You have an opinion, perhaps, that you may bend her by your perseverance. That is a mistake. A man that once comes to this state of sighing and dying has but little chance, because he has surrendered himself and there is nothing more to be won. Were there any possibility of succeeding, it would be by first conquering yourself, dismissing all idea of her partiality for you; for it is owing to this secret vanity and self-flattery that you still pursue. Absolute despair is the first step towards the cure of love. It is either drowning or curing with you at present. As you have not drowned yourself you are in a fair way to be cured.

"I know very well how you missed the matter with this hussy. You appear to be a young man of great sensibility of feeling, and I presume made your addresses with great refinement of thought and manners. You talked to her of flames and darts and flowers and roses, read poetry in the meantime, and thought a great deal of Phyllis, and Amaryllis, and entertained her with names and incidents in romances, and sung and recited soft love songs of Amanda and Phebe and

7. *A Midsummer Night's Dream,* V, i, 7.

Colin; [8] whereas your way was to have talked careless nonsense and sung such songs as Paddy Kelly and Tristram Shandy-o, and told her stories of girls that had ran off with peddlers or gone a-campaigning with the soldiers. These ideas are light and frolicsome and co-natural to springing love. Hence it is that men of but loose and irregular education succeed better with the fair than scholars that are learned in the classics.

"But to bring the matter to a point, the true way is to get another mistress and profit by your experience with the first. No more of sighing and dying in the case, but singing and laughing and jumping like a young fox. Hint a little with respect to certain matters that are between the sexes but let it be done in so delicate a manner that, though she understands you, she is not obliged to do it. What I mean is to make her think you would rather debauch her than marry her. Bring her to this suspicion and I warrant you her whole study will be to entrap you into matrimony. For it is natural for the human mind, when it observes a great security and confidence in another, to imagine there must be some ground for it. It will argue a consciousness on your part of having a good or better in your power. It will impress her with the same idea, and imagination governs the world.

"When the mind is bent upon any object, it is relieved by the conversation of those who understand it and, as it were, dissolved with them in the same ideas." The young man was pleased with the conversation of the Captain and seemed cheered; [he] agreed to join the family and be a little sociable. By degrees he became so; and what by the conversation of the Captain, sometimes explaining and sometimes ridiculing the passion of love, and the young ladies of the family in the meantime rallying him on his weakness, he came a little to his senses (for love is a frenzy) and began to behave like a common man. For it having come out now that love was the cause of his distress and singularity of conduct, some pitied him and others rallied it with good humor and philanthropy. It had, however, become the general topic in the family and was carried down to the kitchen among the servants.

8. Phyllis is a prominent name in Arcadian poetry and in later pastorals such as Edmund Waller's "To Phyllis" and Milton's "L'Allegro," l. 87. Amaryllis is a shepherdess in Theocritus' "Idylls" and in other pastoral poetry; later in Milton's "Lycidas," l. 68. The name Amanda derives from Theocritus' "Amyntas," a nephew of pan in the "Idylls." The form "Amanda" is used as the name of a female character in Smollett's *Peregrine Pickle*. Phebe is best known from Shakespeare's *As You Like It*. In pastoral poetry, Colin is a swain or shepherd. Spenser used the word in "The Shepherd's Calender."

Teague, hearing of it, took it into his head that he must be in love too; and counterfeiting a demure look and absence of mind and walking by himself and living on spare diet, as he had heard the young man that was in love did, he wished to have it understood that his mind was under the dominion of the same passion. This, being observed, was represented to the Captain, who, being at a loss to know what was the matter, called Teague and began to interrogate him. The bog-trotter, with some seeming reluctance, acknowledged that it was love. Said the Captain, "You, in love, you great bear; with whom are you in love?" "That dear cratur," said the Irishman, "that has the black hair and the fair face, and her name is Mrs. Sally, in the house there. She is as fair as the wool on the snow, and gives me the cholic and the heart-burn every time that I look at her fair eyes; God save her soul from damnation but I love her as I do the very food I ate or the cloathes that I ware upon my back."

It appeared to be Miss Sally, a very pretty girl, the eldest daughter of the landlady, who, by the bye—I mean the landlady—was a widow and had two daughters and a niece with her, the handsomest of whom was this Miss Sally with whom Teague had become enamored. For simple and ignorant nature will fasten on beauty as well as the most instructed in the principles of taste.

The Captain, having been a good deal troubled heretofore with the pretensions of this valet in wishing to be a member of the legislature, a philosopher, a preacher, and now a lover, thought he had now a good opportunity of repressing his presumption for the future. There was a young man, a brother in the family, who had been some time in the service as a lieutenant and had leave of absence, at this time, on a visit to his mother and sisters. The Captain well knew that, being in the pride and heat of youth, he would consider Teague's advances to his sister as in insult upon the family and chastise him accordingly. With this view, counterfeiting every possible disposition to serve the bog-trotter, the Captain recommended to him to make a confident of the brother and endeavor to gain his interest with the sister.

Accordingly, one morning when the officer was in his chamber, Teague made his approach, and composing his woebegone countenance as well as he could and explaining the cause of it, solicited his interest with the lady.

There was a whip in a corner of the room with which the lieutenant had been riding; seizing this hastily, he made an attack upon the person of the lover in a manner far beyond what was decent or moderate. The valet, retreating with considerable outcries, made complaint to the Captain, who gave him to understand that, as this outrage was committed by his intended brother-in-law, it must be considered in the nature of a family quarrel, and he could not interfere.

The advances of Teague became the subject of conversation in the family and of much mirth and laughter. The young man who had been in the state of melancholy before described and had been cheered a little was now in a great degree cured by the imitation of the valet. For ridicule is a better cure for love than passion. It is better to make the patient laugh than think.

Having now a disposition to pursue his travels, the Captain sent for his horse and set out.

[*End of Volume I (Philadelphia, 1792). Chapters above are the original Book I, 1, 3, 4; Book II, 1; Book III, 1, 3, 4; Book V, 1, 2; and Book VI, 1.*]

[11]

. . . Towards evening, when the shadows of the trees began to be long, the Captain, bidding Teague trot along side, addressed him in the following words: "Teague," said he, "it is true I am none of your knight-errants who used to ride about the world relieving fair damsels and killing giants and lying out in woods and forests without a house or even tent-cloth over their heads to protect them from the night air. Nevertheless, as in some respects my equipment and sallying forth resembles a knight-errant and you a squire, would it be amiss, just for a frolic, to lie out a night or two, that it might be said that we have done the like. There is no great danger of wolves or bears, for while there are sheep or pigs to be got at they will shun human flesh. It will make a good chapter in our journal to describe you lying at the foot of an oak tree and me with my head upon my saddle under another, the horse, in the meantime, feeding at a small distance." Teague thought it would be an easier matter to write down the chapter in the journal than lie under the trees to beget it. "It is true," said the Captain, "navigators and travellers make many a fiction, and those who have been in battle have killed many that were killed by others or have not been killed at all. But it would ill become a limb of chivalry to deviate from the truth. It will be but about twelve hours' service lying on our backs and looking up to the stars, hearing the howling of wolves and observing the great bear in the heavens, the means by which the Chaldeans, the first astronomers, laid the foundation of the science." "Fait, and I tink," said Teague, "it would be better to be in a good house, with a shoulder of mutton to ate before we go to slape than to have our own shoulders torn by the bears or bruised by lying under great oaks. Of what use is this astranomy? Did any of these astranamers ever shoot down a bear in the firmament to get a joint of mate for a sick person; and what good comes of lying in de woods to be ate up by de snakes, but fevers, and agues, and sore troats to get a long cough and die in a ditch like a dear horse and be nothing thought of but be trown into ridicule like a black-head dat has no sense? It is better to go to a house and get a bed to slape in and warm shates about us than be lying in de dew like a frag, crocking de next day like one of dase and get no good by it."

The Captain had made the proposition merely to amuse himself with Teague, and so did not insist upon it.

Riding one or two miles, the sun was setting and a house appeared in view a little off the road. A lane led up to it with a meadow on one side and a pasture field on the other. On this last there were cattle of cows and sheep grazing. The house in front was a frame building, respectable in appearance, from the height and dimensions, but ancient. There was a considerable extent of clear ground around it and an orchard hard by with at least five hundred apple-trees.

Having lodged chiefly at inns since his first setting out, the Captain had the curiosity to diversify his travels by lodging at a private house this evening. Accordingly riding up to the door and calling out "Halloa," which is the note of interrogation which is used when a man wishes the master or mistress of a family or someone of the servants to come forth to know what he wants.

It happened that the mistress herself came to the door, and seeing a good-looking man in a green old age sitting on a horse-back with his servant ready to take care of his steed should he think proper to dismount, she made a low curtsy, as much as to say, "Sir, I should be happy to know in what manner I can serve you."

"Madam," said the Captain, "to tell you the truth, the night is drawing on and I have been reflecting with myself whether it were better to lodge in the woods or take a house. All things considered, I have thought it most advisable to take a house, and the only question that now remains is whether I can get one."

The lady, smiling with much complacency and inclining her head forward and her middle back, replied, "I should be happy, sir, if this small mansion could afford you an accommodation worthy of your suite." "Madam," said the Captain, "I shall be happy if the guest can be worthy of the accommodation."

"Alight, sir," said the lady, "we shall be happy to receive you." Having alighted, he was introduced to a very decent apartment, where the lady seating herself in a large cushioned chair and pulling out her box took a pinch of snuff and laid the box upon the cushion. She was a good-looking woman, being about fifty-seven years of age with grey hairs, but a green fillet [was] on her left eye-brow, as it seems the eye on that side was subject to a defluxion of rheum which made it expedient to cover it. It could not be said that her teeth were bad, because she had none. If she wanted the rose on her cheek, she had it on her nose, so that it all came to the same thing. Nothing could be said against her chin, but it used her mouth ill in getting above it. She was not very tall, but what she wanted in height she made up in breadth; so that multiplying one dimension by the other, she might be considered as a very sizable woman. After conversing a little while, the lady withdrew to give directions in the kitchen what to provide for supper.

The Captain in the meantime taking up a pipe, which he saw on the mantlepiece, amused himself with whiff.

The old lady in the meantime was in the kitchen, and the first thing she observed was Teague reclining in an angle of the chimney fast asleep. Presuming that he had been inattentive to his master's horse, which had been sent to the stable, she desired a servant to give him a jog and wake him. Teague, awaking, saw the old lady and bespoke her. "Dear madam, what a great happiness it is for poor sharvants to have gentle folks about them. God bless your anours, ladyship; you are just for all de world like my cousin Shala Shagney, the handsomest woman in all Ireland, and was married to Shan Crossan, who had a great estate and a flock of shape into the bargain. She used to say to me when I was aslape, 'Teague, are you awake?' and when I was awake, 'Teague, are you aslape, dear honey?' "

There is something in an Irishman which has an admirable effect upon the fair, whether it is owing to that love-creating lustiness of person and freshness of complexion which they usually possess or the delicacy and quantum of the flattery of which they are not niggardly; nor need they be so, no persons having a greater stock to come and go upon. For so it was that the language of the bog-trotter had gained the good will of this same Hecuba, and she ordered him a tankard of metheglin [9] to make himself merry with the servants.

9. A liquor made of fermented honey and water.

Returning to the parlor, she continued her conversation with the Captain; but her mind running upon Teague, she could not avoid introducing his name with a view to learn some particulars of his history. "This is a civil young man," said she, "that came with you, and of a conversation above ordinary persons." The Captain being an observer of the passions of the mind, as they express themselves in the eye and aspect, saw that Teague had made some impression on the affections of this goodly old maiden gentlewoman. Nor was he displeased with it, for his first alarm was that she would have fastened on himself; but her passion taking this course would be less troublesome. Framing his answers therefore to her questions with a view to favor what had so fortunately commenced, he gave her to understand that, though in the disguise of a servant, Teague was no inconsiderable personage, that he had been a member of Congress one or two years, though by the bye this was stretching the matter a little as he had only had it in his power to be one. But if it is allowable to strain a point at all, it is in the recommendation of one who stands well enough already; for not being taken on the recommendation, there is no deception, and it is but civility to make one more pleased with their choice than they already are.

The Captain said nothing of his having preached or being about to preach, for the idea of sermons and catechisms, impressing the mind with religious awe, is unfavorable to love. As to his being a member of the philosophical society, it could be neither here nor there with a lady, and therefore he was silent with respect to this also.

Supper being brought in, they sat down, but little conversation passed, the mind of the enamorata being more in the kitchen than in the parlor. After supper, the Captain, sitting some time and seeming drowsy, was asked by his hostess if he chose to go to bed. Answering in the affirmative, a servant waited with a candle; and bidding her good night, he was lighted to his chamber.

No sooner had he withdrawn but the old lady sent her compliments to Teague to take a seat in the parlor, where sitting down to a roasted duck just brought in, a few slices of gammon on a plate, a piece of veal, and a couple of roasted potatoes, he was desired to partake, the old lady casting amorous looks at him in the meantime. I say looks; for though she had but one eye to look with, yet looking often, she might be said to cast looks. It was a new thing to the Irishman to be at a table with a servant at his back, and he began now to think that fortune meant to do him justice. And with an ease of self-possession, which some would call affrontery, he did the honors of the table, helping himself and talking as fast as consisted with his disposition to satisfy his appetite. "May it please your ladyship," said he, "I am a poor sharvant now, but I have seen the time when I have ate at as good a table as the Captain my master, though he rides upon a horse and I trot on foot. My uncle, by the mother's side, Shan O'Gan, had a deer park and kept race-horses to go to the fair and the city of Cork; and my father's brother, Pehlim O'Regan, was a justice of the pace and hung paple for staleing shape. I might have been a member of parliament if I had staid at home and went to school, but sending a challenge and fighting wid my own dear cousin, Denis O'Conelly, I had to fly de kingdom, and brought nothing wid me but my brogs and ten guineas in my purse, and am now nothing but a poor sharvant, unless your ladyship would take pity upon me and marry me; for I am wary of this way of tratting after a crazy Captain dat has no sense to curry his own harse. And I have to fight duels for him and keep him from being knocked down like a brute baste, for dis very day when he had a quarrel wid a hastler and was trown upon his back, I lifted him up and said, 'Dear honey, are you dead?' Took de hastler by de troat and choaked him, and he could not spake but said, 'Dear shentlemen, spare my life.' So dat if your ladyship will take me to yourself, I will stay wid you and take care of de harses and cows and de shape, and plant parates and slape wid you and ask not a farthing but your own sweat self into de bargain; for you are de beauty of de world and fasting or slaping I could take you to my arms, dear crature, and be happy wid you."

The lady was by this time entirely won and gave him to understand that in the morning, after consulting a friend or two, the marriage might be celebrated.

I give only a sketch of the courtship that took place, for a great deal was said; and it was near midnight before the lovers could prevail upon themselves to part; when Teague was lighted to his bed, and had as good as that in which the Captain slept which was a new thing to him, being accustomed to pig in with hostlers and servants at the places where they lodged.

The Captain was up early in the morning and astonished not to find Teague stirring. But inquiring of the servants where Teague slept, he was shown up a pair of stairs, which he ascended, thinking he had one or two more to ascend before he reached the garret. But what was his astonishment when he was shown into a room on the second floor where he found Teague snoring on a feather bed with curtains? Waking him, "Teague," said he, "this goes beyond all your former impudence, to crawl up out of the kitchen and get into a feather bed." "Please your anour," said Teague, "to ring a bell and call up a sharvant to bring boots and slippers, for I am to be married dis marning."

The Captain was thunder-struck and, comprehending the whole of what had taken place, saw his faux pas in recommending him to the hostess. And now it only remained to cure the blunder he had made, if it was at all curable.

We are short-sighted mortals; and while we stop one leak, the water rushes in at another. The very means that we use to save ourselves from one evil leads us to a worse. The Captain had need on this occasion of all his address. Composing himself, he dissembled and spoke as follows:

"Teague," said he, "will you, that are a young man and have great prospects before you, consign yourself to the arms of an old woman? Her breath will kill you in the course of a fortnight. The fact is, she is a witch and enchantress; she made the same proposition to me last night, of marrying me, but I declined it. The world is full of these sort of cattle. There was one Shangnesa Circe, in old times, that used to gather all she could in her net and transform them into hogs. Sir Teague Ulysses was the only one that had the sense to keep clear of her music and avoid her. Did you see that drove of hogs before the door when we rode up last evening? They are nothing more than stragglers which she has transformed into swine. I did not sleep a wink last night, thinking of the danger to which you were exposed, and indeed I expected nothing less than to find you this morning a barrow, fattened up for a feast a day or two hence. Did you think such an old haridan as this can have any natural concupiscence for a man? Or if she has, it is for a few days only, until she can make him fit for slaughter. Then by throwing a little water on him or by the bare blowing of her breath, she makes a beef-cow or hog-meat of him; and he finds the knife at his throat and scalding water taking off his bristles and his guts out, and is into the pickling-tub before he knows what he is about. Do you think, Teague, that I have read books for nothing? Have you not seen me in my study, morning and night, looking over Greek and Hebrew letters like partridge-tracks? All this to find out what was going on up and down the world. Many a history of witches and conjurers I have read, and know them when I see them, just as I would my own sheep when I am at home. Better indeed, for unless my sheep are marked I could not know them; but marked or not marked, I know witches;

and if I am not mistaken, this is the greatest witch that ever [has] run. She was all night in my room in the shape of a cat. It is God's mercy that she had not changed herself into an alligator and eat you up before the morning. When I came into the room I expected to find nothing else but bones and particles of hair, the remnant of her repast, but it seems she has thought you not fat enough and has given you a day or two to run, to improve your flesh and take the salt better. The worst thing, after transformation, is the having you cut in order to make you fatter and better pork, which is generally done the first day; and castration is a painful operation, besides the loss of the part. I have had several of my acquaintances served in this manner, falling in with old women whom they took for fortunes but were in reality witches and had dealings with the devil."

Teague by this time was out of bed and had dressed himself in his overalls and short coat and was ready for a march. Indeed he wished to escape as soon as possible. And descending the stairs, going to the stable, and saddling the horse, they both set out without taking leave. It was in this manner Aeneas quitted Dido and got a ship-board before she was awake, and the only difference was that Teague had left no little Iulus in the hall to put her in mind of the father.[10]

[12]

The ensuing day the Captain arrived in a certain city [11] and put up at the sign of the Indian Queen. Taking a day or two to refresh himself and get a new pair of breeches made and his coat mended, which was a little worn at the elbows, he went to look about the city. The fourth day, when he had proposed to set out to perambulate this modern Babylon and called for Teague to bring him his boots, there was no Teague there. The hostler, being called, with whom he used to sleep, informed that he had disappeared the day before. The Captain was alarmed and, from the recollection of former incidents, began to inquire if there were any elections going on at that time. As it so happened, there was one that very day. Thinking it probable the bog trotter, having still a hankering after an appointment, might offer himself on that occasion, he set out to the place where the people were convened to see if he could discover Teague among the

10. *Aeneid,* iv. Actually there was no difference between Aeneas and Teague in this respect. In lines 328–30, Dido regrets that Aeneas leaves her without issue.
11. Philadelphia.

candidates. He could see nothing of him; and though he made inquiry, he could hear no account. But the circumstance of the election drawing his attention for some time, he forgot Teague.

The candidates were all remarkably pot-bellied and waddled in their gait. The Captain, inquiring what were the pretensions of these men to be elected, he was told that they had all stock in the funds and lived in large brick buildings and some of them entertained fifty people at a time and ate and drank abundantly, and, living an easy life and pampering their appetites, they had swollen to this size.

"It is a strange thing," said the Captain, "that in the country, in my route, they would elect no one but a weaver or a whiskey distiller, and here none but fat swabs that guzzle wine and smoke segars. It was not so in Greece, where Phocion [12] came with his plain coat from his humble dwelling and directed the counsels of the people, or in Rome, where Cincinnatus [13] was made dictator from the plough. Something must be wrong where the inflated and the pompous are the objects of choice. Though there is one good arising from it, that there is no danger of my Teague here. He could not afford to give a dinner; and as to funds, he has not a single shilling in them. They will make him neither mayor nor legislator in this city."

"Na faith," said Mr. M'Donald, the Scotch gentleman who had been present at the embarrassment of the Captain on the occasion of the former election, and having a few days before come to the city and, observing the Captain in the crowd, had come up to accost him just as he was uttering these last words to himself: "Na faith," said he, "there is na danger of Teague here, unless he had his scores o'shares in the bank and was in league with the brokers and had a brick house at his hurdies or a ship or twa on the stocks. A great deal used to be done, by employing advocates with the tradesmen to listen to the news and tell them fair stories, but all is now lost in substantial interest, and the funds command everything. Besides, this city is swarming with Teagues and O'Regans, and O'Brians, and O'Murphys, and O'Farrels; I see that they cannot be at a loss without your bog-trotter."

12. Phocion, the Athenian statesman born in 402 B.C. He was the son of a humble craftsman. Elected general forty-five times, he was the virtual ruler of Athens until the democratic restoration in 318 when he was deposed and condemned to death.

13. Cincinnatus was twice called from his small farm to become dictator of Rome (458 and 439 B.C.). After triumphs over the Aequians and others, he returned to his humble farm. Part II of *Modern Chivalry* contains a long mock-epic satirizing an American vigilante society that called itself Cincinnatus.

The Captain, having his fears eased in this particular, returned home, greatly troubled nevertheless that he could not come up with the Irishman.

Reflecting with himself that Teague was inclined to women and that he might have gone to some of those houses which are not in the best repute with the religious part of the community, the Captain thought it might not be amiss to make inquiry. Being informed by the waiter that he had overheard gentlemen at the house in their cups speak of a certain Mrs. Robeson who kept a house of that kind, and, as far as he could understand, it was in such a part of the city, a few doors from such a street.

The Captain having set out, coming into the neighborhood and making inquiry, was directed to the house. Knocking and, on a servant coming to the door, inquiring for Mrs. Robeson, he was shown into a parlor, and in a little time the old lady entered. Being seated, he took the liberty of addressing her: "Madam," said he, "I am not un-acquainted with the style and designation of your house." "Why, as to that," said she, "we do the best we can, but the times are hard, and it is a very difficult thing to pick up a good-looking, healthy girl now-a-days. So many young women, since the war is over, having taken to virtuous ways and got married, has almost broke us up. But I have been fortunate enough to light upon one yesterday that is a rare piece, just from the country; and I am sure——"

"It is not in the way that you mean, Madam," said the Captain, "that I take the liberty to call upon you. I have a servant man of the name of Teague O'Regan that is inclined to women and has been absent some days; and it has occurred to me that he may have come to your house or some other of the like kind, and may be skulking to avoid my service. As he has little or no money, it is impossible he can be much in your way; and I could make it better worth your while to inform on him and surrender him up."

"Teague O'Regan," said the old lady, snuffing, "Teague O'Regan! I would have you know, sir, that no Teague O'Regans come here; we keep a house for the first gentlemen, not for waiters or understrippers or any of the common sorts. There is no half-crown or five shilling pieces here. Teague O'Regan indeed! There is no Teague O'Regan at this house. We have meat for his master. I was saying there was a young woman just now from the country that looks more like a woman of family than a country girl but is so melancholy and mopish that she scarcely speaks and stands in need of someone to talk to her and keep her in spirits. She is fit for any gentleman. Teague O'Regan! Humph! There is no Teague O'Regan puts his foot into my door."

The Captain assured her that he by no means meant to give offense, that though the bog-trotter could not have access to her first rooms, yet he did not know but he might have got in with some of her under maids and be about the kitchen.

The lady, being now appeased on the score of Teague, was in a good humor and renewed her hints to the Captain with respect to the young woman. "She is," said she, "as good-looking a girl as ever came to my house and has not seen a single person but yourself, whom she has not yet seen but may see if you choose; and a very pretty girl she is but keeps mopish and melancholy, as if she was crossed in love and had come to town for fear of her relations and wishes to keep out of sight of everybody."

The Captain, being no stranger to the art these matrons use in their addresses to enhance the value of their wares, was but little moved with the recommendation she had given. But as there were some circumstances in the account of the young woman that were a little striking, his curiosity was excited to let her be called in and present herself. Accordingly, the old lady stepping out, a young woman made her appearance, of considerable beauty but in her countenance expressions of woe. Her blue eye seemed involved in mist, for she shed no tears; her sorrow was beyond that.

"Young woman," said the Captain, "it is easy to perceive that you have not been in this way of life long and that you have been brought to it perhaps by some uncommon circumstances. My humanity is interested, and it occurs to me to ask by what means it has come to pass." The part which he seemed to take in her distress inspired her with confidence; and being requested by him to relate her story frankly, she began as follows:

"My father," said she, "lives at the distance of about twenty miles from this city, and is a man of good estate. I have two brothers but no sisters. My mother dying when I was at the age of fourteen, I became house-keeper for the family.

"There was a young man that used to come to the same church to which we went. He was of the very lowest class, mean in his appearance, of homely features, and a diminutive person. Yet he had the assurance to put himself in my way on every occasion, endeavoring to catch my eye, for he did not dare to speak to me. But I hated him and was almost resolved to stay at home on Sundays to avoid him, for he began to be very troublesome. His attentions to me were taken notice of by my brothers. They were confident that I must give him some encouragement or he would not make such advances. My father was of the same opinion. I assured them I had never given him any encouragement and I never would, that I was as much averse to him as possible.

"I shunned him and hated him. He persisted a long time, almost two years, and seemed to become melancholy, and at last went away from the neighborhood and, as I heard afterwards, to sea. I began now to reflect upon his assiduity and endeavors to engage my affections. I recollected every circumstance of his conduct towards me, since the first time I was obliged to take notice of him. I reasoned with myself that it was no fault of his if his family was low and if he himself had not all that comeliness of person which I wished in a husband; yet he was sufficiently punished, in his presumption in thinking of me, by what he must have suffered and by his going to sea, which he did to get out of my sight, finding his attempts to gain my affections hopeless. I dreamed of him; and scarcely a moment of the day passed but my thoughts were running on the danger to which he was exposed. It seemed to me that if he came back I should be more kind to him. I might at least show him that I was not insensible of his attachment.

"In about a year he returned, and the moment I saw him I loved him. He did not dare to come to my father's house. But I could not help giving him encouragement by my countenance when I met him in public. Emboldened by this, he at last ventured to speak to me, and I agreed that he might come to a peach orchard at some distance from my father's house and that I would give him an interview. There he came often, and with a most lowly and humble behavior fixed my regard for him. Not doubting the violence of his love for me and my ascendancy over him, I at last put myself in his power. Becoming pregnant, I hinted marriage. But what was my astonishment to find that, on various pretenses, he evaded it; and as I became more fond, he became more cold, which had no other effect than to make me more ardent than before. It had been usual for many months to meet me every evening at this place, but now I had gone often and did not find him there. At last he withdrew altogether, and I heard he had left the settlement. Worthless and base as I now knew him to be, and though my reason told me that in person he was still as homely as I first thought him, yet I continued to love him to distraction.

"What was my distress when my father and my brothers found that I was with child? They charged me, though unjustly, of having deceived them with respect to my attachment to this low creature from the first. In fine, my father dismissed me from the house. My brothers, no less relenting than him in their resentment against me, upbraided me with the offers I had refused and the treatment I had given several gentlemen in their advances to me. For, indeed, during the absence of this worthless man, I had been addressed by several; but my pity and compassion for the wretch had so wrought upon me that I could not think of any or scarcely bear them to speak to me.

"Dismissed from my father's house, even my younger brother, who was most soft and yielding in his nature, seeming to approve of it, I went to the habitation of a tenant of my father; there I remained some time, and endeavored to make compensation by the labor of my hands for the trouble I was giving them. But these poor people, thinking my father would relent, had informed him where I was and of the care they had taken of me. The consequence was that, at the end of three months, he sent for the child, of which I had been brought to bed some weeks before, but ordered them instantly to dismiss me, that I might never more offend his hearing with my name.

"I wandered to this city, and the first night lay in the market house upon a bench. The next morning mixed with the women that came to market and inquired for work of any kind. I could find none; but at last meeting with a young woman who felt for my distress, she told me that she had a small room in this city where she had lived some time with an aunt that was lately dead, and that now she supported herself by doing a little in the millinery way, that if I would come and take breakfast with her, and see where she lived, I was welcome. Going with the poor girl, I found her lonely and distressed enough. Nevertheless I continued with her several months. But the work was small that we got to do, and times becoming still worse, I was obliged to sell the clothes that I brought with me, to the last petticoat and short gown, to support ourselves and pay rent. To bring me to the last stage of misery, the poor girl, who was more expert than I was in making any little provision that could be made, fell sick and in a short time died. I could bear to stay no longer in the room, and coming out to wander in the streets like a forlorn wretch indeed and sobbing sorely by myself when I thought no one heard me, I was observed by this woman at whose house you now are, and pressed by her to go home. I soon found what sort of a house it was; and had I not been watched when I talked of going away and threatened to be sent to jail for what it is pretended I owe since I came to the house, I should not have been here longer than the first day."

The Captain, feeling with great sensibility the circumstances of her story, made reply. Said he, "Young woman, I greatly commiserate your history and situation, and feel myself impelled to revenge your wrong. But the villain which has thus injured you is out of my reach in two respects, first, by distance, and second, being too contemptible and base to be pursued by my resentment even on your account. But revenge is not your object, but support and restoration to your friends and the good opinion of the world. As to money, it is not in my power to advance you any great sum; but as far as words can go, I could wish to serve you—not words to yourself only but to others in your behalf. It is evident to me that you have suffered by your own too great sensibility. It was humanity and generosity that engaged you in his favor. It was your imagination that gave those attractions to his vile and uncomely person by which you were seduced. You have been a victim to your own goodness and not to his merit. The warmth of your heart has overcome the strength of your judgment and your prudence has been subdued by your passion; or, rather, indeed, confiding in a man whom you had saved from all the pains and heartfelt miseries of unsuccessful love, you have become a sacrifice to your compassion and tenderness. The best advice I can give you is to compose yourself for this night. Preserve your virtue, for I do not consider you as having lost it. Your mind has not been in fault or contaminated. I will endeavor to find out some person who may be disposed to assist you, and though it may be difficult for you yet to establish lost fame, it is not impossible." So saying, he left the room; but the young woman, impressed with these last words especially, viz., the difficulty if not impossibility of regaining reputation, sunk down upon her chair and could not pay him the compliment of thanks at his departure.

During the night, through the whole of which he lay awake at the public house, he ruminated on the extraordinary nature of this incident and the means which he would adopt to recover this woman from her unfortunate situation.

Thought he, I am in a city where there are a great body of the people called Quakers. This society above all others is remarkable for humanity and charitable actions. There is a female preacher of whom I have heard—a Lydia Wilson. I will inform this good woman of the circumstances, and if she gives me leave I will bring this stray sheep to her. She may have it in her power to introduce her to some place where, by needle work and industry, she may live until it may be in my power, taking a journey to her father and stating the case and giving my sentiments, to restore her to her family.

Early next morning, as soon as it could be presumed [that] the Quaker lady had set her house in order, that is, after the family might be supposed to have breakfasted which was about nine o'clock, the Captain set out and, being admitted, stated to Mrs. Wilson the exact circumstances as before related. The pious woman readily undertook every office in her power. Accordingly, taking leave, the Captain set out for the house of Mrs. Robeson.

At the door, he met a number of men coming out, and on inquiry he found a coroner's inquest had just sat on the body of a young woman of the house, who had the preceding evening suspended herself from the bed post with her garter. He was struck, suspecting it must be the young woman whom he had so much in his thoughts. Going in and inquiring, he found it to be the case, and that they proposed to bury [her] as soon as the few boards of a coffin could be got ready. As a man of humanity, he could not but shed tears and blame himself that he had not given her stronger assurance of his interposition before he left her, that she might not have fallen into despair and taken away her life.

The coffin being now ready, the funeral set out, not for the burying ground of a church yard, but for a place without the city called the Potter's Field. For suicides forfeit Christian burial. Her obsequies [were] attended not by a clergyman in front nor by scarfed mourners holding up the pall, nor was she borne on a bier, but drawn on a cart; and the company that followed her uncovered hearse were not decent matrons nor venerable men, but old bawds and strumpets and cullies, half drunk, making merry as they went along.

Being interred, they returned home; but the Captain, remaining some time contemplating the grave, thus spoke:

"Earth, thou coverest the body of a lovely woman and with a mind not less lovely yet doomed in her burial to the same ground with Negroes and malefactors; not that I think the circumstance makes any difference, but it shows the opinion of the world with respect to thy personal demerit. Nor do I call in question the justness of this opinion, having such circumstances whereon to found it. But I reflect with myself how much opinion, operating like a general law, may do injustice. It remains only with heaven's chancery to reach the equity of the case and absolve her from a crime, or at least qualify that which was the excess of virtue. If the fair elements that compose her frame shall ever again unite and rise to life and, as the divines suppose, her form receive its shape and complexion from her mental qualities and conduct on earth, she will lose nothing of her beauty; for her daring disdain of herself and fate was a mark of repentance—stronger than all tears. Yet had she acted the nobler part of holding herself in life, preserving her mind and body chaste until famine had taken her away or the hand of heaven moved for her relief, she had shone at the last rising with superior brightness, being ranked among the first beauties of heaven, and walked distinguished in the paradise of God. Doubtless the Almighty must blame and chide her for this premature and rash step. Fallen to the last point of depression, he was about to relieve her; and the sequel of her days might have been happy and serene. It was a distrust of his providence. She heard my words though she did not know my heart. And surely it was my intention to relieve her. But she erred against my thoughts; she eluded the grasp of my humanity. For this she will be reprimanded by the Most High and fail of that supereminent glory which awaits heroic minds. Yet, O world, thou dost her wrong in sentencing her to so low a bed. Shall the wealthy but dishonest men, matrons chaste but cold and cruel in their feelings, shall these have a stone built over them and occupy a consecrated spot whilst thou, unworthy, art thrown among the rubbish of carcasses swept from jails or of emigrants unknown as to their origin and place?

"Farewell, lovely form, whom late I knew; and let the grass grow green upon thy grave. Thy sorrows are expunged, but mine are awake and will be so until I also come to the shades invisible and have the same apathy of heart with thee."

[14]

The next day, revolving everything in his mind, it occurred to the Captain that the Irishman might have gone out of town, hearing of an election at a district, and have been elected to Congress. As that body was then sitting, he thought it could be no great trouble to go to the house and cast an eye from the gallery and see if the ragamuffin had got there. There was one that had a little of the brogue of Teague upon his tongue but nothing of his physiognomy; others had a good deal of his manner; but there was none that came absolutely up to the physique of his person.

However, being here, the Captain thought it not amiss to listen a while to the debates upon the carpet. A certain bill was depending and made, it seems, the order of the day. Mr. Cogan, being on the floor, spoke: "Sir," said he, addressing himself to the chair, "the bill in contemplation is, in my opinion, of a dangerous tendency. I will venture to foretell that, if it goes into a law, the cows will have fewer calves and the sheep less wool, hens will lay fewer eggs, and cocks forget to crow daylight. The horses will be worse shod and stumble more, our watches go too slow, corns grow upon our toes, young women have the stomach ache, old men the gout, and middle-aged persons fainting fits. The larks will fall dead in the field, the frogs croak till they burst their bags, and the leaves of the trees fall before the autumn. Snow will be found in the heat of harvest, and dog days in winter. The rivers will revert, and the shadows fall to the east in the morning. The moon will be eclipsed, and the equinoxes happen at a wrong season of the year. Was it not such a bill as this that changed the old style, that made the eclipse in the time of Julius Caesar,[14] that produced an earthquake at Jamaica and sunk Port Royal?[15] All history, both ancient and modern, is full of the mischiefs of such a bill. I shall, therefore, vote against it."

Mr. Bogan was now on the floor and advocated the good effects of the bill.

"Sir," said he, addressing himself to the chair, "I appear in support of the bill. I say it will have a good effect on the physical world especially. The ducks will be fatter, the geese heavier, the swans whiter, the redbirds sing better, and partridges come more easily into traps. It will kill rats, muzzle calves, and cut colts, and multiply the breed of oysters, and pickle cod-fish. It will moderate the sun's heat and the winter's cold, prevent fogs and cure the ague. It will help the natural brain, brace the nerves, cure sore eyes and the cholic, and remove rheumatisms. Consult experience, and it will be found that provisions of the nature proposed by this bill have an astonishing influence in this respect, where they have been tried. I must take the liberty to say the gentleman's allegations are totally unfounded and he has committed himself in the matter of his history, the earthquake in Jamaica not happening in the time of Julius Caesar and therefore could have nothing to do with the eclipse of the sun. I shall, therefore, vote in favor of the bill."

Mr. Cogan rose to explain and said that he did not say that the

14. The solar eclipse of 400 B.C. (Caesar died in 44 B.C.)
15. The Jamaica earthquake of 1692 destroyed the greater part of Port Royal.

earthquake at Jamaica was at the same time with the eclipse of the
sun which happened at the birth of Julius Caesar.

Mr. Bogan rose to correct the gentleman: it was not at the birth
of Julius Caesar but at his death that the earthquake happened.

Mr. Hogan was on the floor, said he thought he could reconcile
the gentlemen on that head. It was well known Julius Caesar lived
about the time of the rebellion in Scotland, a little after Nebuchadnezzar, king of the Jews. As to the earthquake, he did not remember
what year it happened and therefore could say nothing about it.

At this period, the question being called, it was put and carried
by a majority of twenty-five.

The Captain, satisfied with this sample of Congressional debates,
retired and came to his lodging.

[15]

It was about three or four o'clock in the afternoon that someone
who read the advertisement respecting Teague came to the Captain
and informed him that a person answering the description had been
lately employed to teach Greek in the university. Struck with the idea
that the bog-trotter might have passed himself for a Greek scholar,
whereas he understood only Irish, he set out to the university to make
inquiry. Knocking at the door of the principal, he was admitted and,
being seated, addressed him as follows. Said he, "Sir, a pedeseque of
mine (for, talking to the rector of a college, he did not choose to use
the vulgar terms waiter or bog-trotter), a pedeseque of mine whom I
have found useful, save that he is somewhat troublesome in pretending to places of appointment for which he is not qualified, a thing,
by the bye, too common in this country, where men without the aid
of academic knowledge thrust themselves into places requiring great
learning and ability (this he said to flatter the man of letters, as if a
man could know but little that had not been forged or furbished at
his school), I say this pedeseque of mine has absconded for some days,
and I have been able to collect no account of him until last evening,
that a person, having read an advertisement of mine in the gazette,
came to me and informed that one answering the description I had
given, both as to appearance and accomplishments, had been lately
employed as professor of the Greek language in this university. Now,
though I well know this Paddy, as I may call him, to understand no
Greek, yet as he speaks Irish and has much assurance and little
honesty in matters where his ambition is concerned I did not know

but he might have imposed himself upon you for a Greek scholar and obtained a professorship."

The principal made answer that it was true that a person from Ireland had been lately employed in that capacity and that should he be discovered to be an imposter, it would be using the university very ill. The Captain thought so too and, taking it for granted that it was Teague, expressed his surprise that they had not examined him before he was admitted or at least had such proof by letters as would have had ascertained his being qualified. The principal observed that as to examination they had no one at hand to examine, as there were none of the trustees or professors of other branches in the university [who] understood Greek; as for himself, he did not, having not studied it in early life and for a series of years having given himself to politics and mathematics; so that unless they could send out for a Roman Catholic priest or a Scotch clergyman, there was none to examine. The improbability of any person passing himself, above all things, for a master of the Greek language on the score of under-standing Irish was such that it never came into their heads to suspect it, so as to demand letters.

"Had you known," said the Captain, "this bog-trotter of mine (here he forgot the word pedeseque) as well as I do, you would not be surprised at his attempting anything and that he should be now in your academy giving Greek lectures, understanding nothing but the vernacular tongue of his own country." Here he gave an account of his setting up for Congress, etc., as explained in the preceding part of this narrative.

However, wishing to see the raggamuffin that he might unkennel him, he was accompanied by the principal to the chamber of the pseudo professor, considering as he went along in what manner he should accost him, whether he should break out upon him with a direct invective or with ironical words such as, "Mr. Professor, you must be a very learned man, not only to understand Irish, but Greek. But perhaps the Greek and Irish language are much the same. It must be so, for I know that a few days ago you did not understand a word of this, and to acquire a dead language in such a short time would be impossible, unless the living tongue was a good deal akin to it. But I had never understood that Irish had any more affinity to the language of Athens and Sparta than the Erse or the German or the Welsh; however, we must live and learn, as the saying is. You have shown us what we never knew before."

Conning a speech of this sort in his own mind, with a view to divert the principal and amuse himself with Teague, he entered the chamber of the professor, who sat in an elbow chair with Thucidydes before him.

What was the surprise of the Captain to find that it was not Teague!

In fact, it was a person not wholly unlike him, especially in a tinge of the brogue, which he betrayed in his discourse; for though the professor was really a man of education, having been early sent to St. Omer's, where he had studied, being intended for a priest, and understood not only the Greek and Latin but spoke French, yet in the pronunciation of the English tongue, he had that prolongation of the sound of a word and articulation of the vowel O which constitutes what is vulgarly called the brogue, as being the pronunciation of the native Irish, who being a depressed people, are most of them poor and wear a kind of mean shoe which they call a brogue.

After an apology to the professor for mistaking him for a certain Teague O'Regan whom he had in his employment, at the request of the professor, the principal and the Captain took seats.

The professor said his name was not O'Regan, being O'Dougherty, but he knew the O'Regans very well in Ireland. There was a Paddy O'Regan in the same class with him at St. Omers when he read Craike. That he was a good scholar and understood Craike very well, and he would be glad if he was over in this country to teach Craike here; it appeared to be a very scarce language; but he had become a praste and was now a missionary to Paraguay in South America.

The Captain, punning on his pronunciation of the word Greek and willing to amuse himself a little with the professor, could not help observing that he was under a mistake as to the scarceness of the Craike language in these States. That there were whole tribes who spoke the Craike language; there was that of the heron, and the raven, and several other fowls. A German professor, who was present, apprehending the Captain to be under a mistake and willing to correct him, observed, "It is," said he, "the Creek language that the professor means." "As to that," said the Captain, "it is also spoken plentifully in America. There is a whole nation of Indians on the borders of South Carolina and Georgia that speak the Creek language; men, women and children."

The professor, knowing more of the classics than of the geography of these United States and of the heathen gods more than of the aborigines of this country, expressed astonishment. "If what you tell me be a trut," said he, "it is a crate discovery; perhaps dese may have de fragments o' de books o' de philosophers and poets that are lost, and de professors cannot come acrass in deir own countries; but I have tought dat de Craike language was spoke only in de Morea and a little in Russia and Constantinople."

The Captain assured him, the principal favoring the mistake by a grave face and bowing as the Captain spoke, that it was absolutely the vernacular language of these people.

"Why den," said the other, "do dey not get professors from amongst dese to tache Craike in deir colleges?"

"Because," said the Captain, "we have been heretofore on hostile terms with these Indians, and it is but of late that we have made a peace. But now, it is to be presumed, we shall have it in our power to procure from them able teachers."

The professor was alarmed at this, as supposing it would supersede the necessity of his services or at least much reduce the price of his tuition. He could have wished he had not come to this quarter of the world and was almost ready in his own mind to bind up what he had and go back to Clougher.

So ended the visit to the university, and the Captain withdrew.

[16]

Our chevalier was now at his wits' end, not being able to conceive of any other place of amusement in which Teague might be found, when all at once it came into his head (led to it, perhaps, from the reference in his late conversation to the Indian tribes) that probably he might have fallen in with the Indian treaty-man and have been prevailed upon to personate a chief. It appeared to him, therefore, advisable to go directly to the Secretary at War, to know if any party of Indians had been lately there to negotiate a treaty.

Being introduced and after some ceremony accosting the Secretary, he gave him to understand why it was that he had the honor to wait upon him, viz., that he had a servant of the name of Teague O'Regan, an Irishman, who had been absent some days and that, from a circumstance which happened in the way to the city, he had reason to suspect he might been picked up by a certain Indian treaty-man to supply the place of a Welsh blacksmith who had died and had passed for a chief of the Kickapoos.

The Secretary was a good deal chagrined, believing the Captain to be some wag that had come to make this inquiry by way of burlesque on the Indian treaties, and with some irritation of mind, gave him to understand that there had been no Indian treaty-man or Kickapoo chief there, that no treaty had been held with the Indians for above a month past, since the king of the Togamogans had drawn goods; but treaty or no treaty, it ill became him, in the appearance of a gentleman, to throw a burlesque upon government by insinuating that his Irishman could be imposed upon them for a chief.

"I mean no burlesque," said the Captain, a little irritated in his turn. "I have had too much trouble to keep him from the Indian treaty-man that was coming here to be disposed to jest with so serious an affair. The hairbreadth escape of going to Congress or being licensed as a preacher or being chosen as a member of the philosophical society was nothing to this, as it was so difficult to guard against it, the Indian recruiters imitating savages not only in their dress and painting but in the dexterity to way-lay and surprise."

"I wish you to know, sir," said the Secretary, "that I comprehend your burlesque very well. But though you and others may misrepresent our policy in the Indian treaties, it is base irony and ridicule to insinuate that the Indians we treat with are not chiefs."

"Chiefs or no chiefs," said the Captain, "I am not saying nor care, but only wish to know if you have been instituting any treaty with my Teague who has been absent some days."

"I will be much obliged to you to withdraw from my office," said the Secretary.

"I shall withdraw," said the Captain, "and not with that respect for your understanding and politeness which I could have wished to entertain. I have addressed you with civility, and I was entitled to a civil answer; but I see the 'insolence of office' is well enumerated by the poet among the evils that make us sick of life. Your humble servant, Monsieur Secretary. I shall trouble you no further."

[17]

Returning to the Indian Queen, a play bill for the evening had announced the performance of the tragedy of *Macbeth* and a farce called *The Poor Soldier*. A party of the gentlemen from the public house had taken a box, and the Captain agreed to go with them to the play. Having delivered their tickets and being admitted to the box, it struck the Captain to cast his eye upon the pit and galleries and observe if he could anywhere descry the physiognomy of Teague. As before, when with the same view he surveyed the members of Congress, he could discover several that a good deal resembled him but yet not the identical person. The curtain being now drawn, the play began. Nothing material occurred during the performance of the tragedy, save that when the witches came in, there was one in her cap and broomstick whose features a good deal resembled the Irishman's and who, had she not been an old woman and a witch, might have passed for Teague. The Captain was struck with the resemblance of feature and long frame of the bog-trotter, covered with a short gown and petticoat; and borrowing a glass from one that sat in the box with him, endeavored to reconnoitre more perfectly, and could have sworn that it was the mother or sister of Teague, that had just come from Ireland and joined the Company.

The tragedy being ended, the farce began to be acted; and who should come forward in the character of Darby but the long-sought-for Teague. The fact was he had before appeared in the tragedy in the character of an over-grown, red-headed witch. It was more natural for him to appear in the character of Darby his own countryman, for he spoke with the brogue naturally and not by imitation. The managers had had him all the while of his absence from the Captain under tuition, teaching him his part, which was not difficult to do, the manner and pronunciation being already his own.

It was this that induced the managers to take him up as a substitute, the person who actually played the part of Darby being at this time out of the way. As the natural squeal of a pig is superior to an imitation of it, so it was allowed by the audience that Teague exceeded the pseudo Irishman that usually performed this part. All were pleased but the Captain, whose sense of propriety could scarcely restrain him from throwing his cane at the bog-trotter. Thought he with himself, what avails it that I prevented him from taking a seat in a legislative body or from preaching or being a philosopher if, after all, he has relinquished my service and turned player, a thing no doubt fitter for him than the being a senator or clergyman or philosopher because he can appear in some low character in the farce or comedy and come off tolerably enough. For though among the dramatis personae of learned bodies, there are Tony Lumpkins and Darby M'Faddins in abundance, yet there ought to be none; and Teague had better be on the stage than in such capacities, since he must be somewhere. But to leave me without notice, after all my civilities to him, is ungrateful and deserves all that I can say bad concerning him. I shall give myself no further trouble on this head but let him take his course. I must endeavor to find another servant who can supply his place.

[18]

Just at this moment a waiter coming in told him there was a person without, that is, in the bar-room, who wished to speak with him. Going out, who should strike his optics but Teague.

The fact was, being elated with the success of his performance on the stage, attributing that to art which was nature itself, he had counted more upon his accomplishments than he ought to have done and had made advances to the mistress of the manager, who was also an actress and, not greatly coveting an amour with the bog-trotter, made a merit of the circumstance to induce an opinion of fidelity and informed the manager of the presumption of the Irishman. The manager in the most unbecoming manner, without either citation, examination, trial, conviction, or judgment, but laying aside all forms of law, had instituted an original process of himself, and laying hold of a horsewhip had applied this implement to the back and shoulders of Teague; and as the Irishman made an effort of resistance at the first onset, the manager had been under the necessity, by turning the butt end of the whip, to knock him down, which he did by a stroke about the left eyebrow, which not only bereft him of senses for the present but [gave him] a discoloration of the eye for some days and a scar probably his whole life after.

It was this incident had induced him to leave the theatre and brought him back to the Captain, whom he now accosted in the following manner: "Dear master, for de love of shalvation, forgive a poor sharvant dat has been killed dis marning with a great cudgel, just for nothing at all but not pleasing a damned whore dat wanted me to stale de manager's cloathing and go off wid her. This is all that a poor sharvant gets by being hanest; but by Shant Patrick and de holy crass, it is what I deserve for laving de sarvice of a good master as your anour, and taking up with bog-trotters and stage players that would sooner take a cup of wine dan de holy sacrament and get drunk every night in de wake and go to de devil head foremost; but if your honor, dear master, will forgive de past and my running away and laving you, I will come back again and sarve you to de day of judgment or any langer time dat your honor plases, and clane your boots and spurs and rub down de bay harse; de poor old crature, how aften I have tought of him when I was in my rambles and he was aslape, laste

dey should chate him of his oats and give him nather hay nor straw
to ate; for I always liked to take care of a good harse and a good
master, and aften tought of your honor when I was amang de bog-
tratters of de stage, and gave you a good name and was always talking
of you and forgot my part and put de managers in a passion, who fell
upon me and bate me like a dog."

The Captain saw the inconsistency in the relation, one while
alleging the tale bearing of the mistress as the occasion of it; again, a
deficiency in the recital of his part. But expecting no truth from the
Irishman, [he] cared very little how it came to pass. The principal
thing that occupied his thoughts was whether to receive the bog-
trotter or dismiss him. He reflected with himself on the trouble he
had had with him on his various pretensions to advancement, his
uneasiness of mind and fatigue of body for several days past in examining stews, methodistical conventicles, rummaging philosophical
societies, attending elections, and listening to the debates of Congress
to see if he could anywhere observe his physiognomy or distinguish
his brogue. He could not think of subjecting himself to such un-
certainty in the attendance of any servant with such preposterous
ideas as being a legislator, philosopher, etc. Again he considered that
probably this last chastisement he had received might have a good
effect in curing him of the freaks of his ambition, and a mind broken
and reduced by disappointment is in a mellow state and more capable
of receiving the seeds of good advice than a mind full of vanity or
pride that has never yet received blows. Deliberating on these grounds,
his humanity prevailed and he determined to receive the ragamuffin
into favor.

This being settled and learning from the Irishman in what manner
he had been inveigled and drawn away by the manager to go upon
the stage and that it was only because Teague had made advances to
a woman that was a whore already that the manager had made such
an attack upon his person, he wished to punish him if it would appear
to be within the province of the law to do it. Accordingly inquiring
what principal lawyer there was in that city, [he] was informed of a
certain counselor Grab. Taking Teague with him, he set out to consult this gentleman. Counselor Grab was in his office among large
shelves of books, or shelves of large books, not as the Latins say, *Co-
operatus, aut obrutus, sed comitatus libris,* that is, In the midst of his
books. He had on a pair of spectacles, not so much on account of age
as to make the client believe that he labored under a premature want
of sight from much reading, or because a pair of lenses, magnifying

the organs of vision, gives the appearance of a larger eye, which has a good effect on the person consulting, impressing the idea of a broader view of things that are before it.

Entering, the Captain addressed himself to the counselor and gave him the outlines of the injury done to Teague, the counselor in the meantime suspending his reading in a large book which he had before him, printed in Saxon letter, and raising his head until the glasses of his spectacles were brought to bear upon the physiognomy of the Captain.

The Captain, having finished his account, referred him to Teague, the subject of the battery, for a more particular detail of the circumstances. Teague was glad of the opportunity of speaking before a learned lawyer and was beginning to give a relation of the whole affair, but the Captain stopped him, bidding him wait until the lawyer should himself request him to begin. The lawyer was silent. After having reconnoitered with his glasses, one while the Captain, another while Teague [talked], he dropped his optics and began to read again. The Captain, thinking he had not been sufficiently understood, recommenced the narration and gave an account of what he himself had suffered from the inveigling and detaining his servant and the visible injury which the servant himself had sustained. The lawyer was still silent; and though he had eyed him while speaking, as a Tuscan astronomer would the moon, yet he applied himself again to the reading the black letter that was before him.

The Captain thought it strange treatment and was for some time at a loss to know what to think of the matter. But recollecting, opportunely, that the circumstance of a fee had been omitted, he took out his purse and threw down two dollars. The lawyer seemed a little moved but cast his eye again upon the black letter. Finding the two dollars not sufficient, the Captain threw down two more. The counselor raised his head from the book, and you might discern some dilitation of the muscles of the face, as bespeaking an approaching opening of the voice; but still there was silence and might have been to this hour had not the Captain recollected at this moment what he had all along forgot, that half a joe [16] was the fee of a lawyer. Doubling, therefore, the four dollars that were already down, the lawyer came to his voice, the organs of his speech were loosed, and taking the glasses from his eyes, he gave his counsel as follows.

Said he, "You have a double remedy in this case, against the

16. About $8.80.

manager who inveigled and against the servant himself. Against the servant on the act of Assembly, if indented; [17] at common law, on the contract to serve. For even a servant at will, and not engaged for any special time, is not at liberty to desert the service of his master without reasonable notice first given. So that you may have your remedy against the servant, in the first instance, by bringing the matter before the court of quarter sessions and having time put upon him, as the phrase is, for this dereliction of your service; or, in action on the contract, express or implied as the case may be, wherein he shall repair in damages the loss sustained."

The bog-trotter was alarmed at the idea of an action against him and, looking wistfully at his master, exclaimed, "Dear master, will you trow de law upon me, dat am as innocent as a shild unborn and would go to death and damnation for you? Dear master, I suffered enough by de cudgel of dat player for all de running away I have done; and, God love your shoul, keep de law in its own place and not let it come acrass a poor sharvant dat has nathing but as he works and trats about, but let dese great big books of his honor de lawyer spake to de manager for his deceiving a poor sharvant and putting it into his head to run away and lave a good master and his bating him wid a great cudgel into de bargain."

"I have no desire," said the Captain, "to pursue the bog-trotter as he has made acknowledgments for his fault but would want the utmost rigor of the law to be put in force against the player."

"You have also in this case a double remedy," said the counselor, "by prosecution on the part of the servant and on your part. Nay, the servant himself has a double remedy, for he may prosecute by indictment, or bring his action of assault and battery, or both. I would recommend the action only, because, where no indictment is prosecuted and the civil action only brought, exemplary damages may be given as well as reparatory. For in the civil action it will affect the minds of a jury that the party has already suffered all that is in the nature of punishment by a criminal proceeding and nothing remains with them but to give reparatory damages. On the part of the master two kinds of action may be brought, either an action of trespass, *vi et armis,* laying a *perquod servitium amisit,* or simply an action on the case for the consequential damage of inveigling the servant."

"As to the number of remedies," said the Captain, "or the kind of them, I care very little how many there are or what they are. I want

17. Act of Pennsylvania Assembly governing terms of indentured servants.

only a good remedy. Give me a good swingeing one against the rascal, and I care very little what it is called."

"I shall then," said the counselor, "advise simply an action of the case, and count generally on the inveigling and detaining and rendering unfit for service while in his power. In this mode, the whole circumstances of the injury may be brought together and summed up into one point of view and, enhancing the quantum of damages, can expatiate on the value of your servant and the special occasion you had for his service at this particular juncture; for I make no doubt he is a valuable servant and that it has been an irreparable injury to you to have been defrauded of his service at this time."

"As to his value," said the Captain, "there can be no doubt, not only as a servant but in other respects. I have been offered, or at least I suppose I could have got, an hundred pounds for him to be a member of Congress or to preach or to go to the Philosophical Society or to be an Indian treaty-man, but have refused every proposal made him or me for these purposes; and . . . to have him kidnapped and taken off without fee or reward and employed as an actor and beat and rendered useless, at least for some time, into the bargain, is too much for any man to put up with. If there is law in the land, let it be put in force and this man made an example."

The counselor had no need of spectacles to give himself the appearance of a glaring and broad look on this occasion, for the words of the Captain made him stare sufficiently without the aid of a magnifying medium to enlarge his optics. He began to take him for a madman, at least in some degree deranged in his brain, to talk of his servant being in request for a member of Congress and the like.

"Yes," continued the Captain, "he not only inveigled away a servant that was thought fit to be a member of Congress and a preacher and an Indian treaty-maker and a philosopher and what not, but has kept me these three days trotting after him and trying to find him at election places and in Congress boarding houses and the hall where they have their debates and churches and pulpits and chambers of philosophical societies and professorships and where not, to see if I could find him, while this manager had him in the meantime at rehearsals, teaching him the art of mimicry for the stage."

The counselor in the meantime had reflected with himself that whether madman or no madman the Captain had money and might be a good client, let his cause be what it would. And so composing the muscles of his face, [he] seemed to agree with him and observe that doubtless the quality and capacity of the servant would be taken into view in estimating the damages; that if it appeared he was not only fit stuff for a servant but to be advanced to such eminent offices as these, not only the inveigling the embryo legislator, preacher, and philosopher but the assaulting and beating him, and by that means disabling him from immediate service, must be viewed in the light of an atrocious injury and insure a verdict accordingly.

"Very well," said the Captain, "and I shall wish to have the matter determined as speedily as possible as I may be but a few days in town. And besides, as the marks are yet apparent on the face and, I suppose, back of the bog-trotter, it will appear to the judges and jury, without the trouble of witnesses, what damage he has sustained."

"The process of law," said the counselor, "is tedious but certain. You cannot expect a trial in this case until the third or fourth term, that is nine months or a year."

"How so?" said the Captain. "Because," said the counselor, "it is now two months or upwards before the court to which the writ will be returnable. Even if a declaration is then filed, the defendant may imparl until the succeeding term, which is three months, when, if there is no demurer general or special, a rule to plead will be taken, which may not be put in until the succeeding term of three months again. At this term, if there is no replication, rejoinder, surrejoinder, rebutter, or surrebutter to draw up and file, while the defendant may crave a term, issue will be joined and at the next term trial. But even after a verdict there may be the delay of a term, on a motion for a new trial depending; so that in the law there is delay, but this delay is the price of justice."

"It is a price," said the Captain, "that I will not give for it. If you will bring it about in a short time to have this fellow flogged, even with half the stripes he has given my servant, I shall not think the half joe thrown away, but to be a year or half a year about the business is putting the matter so far off that it may as well be omitted altogether. If you could only get him sentenced to take a kick or two from my foot, or Teague's, before we leave the city, I should be satisfied."

"The *lex talionis*," [18] said the counselor, "makes no part of our law. You can punish only in estate, not in person, for simple assault and battery, such as this is."

"Do you not hang a man for murder?" said the Captain. "And

18. Law of retaliation, as in the Old Testament.

why not punish personally for an assault and battery?" "Because it is our law," said the counselor, "and in a civil action, the object is damages."

"A civil action and damages are strange phrases," said the Captain. "How can civility and damages be reconciled?"

"These are technical terms," said the counselor, "which persons not of the profession are at a loss to understand, but have in themselves a distinct and sensible meaning."

"Let the terms mean what they will," said the Captain, "it all comes to this at last—there is no getting at the manager under a year or two years' race for it, before which time Teague will have forgot the abuse he has received and I my trouble in running after a strayed Irishman through this city; and, therefore, it may be as well to give the matter up and sit down with the loss."

"That as you please," said the counselor, and putting on his spectacles, cast his eyes again upon the black letter.

The Captain, without bidding him kiss his backside, beckoned to Teague to follow him and withdrew from the chamber.

Having retired, "Teague," said the Captain, "this thing of law has been well said to be a bottomless pit. The way to it is like that to the shades:

> Facilis descensus averni;
> Sed referre gradus, hic labor, hoc opus est [*sic*].[19]

This pettifogger seemed to have a thousand remedies at his command and yet none that would serve us, as the redress, if any, is to be postponed to such a distant day. I have heard a great deal of these cattle, and I believe they are best off that have the least to do with them. They have so much jargon of technical terms that the devil himself cannot understand them. Their whole object is to get money, and, provided they can pick the pocket of half a joe, they care little about the person that consults them. The first loss is the best. You had better put up with the currying you have got than have my pocket picked on pretense of redress a year or two hence which may perhaps prove a century."

Teague was content to put up with the drubbing and have no more said about it.

19. *Aeneid,* iv, 126, 28–29. Brackenridge's memory was faulty. The passage reads: "—Facilis decensus Averno . . . sed revocare gradum . . . hoc opus, hic labor est." "Easy the descent to hell . . . but to recall your steps . . . this is the task, this is the labor."

[19]

The Captain had consoled himself with the idea that Teague was now cured of his folly and would no more be disposed to entertain notions of ambition and unreasonable projects. He was disappointed in his hope, for that very evening the Irishman, washing down the recollection of his woes with some exhilarating drink and, though not intoxicated but enlivened only, he came to the Captain. Said he, "Dear master, what would your anour think if a poor sharvant should turn lawyer and get a half-joe when a customer comes to consult him in de morning? Would it not be better dan currying a horse and tratting about like a big dog with no sense to live like a man of fartune and have a big house over his head and about him and take half-joes from paple dat come to him about deir quarrels and batings through de town and sending dem aff as wise as if day had never come to him and de great spectacles to look like a blind man dat was blind before he was born and could see more dan two or three other paple for all dat and was a canjurer and a wizzard and could take money for nating? Would it not be better, master, than tratting like a fool and disrupting wid paple and having nating to lay up but be as poor as a church mouse or a rat all de days of our life and paple laugh after us when we are gone?"

The Captain was thrown into a reverie of thought by the speech of the bog-trotter, reflecting that his presumption and folly were incurable, for, notwithstanding all that had been said to him or suffered by him, his natural propensity remained the same, according to the maxim—*Naturam expellas bifurca, usque recurret* (You may toss out nature with a pitchfork, she will still come back upon you). Not so much from any further view of reclaiming him as from indignation and resentment against his presumption, the Captain projected in his mind a farther means of chastising him. He had heard of a workhouse in this city into which refractory servants are committed and put to hard labor, such as pounding hemp, grinding plaster of Paris, and picking old ropes into oakum.[20] He resolved to have the ragamuffin put into this a while. Counterfeiting, therefore, an approbation of his project of becoming a lawyer, "Doubtless," said he, "the profession of the law is a profitable business, where money is very easily got by the bare breath of the mouth. Nevertheless, it requires time and study to qualify for this profession. Nay, the intro-

20. Picking apart the fibers.

duction to the study, by being put under an eminent lawyer in full practice, is itself very expensive. An hundred pistoles [21] is sometimes the fee. This I could not very well afford, but I have an acquaintance in this town who, I am persuaded, would be willing to oblige me and will take less. I will call upon him early tomorrow and settle the contract."

Accordingly the next day, calling on the keeper of the workhouse, he gave him an account of his refractory servant and, with a gratuity of a couple of guineas, obtained his consent to take the bog-trotter under his direction and give him a few lessons in picking oakum and grinding plaster of Paris and pounding hemp, not withholding in the meantime a seasonable application of the cowskin in the intervals of study of these several branches of the law. For the idea was to be imposed upon Teague that this was an office, or as it were an inn of court, or chamber of the Inner Temple, and that the several flagellations and grindings and poundings were so many lessons and lectures to qualify him for the practice of the law.

It happened, fortunately, that the keeper of the workhouse was well qualified for the task, for in early years he had been put an apprentice to an attorney and had some opportunity of attending courts and hearing the names of books to which the advocates referred in their pleadings. But having a turn for extravagance and a dissolute manner of life, he had come to poverty and, through various scenes, to jail. There, by address, he had gained the good will of the jailor's daughter, whom he married; and, by the interest of his new father-in-law, having obtained his liberation, he was, from acting as deputy jailor in a series of time, at length promoted to be the keeper of this workhouse. Indeed from his employment, being acquainted with the prisoners and finding himself sometimes interested in their fate and being led to attend their trials, he had, even in his last capacity, been a good deal about courts and heard law phrases and books mentioned.

Accordingly when Teague was introduced, which was that very afternoon, he had at his command the names of the abridgers and reporters and commentators of the law and the technical terms in the commencement and process of a suit, so that, when the key was turned and, after having stript him of the linen doublet that was upon him, he began to give him the first application of the cowskin,

21. The double escudo of Spain, a gold coin worth approximately four dollars; but the term was applied generally to a variety of gold coins of Europe worth about the same value.

he told him this was reading Wood's Institutes; and when, after this, he was sentenced to an hour or two's hard labor at grinding plaster of Paris, this was called Coke upon Littleton; and when the employment was varied, pounding hemp or picking oakum, it was called Hawkin's Pleas of the Crown or Foster or 4th Blackstone, etc. When the poor bog-trotter, reduced to a skeleton living on bread and water, complained of the hard usage and offered himself a servant for life to curry horses and brush boots to any Christian creature that would take him out of that place, he was told that, as he had begun the study of law, he must go through with it, that this was but the commencement of the suit, that in a year's time he would learn to file a declaration, in another to put in a plea, in a third, to join issue, and in a fourth, to conduct a trial, that unless a bill of exceptions had been filed or there was a motion in arrest of judgment or writ of error brought, he might be admitted the fifth and begin to practice the sixth year. At all events, provided he would submit himself with due application to fasting and cowskinning and grinding plaster of Paris, pounding hemp, and picking oakum, he might be a lawyer the seventh year and wear spectacles, like counselor Grab, and take half a joe when he thought proper.

I know not by what simile to represent the howl of the Irishman at this prospect of the duration of his woes. It was like that of a wolf at the bottom of a well or a dog that had lost his master or a cow her comrade or some forlorn wanderer that has missed the way and given up all hopes of being extricated from the wilderness. At the various applications of the cowskin, he had jumped and cursed and sworn and prayed and beseeched and promised a thousand services, of currying horses and brushing boots and trotting wherever he was ordered, provided they would set him at liberty. When employed at the hard labor before mentioned, he had groaned and cursed the law, the counselor, and the half-joe. Ah, thought he, if my dear master, the Captain knew how hard a ting it was to study law and to fast widout ating or drinking and be bate wid a cowskin, he would not have given de hundred pistoles, nor de half of it, to have had me kicked and cuffed in dis manner. I would give body and shoul into de bargain if I could see him once more at dat iron gate there to spake to him and besache him to take me out of dis purgatory. He was a good master, and when I was a fool and wanted to be a member of Congress and prache and be a phalosophar, he told me, "Teague, you are a fool," and what dey would do wid me there, how dey would bate me, ate me, and take de skin off my back and make a cow or a shape od me; and now I am worse than a cow or a shape or a harse in de tame, for I am cut and curried black and blue till my flesh is raw and a cholic in my belly wid fasting; and all to stoody dis law. De devil take counselor Grab and de half-joe.

[20]

The Captain had now leisure to reflect on the predicament in which he left Teague, and, thinking he might have had what was sufficient to cure him of his folly or at least restrain it, thought of making a visit to the house of employment or sending to liberate the valet.

This thought running in his head, he naturally suggested it to a gentleman with whom he was at this time in conversation on in different subjects, the gentleman lodging at the same inn or public house and seeming to be a person of considerable shrewdness and discernment not only of the affairs of men in general, but of the special spirit and character of these times.

Said the gentleman, "The folly of your man has certainly been very great to suppose that he could be qualified to sustain the profession of an advocate and to practice law. For, though in this as in most other professions, the race is not always to the swift nor the battle to the strong but [to] the people that showeth favor, that is, take up an opinion of abilities where there are none; yet your servant, having so little even of the semblance of qualification, it would be counting too much on the circumstance to promise great success in his case. His prospect of advancement would be much more certain in the political career. You seem, by your account, to have discouraged him in taking a seat in the legislature and would not wish now to contradict yourself; yet why not indulge him im taking a place in the executive of some government? As far as I can see, with that ambition which is natural to him, you will find him but of little use as a waiter, and you may as well let him do something for himself as not. If appointed in the department of finance, he can use clerks and, in a very short time, he may learn to write his name so as to give his signature to any paper; and this, with the help of clerks to do the accountant business, would be sufficient. At least there have been those in these departments who have been approved and yet could do little more. Should he even become a governor furnished with a secretary, he can be at no loss to compose his messages or other communications to individuals or public bodies.

"But what I would propose, and will suit him best, will be to go into the general government and under this the diplomatic line will be eligible. He might be appointed consul to the port of Cork or Dublin or the Barbary States or other places. Or he might go as ambassador to the grand mogul or envoy extraordinary to the king of England or other princes or potentates in Europe.

"If you should think of favoring him in his career, it will be necessary for him to appear at the levee of the president, that he may be introduced with a certain gradual etiquette of advancement."

"What!" said the Captain. "Introduce a ragged bog-trotter to the President of the United States!"

"Not ragged," said the gentleman. "You can have a pair of breeches made for him and put shoes upon his feet. A sword will be necessary and some other articles of equipment. And when you bring this into view with his making his fortune, you will not consider it as advancing much for a person whom you wish to serve."

The Captain began to think there was weight in the observations of this gentleman and that it might be proper to let the bog-trotter have a chance of doing what he could. Accordingly, he wrote a note to the keeper of the house of employment to liberate him for the present.

The state of politics at this time and the prospect of Teague's advancement we shall leave to the third volume of this work.

[*End of Volume Two (Philadelphia, 1792). Chapters included are the original Book II, 1; Book IV, 1, 2, 5, 6, 8, 9; Book VI, 3, 4; and Book VII, 1.*]

[21]

. . . the Irishman was certainly in no very decent apparel to appear at the court, even of a republic. The jacket and trousers, or overalls as some call them, that he had upon him, though of rough materials, being a coarse tow linen that had not had but one boiling before it was made up, were not even whole, what is more, not clean. Not that he had voluntarily on some great occasion for a public or private calamity, as was the manner of the Jews, rent his garments and put on sackcloth and strewed ashes on his head, but what came to the same thing; by lying by the fireside at night and wrestling in the day with the hostler and servants at the tavern, he was reduced to the same raggedness and ash-powdered state.

Nevertheless, though there might not have been time to have

washed his duds, yet a patch or two might have been put upon his vestments, a considerable impression having been made upon his flank by a sharp point and his rear being uncovered a handsbreadth or more; unless indeed his breeches had been taken off altogether and he had come forward, a real *sans culotte*,[22] without anything on his backside at all.

[22]

Having waited with impatience for the evening, the Captain, with the candidate, set out for the levee. Arriving at the door, the Captain entering first and Teague just behind, he addressed the President. Said he, "May it please your Excellency, here is a young man whom I take the liberty to introduce as a candidate for state employment. He has been offered a seat in Congress. But it appears to me that a place in the executive department would suit him better. His name is Teague O'Regan and he has been for some time a servant of mine, a bog-trotter, but I believe I could now spare him if your Excellency has occasion to make use of him." The Attorney General and several others who were present were a good deal confounded at the proposition. A little lean Frenchman in the room with a sword by his side was astonished and expressed above an hundred foutres [23] to himself in the compass of a minute. I do not mean that he spoke out but thought them to himself in a short space. A British consul present, who was a man of philosophic turn of mind, could not but reflect on the nature of a republican government and the extraordinary assurance of the lowest class to pretend to offices.

The President, in the meantime contemplating the object, made a pause. But after some time recollecting himself, bowed to the Captain and to Teague and signified that doubtless proper notice should be taken of the merits of the gentleman and provision made for him. This he said, bowing at the same time in a circular manner and turning round as if to converse with another person to whom attention was, in his turn, due. Teague in the meantime, advancing with his mouth open and both his arms stretched out, was about to harangue in his own dialect, as plase your honour, etc. But an aid of the President, or someone concerned in the ceremonial of the occasion, touching the Captain and Teague and, conversing with them towards the door, gave them to understand that they might depart for the

22. Without breeches.
23. French obscenity meaning to copulate; also a worthless fellow.

present and that there was no manner of question but that his Excellency had taken a note of the matter and, when any appointment was about to take place, the gentleman would be remembered.

[23]

From the reception at the levee, which the Captain thought favorable, he began to entertain more confidence in the advancement of Teague and, under this impression, thought it now advisable to begin to take some pains with his bodily appearance and, by the next interview, produce him to the best advantage.

To conduct this by system, the first thing was to heave him down, as it were, and scrape off his barnacles. This was done by ordering into an apartment of the kitchen at the Indian Queen a tub of warm water. His overalls being stript off and putting his feet and legs in this, with hickory ashes and a pint of soft soap, the hostler was occupied an hour or two in the necessary lotion and friction until the upper skin began to come off and the natural complexion of his flesh to appear. After this, being stript altogether, his whole body underwent the same operation, the Captain standing by and ordering his joints to be stretched in the manner of the Turks in their baths. After this a clean shirt was put on him and the usual attire of a common man.

[24]

The next thing to be done towards forming the bog-trotter to some degree of decency was the teaching him some more easy movements of his person so as not to lift his feet so high or make such long strides, as not being necessary where there were now no sloughs or ditches to leap over but carpets or plain floors to step upon. This, with the instructing him in what manner to turn his toes out or at least to keep his feet parallel in walking, and [in] turning round to throw one heel into the hollow of the other foot, at the same time in what manner to bear his arms and head and to preserve or incline his body in receiving or returning a salutation. Considering by what means this was best attainable, the Captain thought to himself it might be advisable, in the first instance, to employ a dancing master. For though the lessons of such a teacher might not give ease of behavior all at once, yet these might lay the foundation of it. For no man ever came from the hands of a dancing master with a natural ease and flexibility of joint and limb, yet being taught to move by rule at first, in the course of mixing with good company the wire edge of art would wear off and an ease of demeanor be attained. For this reason he thought proper, the next morning, to send for Monsieur Douperie and to address him as follows:

"Monsieur Douperie," said he, "here is a young man of some talents, as the world supposes, though I never could find them in him, who is in a fair way to be introduced into the political and probably the gay world. And as he is but rustic and awkward in his movements, I would wish to have him polished; not that I expect he can attain to great perfection in the highest species of the dance, such as the minuet or the cotillion or even the maneuvers of a contre dance, but simply in the position of his feet and to step and move with propriety. For I do not think it necessary for a statesman that he be a proficient in the saltatory art, but simply that he be able to bear himself upright and to enter a room in an easy manner and not take too long strides in walking across the floor."

The Frenchman, eyeing Teague, thought with himself that he was but a rough subject to work upon. Nevertheless, concealing his sentiments, as the manner of the nation is polite and compliant, he replied. "Monsieur Capitaine," said he, "ver great sensible of de honneur que vous me faites,[24] de attitude of dourself be so ver natural, dat prove de high degree que vous acquis [25] in de art dat I tashe and trow un grand lustre on de talents dat I possede."

Such was the compliment to the Captain himself, though, by the bye, he was but a plain man and had never been taught to dance.

Monsieur Douperie continuing, turned his attention now to the bog-trotter. "Dis Monsieur," said he, "appear de best calcule of de vorld for de danse. Sa taille,[26] ver good; his limb, promettent.[27] Ver much en faveur of his talents futures. His muscle et son apparance nerveuse confirm me of his strense in de execution. His eye be very good pour fixet son visavis his partner. Tout me promet un grand expectation make Monsieur most egal myself in de art of de danse." [28]

"As to that," said the Captain, "I would not have you too sanguine.

24. That you offer me.
25. That you acquired.
26. His shape.
27. Prominent.
28. "His eye is very good for looking his partner in the eye. All of this promises me a great expectation of making the gentleman equal to myself in the art of the dance."

You do not take into view the low state in which he is and what pains will be necessary before you can bring him to that point where you begin with others. So low is my opinion of his present grade in point of manners that I had thought of putting him a while under the care of a person skilled in breaking oxen, that he might be taught to move by rule in some rough way at first before I would trouble you with giving him the nicer precepts that respect the locomotive art."

"Tres plaisant, Capitaine, ver plaisant," said the dancing master, "mais, j'me promet dat Monsieur make ver good proficiance in ver short time." [29]

The Captain, now thinking proper to withdraw, left Teague to his lessons.

[25]

Having bestowed some pains to cultivate the personal movements of the bog-trotter, it now remained to endeavor to improve his manners. This the Captain undertook himself, and, though he had not read Chesterfield, yet he had some common ideas of decency and delicacy in habits and behavior. On this point, addressing his pupil, he began.

"Teague," said he, "you have now got, in literal terms, your rough coat off, that is, you have some better dress than what you used to wear. You have also had some lessons in what manner to stand or move your feet, as there may be occasion. It now remains to instruct you with regard to habits of delicacy in some matters. You must be careful to keep your hands and face clean, pair your nails, and let no black be under them. Wash the inside of your mouth and brush your teeth, keep a handkerchief and wipe your nose with this, not with your bare hand. When you cough, spit out, even should there be nothing to spit, lest the imagination of another may suppose that there is. You must not belch or break wind from your mouth or from any other part. By the bye, Teague, I have my fears of you in this last particular, for you know you have not been always careful in trotting with me to observe a delicacy in this respect, and it would be the devil in hell if, in a company of ladies, an indiscretion of this kind should escape you.

"In the next place you will be careful to avoid scratching your head or putting your hand in the waistband of your breeches or

29. "Very pleasant, Captain, very pleasant, but I promise myself that the gentleman will make very good progress in a very short time."

turning your back to the fire and pulling up your coat behind, which is the way of the vulgar. Put but a small quid of tobacco in your mouth, not swell the cheeks as if you had robbed a weaver of a ball of yarn and put it there. Do not spit on a floor if you must spit. In eating, sit close to the table, do not put your nose too near the plate, put but a little in your mouth at once, do not speak while your mouth is full or while you chew. If anyone speaks to you in this predicament, bow, as much as to say I will answer you presently. Drink healths sparingly, if at all. Do not blow in your cup to cool your tea. Keep your infirmities to yourself, and do not complain of costiveness or laxativeness, of pains in the bowels, etc. A gentleman should have no complaints, unless to his physician, of anything but the gout or a fever or the like. Give no information of a bad digestion, or [of] food being heavy or light to your stomach, of your agreeing with this or that food but its not agreeing with you, as the vulgar say, that is, as we shall understand you, it gives you the belly-ache. Take care not to value yourself on your eating, as that will show a gross mind, or on your drinking much, as that is but a low ambition. Sing no bawdy songs, especially among ladies, such as Brian O'Linn, and Arthur O'Bradley or that about Tristram Shandy-o. For though these were suitable enough to your former station, and such as you have been accustomed to sing among the girls at the taverns, yet they will not pass among more refined company. You must get some more fashionable airs, such as the Bird or Guardian Angels or the like.

"Even at clubs, among gentleman, I would recommend it to you to avoid lewd and indecent songs, especially if they are of the gross and disgusting kind. As you are an Irishman, a verse or two of Lango Lee might be excusable perhaps. It is true that in the higher ranks, among both males and females, the double intendre is sometimes used; but unless it is with great delicacy and relieved by singular wit, it is not admissible.

"There are rules of good manners which you are to observe. Such as when you walk with any person, let them walk next the wall; if you are about to enter a room with another, let him enter first, or if about to sit down, give way to another who is also about to sit down. Decline the higher seat. You must not talk too much, especially about yourself, boasting, as I have heard you do sometimes, of jumping and trotting and how you could wrestle and the like. I am afraid, Teague, that after all the pains I am taking with you, you will spoil the broth by some outbreakings of your old tricks and habits in some way or other. However, since I have suffered myself to be persuaded to try the matter, let it go on. We shall see the issue of it." These are the outlines of some of the hints upon manners given by the Captain.

[26]

The circumstance of having been at the levee and having made a speech in the beer-house, which had been much approved, and, above all, it being announced that he was a candidate for state employment, had made the bog-trotter a pretty general theme of conversation. Sundry persons who were expectants upon government had procured themselves to be introduced to him, as supposing that when in office, by and bye, he might have it in his power to do them service. Even by those that were in government, in the legislative, executive, or diplomatic line, he was not neglected. Several members of Congress had left cards. Assistants and deputy assistants in office, foreign consuls, two or three directors and cashiers of banks had waited upon him and paid him their compliments.

His name became known in the gay world and by a gradual introduction he had become acquainted in some of the best families of the city. The ladies, in general, were much taken with him. They thought him a plain, frank, blunt-spoken Irish gentleman, not harassing them with deep observations drawn from books or an ostentation of learning but always saying something gallant and complimentary of their persons or accomplishments, such as "God love your shoul, my dear cratur, but you are de beauty of de world. Sleeping or waking, I could take you to my heart and ate you wid de very love o'd' my shoul dat I have for you. De look o'd' dur face, like de sun or de moon, run trugh me and burn up like a coul o'd' de fire; dat I am shick and fainting to take du to my arms, my dear cratur."

Declarations of this nature, made without any ambiguity and warm and violent in their nature, had rendered him, as I have said, pretty generally a favorite of the ladies, far indeed beyond anything which the Captain, simple and ignorant of the world, had ever imagined. His astonishment, therefore, was not small a day or two after this, when, walking the street, he saw a carriage pass by with a gentleman and lady; and, on asking whose carriage that was and who the gentleman that was in it, for he was struck with some resemblance of the bog-trotter, it was answered that it was the carriage of Mr. Haberdasher, a merchant of the city, whose lady was taking an airing it would seem with Major O'Regan, a member of Congress, or ambassador, or something that was just come to town. God Almighty!

thought the Captain. Is it possible? I see that I have been a fool all my life and, though just going out of the world, am but beginning to get experience to live in it. I had been led by his own confidence and by the opinion of others, though with great doubts on my part, to suppose it possible that he might have come to be of some respect in government, the discharge of an office requiring rather solid than brilliant parts; but that in so short a time, or indeed after any period, he should become a favorite of females of taste and fashion never entered into my head at all; and forsooth, they have given him the appellation of Major, though he is about as much a major as my horse.

Such were the ideas which the circumstance of Teague in a carriage with a fine lady naturally produced in his mind. Nor indeed should we think them unreasonable were it not that we know there was nothing extraordinary in the case. For though abstractedly considered, it would seem improbable that the female mind of great delicacy and refinement should be captivated by a rough and gross object; yet we know that the fact is in nature, and we must leave it to the philosophers to account for it. Nor will this be any difficult task when we consider the powers of imagination. Here was a new object, unknown as to its origin and high as to its pretensions and, what is novel and not fully comprehended, lofty in its nature. [It] has a supereminent dominion over the human mind. Hence the proverb, "Far fetched and dear bought is good for ladies." But on the present occasion a particular principle operated in favor of the bog-trotter, viz., the taste and fashion of the day. For, as in the age of chivalry, a knight was the only object in request and, at the beginning of the revolution in America, a Baron or a Count from France or Germany was the tone, so now, since the adoption of the Federal Constitution, the [appetent] offices of government are the only characters in vogue. And as in the first instance, mere squires had been taken for knights and passed very well, and in the second case, tailors and barbers had slurred themselves for gentry or nobility, what could hinder the bog-trotter from availing himself of the whim of the day and be taken for a person qualified to fill any place in government from the bare pretending to it? And being once taken for such, what prodigy was there in his being in request with the females and all the first families of the city, who might be ambitious and vie with each other in having him married to a niece or a daughter, that so being raised above plebians by the connection, they might be considered as of a patrician degree? Let the principle be what it would, whether taste or ambition, the fact was that the bog-trotter was courted and caressed by all the first people. There could be no card party without Major O'Regan. A young lady sitting by a gentleman in any house and seeing him pass by would start up and run to the window and say, "O, there is Major O'Regan." When he was in company and would laugh and put out his tongue, as if he was about to sing Lillibullero, the young ladies would laugh too, not that there was any jest in what he or they said, but just because the Major had laughed. When he would put out his paw to touch the hand of any of them, "O la! Major," one would say; "O now! Major," another would say; "Don't now Major," a third would exclaim, rather to attract his attention than to repress his advances. The fact was there seemed to be a kind of Teagueomania among the females so that all idea of excellence, personal or mental, was centered in him, and all common lovers were neglected or repulsed on his account. A melancholy instance of this kind occurred to the Captain the following day, when walking by the margin of the river on which the city stood and towards a grove of wood which skirted it on the south. He observed a man sitting on a tuft of the bank, with his head reclining forward in a melancholy position and looking down upon the wave beneath him in the manner in which Achilles is described by the poet Homer as looking on the purple ocean and complaining to the goddess Thetis of the injury done to him when the maid Briseis had been taken from his arms by the order of Agamemnon.[30] Sensibly touched with an appearance of woe in any case, the Captain could not avoid advancing and accosting him. "Sir," said he—but what need I take up the time of the reader with stating particularly the words of the address. It is sufficient to say that, with all necessary delicacy, the Captain gave him to understand that he took a part in his misfortune, if there was any upon his mind, and would think himself extremely fortunate if by language or acts he could alleviate his griefs.

"Sir," said the other, "it is impossible. I am an unhappy man, who has been for some months in love with a young lady of this city and whose affections I had conceived myself to have engaged by the most unremitting attention. I had counted upon her as my wife, and in all my industry in business, which is that of a merchant, I had my thoughts directed to the provision I hoped to have it in my power to make in order to support her with dignity and affluence. Yet within these few days, her attention is engaged and her affections alienated by a certain Major O'Regan who is or is about to be engaged in some public employment."

30. *The Iliad*, I.

"Major O'Regan," said the Captain, laughing. "Is it possible!"

"Do you know him?" said the gentleman.

"Know him," said the Captain. "He is my bog-trotter. He has been my valet de chambre this three years and of late my hostler and boot cleaner in my travels to this city. I believe I could prevail with him, for a pair of breeches or so, to resign his pretensions to the lady."

At this, the eye of the inamorato began to resume its lustre and the paleness of his countenance to give way to some freshness of complexion. "Give me your name and the name of the lady," said the Captain, "and call upon me tomorrow at the Indian Queen about nine o'clock, and I will endeavor to make such terms on your behalf with this same Major O'Regan that he will give you no further trouble on the score of the lady."

The inamorato expressed his thankfulness with great animation and fervor and accepted the invitation to wait upon him at the time proposed, informing him at the same time that his name was Williams and that of the lady was M'Cracken, a daughter of an alderman of the city of that name.

The Captain, coming home, addressed the bog-trotter as follows: "Major O'Regan," said he, "for that I find is the title which they have given you, there is a young lady of this town of the name of M'Cracken whom you have by some means engaged to think favorably of you to the neglect of a former admirer, a Mr. Williams, a merchant of this city. This gentleman had a claim upon her from a prior attention, and though there is no muncipal law that constitutes it a wrong in you to interfere, yet humanity will dictate that it is a wrong. Because it is a small thing to a man whose affections are not engaged and who has yet wasted no time upon an object to decline attention to it or relinquish it. But to him who has set his mind upon this or that lady, it is death to be repulsed; and a man of honor and delicacy of feeling, who sees the advances of another which are well received, will not interfere, even though the object might be agreeable to him. Much less will he amuse himself at the expense of another by paying attention when it is his own vanity alone that he consults in showing in what point of view he could stand if he should think proper to persist. I hope better things of you, Teague, and that you will conduct yourself on the principles of honor and humanity; you will resign this flirt, for such I deem her who"—he was going to say who could be tickled with you, but, having a point to carry with Teague, he chose to use soft words—"who," continued he, "could so readily change one lover for another. What security have you for the affections of one of so versatile a mind? Mr. Williams is a merchant and has cloths in his store. He will give you the pattern of a pair of breeches to decline your pretensions and resign the jade to him who had first cast his eye upon her."

Teague, much more from this last part of the argument than from the fine sentiments of delicacy which were laid down in the first of it, consented to relinquish the dulcinea;[31] and so when Mr. Williams called at the hour proposed, an order for the making of a pair of breeches was given and the bog-trotter pledged his word that he neither would laugh, talk, walk, or ogle with her any more.

Shortly after this, while reading a newspaper, the Captain heard two men conversing at the opposite end of the saloon in which they sat, one of them expressing his concern that, having a cause to be tried before the court then sitting, his lawyer Mr. Hardicknute could not attend, being indisposed, and as it was alleged, from a disappointment in love by a Miss Thimbleton who was of late, as it appeared, taken with a certain Major O'Regan, an Irish gentleman of some note who had taken notice of her.

Inquiring the residence of the gentleman and being informed, the Captain, ever prompt to do offices of humanity, immediately calling for Teague, who was in the bar room with the waiter getting him to write a love letter for him, set out on a visit to lawyer Hardicknute, and being admitted to his chamber, where he lay languishing in bed, accosted him, giving him to understand that he knew the cause of his complaint, not by feeling his pulse as did the physician of Demetrius who was in love with Stratonice,[32] nor by any power of conjuring but simply by hearing it from a client who was interested in his recovery; and that in consequence of this information he had come to relieve him and had brought the identical Major O'Regan along with him, who for half a johannes[33] was ready to resign all pretensions to the lady. This the Captain presumed from his influence with the Irishman and from his succeeding on the former occasion.

The sick lawyer, at this, sat up and, having put on his gown and slippers, expressed great thanks to the Captain and the Major and very readily handed a half-johannes from his bureau and, calling for pen, ink, and paper, for he was not sufficiently restored to go to his office, he signified that it would be proper the Major should give

31. A mistress or sweetheart, from Don Quixote's Dulcinea del Toboso.
32. Stratonice was one of the wives of Demetrius II, who reigned in Macedonia from 239 to 229 B.C.
33. Half a joe, about $8.80.

him some instrument of writing as evidence of the contract. It was agreed on the part of the Captain and the bog-trotter, and the lawyer wrote as follows:

> Know all men by these presents, that I, Teague O'Regan, Major, am held and firmly bound into John Hardicknute in the sum of one hundred pounds, money of the United States, well and truly to be paid to him the said John, his heirs, executors, administrators, or assigns. Given under my hand and seal this second day of June, in the year of our Lord one-thousand seven-hundred and ninety-one.

> The condition of the above obligation is such that if I, the said Teague O'Regan, shall withdraw all attention, courtship, or wooing on my behalf from a certain Martha Thimbleton, lady, then the said obligation to be void, otherwise to remain in full force and virtue.

his
TEAGUE ⁺₊ O'REGAN
mark

This matter being fully settled, the Captain and the bog-trotter took their leave and departed. On their way home, a man was seen to run across the street, dressed in black but without hat, coat, or breeches on. The Captain conceived it must be some mad *sans culotte,* or unbreeched person, that had come over from Paris and was running through the streets here in order to bring about a revolution. But on inquiry, he was informed that it was the Rev. Mr. M'Whorter, a young clergyman who had been deranged in his understanding on account of a preference given by Miss Fiddle to a certain Major O'Regan who had seemed to have engaged her affections; that it was first discovered on the preceding Sunday, when in his prayer instead of saying "give us this day our daily bread," he repeated, "give us this day our daily Miss Fiddle," and instead of saying, "deliver us from evil," as he ought to have done, he said, "deliver us from Major O'Regan"; that ever since he had been getting worse and now had thrown off a part of his garments and, exposing himself in public, appeared to be mad altogether.

The Captain, thinking on the subject, was about to parody that line of the poet and to say:

> Ye Gods what havoc does O'Regan make
> Among your works.

But repressing all poetical flights, he wished to lose no time but as speedily as possible to wait upon the unfortunate ecclesiastic and, by easing his mind, remove his derangement. Accordingly, pursuing the clergyman and having had him seized and conveyed to a chamber, he endeavored to make him sensible that Major O'Regan, the cause of his misfortune, who was there present, was ready to quit claim to Miss Fiddle and give him no cause of uneasiness any farther. For this, on their way, the bog-trotter, in consideration of an interest in the clergyman's prayers, had promised to do. But poor Mr. M'Whorter was too far gone. He could talk of nothing but some incoherent jargon consisting of a mixture of scripture and profane language, one while about Miss Fiddle and Major O'Regan, another while of Daniel in the lion's den and Jonas in the whale's belly and the devil running into swine. He would imagine sometimes that the devil was in himself and would squeal like a pig.

The matter being thus hopeless, they set off to come home. On their way they fell in with a man who called himself a doctor and had a blistering plaster in his hand and a gallipot [34] and a clyster pipe tied with a string about his neck and hanging down his back and had alarmed two or three ladies just before, offering his services in the way of his profession. On inquiry it was found that it was the celebrated Doctor Cataplasm that had lost his senses within three days past on account of a Major O'Regan, [who] was likely to carry off Miss Blasm, to whom the doctor had been a suitor for several years and with whom he had been just on the point of marriage. Despairing from the late experiment of doing anything with mad people, the Captain waived any trouble with the doctor, but looking sternly at Teague, "This will never do," said he. "I cannot reconcile it to myself to be in the most distant way accessory to so much mischief; and as, from a deference to the judgment of others and to your importunity, I have suffered myself to be the means of introducing you to this sphere, I must take care to repair the injury as far as may be in my power or at least prevent any increase of it as much as possible. If there is some talismanic charm, God knows what it is, in your person or appearance that makes you thus formidable to the peace and happiness of others in giving this success among the females and if you have not generosity or moral sense of duty to use your advantage consistent with humanity, it is full time you should be checked and drawn from this sphere altogether and sent to your former bog-trotting or put into the state, if you can get there, that honest men may marry their wrenches whose affections they had previously engaged."

The bog-trotter was somewhat obstreperous or, as the vulgar say, "obstraphilous" on the occasion and seemed to signify that he would not desist but would pay attention to whom he thought proper.

34. A small ceramic medicine bottle.

The Captain saw that it was a difficult matter to lay the devil he had raised and his hopes rested in this, that he was but the bubble of a day and that, though light-headed young women in the unfortunate cases mentioned had given him a visible preference, yet it was rather to torture their former lovers with a view to try the strength of their passion than with any intention seriously to make choice of him and finally accept him for a husband. For he could not think it possible that a woman of fashion and education would ultimately be willing to give her hand to such a ragamuffin. If indeed he could come to be a judge or a governor, such a thing might take place; but as it was, it seemed to outrage all credibility.

In this he was mistaken, for but the very next day he was waited on by Mr. Mutchkin, a merchant of the city, who was in the wholesale and retail way as a grocer and who had an only daughter, Miss Mutchkin, to whom the Irishman had made his most serious proposals. It was to her, by the assistance of the waiter, that he had been writing love letters. Mr. Mutchkin, a cautious man, before he would give his consent to the match thought proper to call upon the Captain, whom he understood to be the uncle or guardian of the young gentleman, with a view of inquiring into his expectations.

"Expectations!" said the Captain. "Why just this, that if he should chance to get into office, it is well, and if not he must return to his bog-trotting." "Bog-trotting!" said the merchant. "Aye, bog-trotting," said the Captain. "What else would he do? It is but ten days or thereabouts since he quitted it; and since, by taking him to levees and beer-houses and rubbing and scrubbing him and teaching him to dance and giving him lessons of manners, he has been made fit to appear in the gay world. He has but that pair of breeches that you see to his backside and a pattern not made up yet, that merchant Williams gave him; and for my part I have done all for him that I can do. There is just the truth, Mr. Mutchkin, and if you choose to take him for a son-in-law, you are welcome; but as, thank God, I have preserved a principle of candor and honesty all my life, I will not deceive on this occasion; and if the match should prove unfortunate, you will not have me to blame."

Mr. Mutchkin expressed, by the staring of his eye, his astonishment; and as soon as he could speak, thanked the Captain for his candor and declared his resolution that if Major O'Regan, as he had the assurance to call himself, should again come to his house, he would turn him out of doors; and that if his daughter should give him the least countenance for the future, he would disown her entirely. He had taken the greatest pains with her in her education. She had been taught all the polite accomplishments that could become a lady, dancing, music, painting, reading French, the belles lettres, geography, etc., and if, after all this, she would throw herself away on a ragamuffin to the discredit of the family, he would no longer take notice of her.

"Fair and softly," said the Captain, "I have a word of advice to give on the subject. It is true I have not travelled much through the world so as to visit France, Italy, Spain, or Portugal, nevertheless I have some general knowledge of the principles of human nature, not only from books but from my own observations of the small circumstances that have fallen in my way, and reflection upon them. And [I] have found that in the intellectual province, as well as in material works, art accomplishes more than force; nay, as in mechanism, the arch is strengthened by the very weight you put upon it, so where the imagination is concerned the attachment is fixed by an opposition to it. Hence it is that the dissuasion of parents, guardians, or friends is often so ineffectual with their daughters or wards in matters of love. It will behoove you, on this occasion, in order to accomplish your object, to conceal your knowledge of the circumstances communicated, to allow the bog-trotter free ingress and egress as usual, and to affect to speak of him with respect. Leave it to me to say such things to the young lady, as under pretense of recommending her lover, will be effectual to disgust her and remove her attachment."

Mr. Mutchkin, impressed with the sincerity and good sense of the Captain, consented to be guided by him in this business and, accordingly going home, was silent to the mother and daughter with respect to the conversation he had with the old gentleman who was considered as the uncle of Teague. And the following day . . . the Captain waited upon the family and was introduced by Mr. Mutchkin, who, retiring under pretense of business, left him alone with the daughter and mother to make use of the means he had proposed. For Mr. Mutchkin well knew that O'Regan was a great favorite with the mother and that it would be as difficult to convince her as the daughter of the imposition in his character. Nay, as she had promoted the match, her pride, unless she herself was the first to detect the imposture, would hinder her from seeing it or at least acknowledging it at all.

Being seated, conversation ensued, and Mrs. Mutchkin paid the Captain many compliments on the fine figure and address of his nephew. Miss Mutchkin hung down her head and blushed, as being in the presence of the uncle of her lover and hearing the name of Major O'Regan mentioned. "Why, madam," said the Captain, "I understand that the bog-trotter has been well received in your family. It is true I am not his uncle, nor is he a major; nevertheless, many uncles have had worse nephews and there have been majors that did not perhaps ever see so much service, for I have understood from himself that he was enlisted once when he was drunk and was a while in the barracks in Dublin, but got off when the matter came to be examined and it was found that advantage had been taken of him. For the Lord Lieutenant had given strict orders that in the enlistments the utmost fairness should be used; nor indeed was it necessary in time of peace to take advantage, because there were men enough to be got voluntarily and deliberately to enter the service. Nor indeed had Teague himself any objections to be a soldier but that his constitution had not given him that courage which is necessary to enable a man to face an enemy with fire arms. He could cudgel at a fair or the like, where he was supported by others that would take the weight of the battle off his hands, but except to wrestle at carnish-hug, as he calls it, with an hostler now and then, I never knew him fond of any contention whatsoever. I understand that he has been fortunate enough to render himself agreeable to the young lady, your daughter, and I congratulate myself on the prospect of having so accomplished a young woman to be the wife of my domestic. I have had him now these three years. I bought him out of a ship of Irish servants. He has been always faithful to me in the offices in which I employed him, such as brushing boots and rubbing down my horse. It is true his manners were a little rude at first, but I have taken a good deal of pains to teach him some of the outlines of a decent behavior, such as to blow his nose with a handkerchief and keep from breaking wind in company, a practice to which he was a good deal addicted at his first setting out; and though he takes long strides, as you may see, from wearing brogues and bog-trotting, yet in the course of time this and other habits may be broke by being in good company. He has made considerable improvement in the short time I have taken pains with him. Though but ten days since he was heaved down and curried and brushed up for a gentleman, he has learned to chew food without greasing his chin and cheeks. If he should fall into the hands of a lady of taste, as he is like to do, she may improve him still more. It will be of particular advantage to him to get a woman that can write and read, as I understand Miss Mutchkin can do very well; for, as he can neither read nor write himself, it is necessary that there should be one of a family that can. He has been fortunate at the taverns where we lodged to get the waiters to write and read billets to ladies; but such cannot be always at hand for these things, but a wife may. It is true his hopes in government are uncertain as to being an ambassador or consul, but he may get to be a valet de chambre to one of these. And though the ambition of Miss Mutchkin may not be so much flattered as to be a lady of a minister, yet true happiness is to be found in contentment. And the love she has for his person may make amends for the want of rank and honor, much more for the want of fortune, for riches are but dross and the maid of a kitchen may be as happy as the mistress in the parlor. His fortune indeed is not much. He has nothing of his own but what dress he wears and a pattern of a pair of breeches not yet made up. My estate is but small, consisting in a farm and implements of husbandry with a couple of horses, one of which I have rode from home while he bog-trotted by my side. Nevertheless, if he marries Miss Mutchkin I will endeavor to do something for him and for two or three years to come will engage to find him in breeches and waistcoats."

The young lady was confounded and withdrew. The mother was silent and with all her heart wished the Captain gone that she might digest her mortification in private. The Captain saw all this; but without seeming to see it, preserved a grave countenance. And with some apology of having an engagement so that he could not have the honor of longer conversation, he took his leave.

The dialogue that took place after this between the mother and the daughter may be more easily imagined than expressed. It was concluded that when O'Regan came next to the house the porter should be ready with a cowskin to give him a suitable reception.

Mr. Mutchkin, coming in, was made acquainted with the discovery of Major O'Regan's history. Affecting to be as much astonished as themselves, he observed that it would be however proper to dismiss him with civility, as he had been received in the capacity of a suitor. Here Miss Mutchkin again blushed, not as at first, with an affected blush of modesty when Major O'Regan was at any time mentioned, but with the blush of confusion and shame. The mother discovering in her countenance all the emotions of wounded pride and ungovernable resentment, avowed her determination to have him received with a cowskin by the porter. Mr. Mutchkin, affecting to acquiesce, as these were matters in which he did not wish to concern, did but confirm the resolution.

Accordingly that evening, when the bog-trotter, being on the point of marriage as he thought, came to take tea with Miss Mutchkin, ringing the bell and being admitted, a stout fellow, an Englishman who served in the capacity of porter, being prepared with a very heavy cowskin, made an attack upon him. The Irishman exclaimed and called out for Miss Mutchkin. "O! God love your dear ladyship, Miss Mutchkin, by shaint Patrick, by de holy apostles, I shall be kilt and murdered into de bargain! O! I shall be kilt and murdered. God love your shoul stop wid your cowskin till I says my prayers and spare my life; O! I shall be kilt and murdered. O! dis night, in de house here. Miss Mutchkin, where is your dear ladyship, to look upon me wid your eyes, and save me from dis bating? O! I am kilt and murdered."

Saying these words, the porter had kicked him out of the house and, shutting the door, left him to his exclamations in the street.

Coming home to the Captain, he made a woeful complaint of the disaster that had befallen him, which the Captain took care not to alleviate but increase, alleging that it must have been some former lover of the lady who was exasperated at the preference given and took this method of revenge, that he now saw how dangerous it was to interfere with men of spirit in their courtships and he ought to be more careful for the future.

[27]

Taking advantage of the humiliated state of mind in which the bog-trotter now was, from the later cow-skinning he had received, the Captain thought he could be drawn off from an extreme attention to the ladies and engaged to apply to the qualifying himself for state affairs. Accordingly continuing his address to him, he observed that, though gallantry and waiting upon ladies was very agreeable, yet prudence ought to be observed not to create enemies by seeming to engross their attachment so as to put a man in danger of duels and cow-skinnings. At the same time it behooved a man not to suffer his gallantry to interfere with business; and more especially in the early stages, when he was about qualifying himself for any occupation or appointment, that, as he (Teague O'Regan) was a candidate for state affairs, he ought to check his career and withdraw himself for some time from the gay circles in order to acquire some small things which were necessary to the creditable and convenient discharge of a public function, such as learning to write his name if possible. As to learning to read or write generally, that would be a thing of years, if at all acquirable at his period of life. But he might be taught to imitate the few characters that composed his name in such a manner as to pass for it, so that when he had to sign dispatches or commissions or the like he need not be under the necessity of making his mark like an Indian at a treaty, but might do something that would pass for a signature in letters of the alphabet. So providing him with a room and placing a table before him with an inkstand and strewing some papers and furnishing him with spectacles, as if he [were] already making out dispatches, he began to instruct him in making the letters, T, E, A, G, U, E, etc.

But he had scarcely begun when the waiter, coming in, delivered a parcel of cards and billets for Major O'Regan. The Captain, instantly reflecting that this correspondence with the gay world would undo all that he was doing and draw off the bog-trotter from his lessons as soon as the smart of the cow-skinning had worn off, saw it necessary to read the billets as from different persons and containing language different from what was in them. The cards being chiefly from men in public employment, he read as they really were. Opening one of the largest of the billets, "Aye,' said he, "there is more of it. Do you know this Johnston that seems so much enraged about Miss Muslin to whom you have paid some attention?" By the bye, it was a billet from Miss Muslin, to whose acquaintance it would seem he had been introduced, but the Captain read Johnston. "By de holy fathers," said Teague, "I know no Johnston." "He sends you a challenge," said the Captain, "to meet him on the commons this evening at six o'clock with a brace of pistols and a second to determine whether you or he has the best right to pay attention to this lady." We shall give the billet as written by the lady and as read by the Captain.

As written by the Lady:

> Would wish to have the pleasure of Major O'Regan's company this evening at tea. Lawyer Crabtree and Doctor Drug will be here, and you know we shall split our sides laughing at the ninnies. You're so full of your jokes that I want you here. Dear Major, don't be engaged, but come.
>
> Yours sincerely,
>
> Patty Muslin

As read by the Captain:

> Sir,
>
> You will instantly do one of two things, either relinquish your attention to Miss Muslin and be no more in her company or meet me this evening precisely at six o'clock on the commons at the back of the Potter's-field

with a brace of pistols and a second, to take a shot. I shall have a coffin ready and a grave dug for whichever of us shall have occasion to make use of it.

Your humble servant,

Benjamin Johnston

In the same manner he read the other billets, converting them from love letters into challenges to fight with mortal weapons or into declarations of cudgeling and cowskinning if he interfered any farther in his attention to such and such ladies.

The bog-trotter began to think the devil was broke loose upon him and very readily gave the Captain leave to write answers, declining all combats and declaring his compliance with all that was requested of him.

The waiter was the only person who, by receiving the billets and handing them in the absence of the Captain and reading them to Teague, might inflame his mind with the thoughts of the fine ladies and gay circles from which he seemed to be just recovered. Taking him aside, therefore, and accosting him, "Mathew," said he, for that was the name of the waiter, "I do not know that I ought to find any fault with your giving your service for some time past to my Teague in reading the billets directed to him and in writing his answers, but I desire that there may be nothing more of this. As he is about to be closely engaged for some time to come in acquiring some scholarship and preparing to enter on some state appointment, I do not choose that his mind should be taken off by affairs of compliment or love. All billets therefore directed to him you will for the future hand to me." The waiter promised compliance and said it was all the same thing to him, as all he had done was to oblige the bog-trotter, and if it was disagreeable to him (the Captain) he should do no more of it.

However, Teague continuing still to have some hankering after the company of the ladies so as not to have his mind so much upon learning to write the characters of his name as the Captain could have wished, he found it necessary to engage the barkeeper to assist him in personating now and then someone who had come to demand satisfaction for the interference of the bog-trotter in affairs of love, that by keeping up the alarm on his mind he might the better confine him to his studies. According to the plan agreed upon, the barkeeper knocking at the door and the Captain opening it a little and demanding his business, "Is there not a Major O'Regan here," he would say with a counterfeited voice, "who has pretensions to Miss Nubbin?" (One of those who had sent billets.) "I wish to see the gentleman and try if I can put this sword in his body." (By the bye, he had a long sword.) "God love your shoul," would O'Regan say, "dear Captain, don't let him in. I shall die wid fear upon de spot here, for I never fought a man in cold blood in my life." Here the barkeeper, as recognizing the voice of O'Regan, "Yes," would he say, "I find he is here. Let me in, that I may put this through him. I had paid my addresses to Miss Nubbin and was just about to espouse her when, unlike a gentleman, he has interfered and turned her head with his attention. By the New Jerusalem I shall be through his windpipe in a second." Teague, hearing this and raising the Irish howl, would redouble his entreaties to the Captain not to let him in. The Captain would say, "Sir, if you mean to make a pass at him you must make it through me, for I shall not stand to see a domestic run through the body and his guts out while mine are in. You may therefore desist, or I shall have you taken into custody as a breaker of the peace." With this he would shut the door, and the bar-keeper would go off cursing and swearing that he would have revenge for the insult that had been offered him by the Irishman.

By these artifices, certainly innocent as the object was good, for it can be no injury to deceive a man to his own advantage, by these artifices the Captain succeeded in preventing a correspondence with the gay world and detaching the mind of his pupil from the gallantries of love. But when any member of Congress or office of state called upon him, he was admitted. Traddle called frequently and declared that he had no resentment on account of Teague's proposing to be his competitor at the election in the country, but wished him success in obtaining some appointment where his talents might be useful.

[*End of Volume Three (Pittsburgh, 1793). Chapters included are the original Book I, 2, 3, 5, 6, 8; Book III, 1; and Book IV, 1.*]

[28]

Notwithstanding the fairy scene of imagination with respect to the advancement of Teague in which the Captain had suffered himself to be engaged, yet sometimes he would begin to doubt with regard to the reality of the prospects and to question whether, after all, it was probable that the executive of the United States would think him adequate to the discharge of judicial or ministerial functions and appoint him accordingly. Ruminating one day on this subject, a servant presented a billet. It was from the President of the United

States, expressing a desire to see the Captain and to converse with him relative to the appointment of the young man in his service of the name of Teague O'Regan to some office in the government. Nothing could be more opportune, for the Captain at that moment, weary of his charge and despairing of success, was just about to relinquish all further prosecution of his object and to remand Teague to his boot-cleaning and horse-currying as formerly. It may easily be supposed that he lost no time in having his coat and hat brushed and setting out to wait on his excellency. Presenting himself, he was asked to sit down, and the conversation opening on the subject of Teague and his qualifications for office. The Captain, not willing to be the means of deception in the introduction of his valet, thought proper to deal candidly with his excellency and to give him an exact account of the education and history of the bog-trotter; that if, on a full view of his character, he should think proper to appoint him, the responsibility might lie with himself. "For to be candid," said the Captain, "I should doubt the expediency of appointing him, in the first instance, to any of the higher offices of government, such as Secretary of State or even that of Secretary at War; though, I presume, requiring less talents than the former, the business of a soldier lies more in the heart than the head. As to Secretary of the Treasury, I should bar that altogether, as it might be unsafe all at once to trust him with much money until he had given greater proofs of fidelity in this particular than those of his rank are usually found to possess. The diplomatic line might suit him best were it not that the sending him off the continent will put him out of the way of that superintendance which for some time I myself am willing to take of him until he shall have acquired habits of diligence and principles of integrity in business." The President smiled, doubtless at the idea of the *sans culotte* (for such I figuratively call him, because he had now got on breeches) being at all in the way of appointment to such trusts, for a thought of the kind had never come into his mind. He was thinking of an office of much less dignity and which came nearer to the capacity and grade of ordinary education. It was that of an excise officer. Having mentioned this, the Captain approved of it and thanked his excellency and took his leave.

Teague, having received his commission, was elated beyond measure and impatient to set out to his district in order to enter on the functions of his office. The Captain, having purchased him a horse, for he refused to bog-trot any longer, the revenue officer took leave of his old master, who had previously given him much good advice with regard to duty in office, and promised to follow him as soon as he could provide himself with another servant, that he might be on the spot to give him countenance and assist him occasionally with such farther lessons of prudence and morality as his experience in life might enable him to give and which it could not be unbecoming in one of his age, however dignified by office, to receive.

[29]

Teague having thus departed, it became the Captain to look out for another servant; and deliberating on this subject, Mr. M'Donald, the Scotch gentleman of whom we have before spoken, happened to enter. The Captain explained to him the circumstance and made inquiries with regard to his knowledge of anyone that chose to be employed in this way and might be fit for the service. Said Mr. M'Donald, "I ken [35] a lad right weel of the name o' Duncan Ferguson, frae about Perth in Scotland, that is trusty and vera fit to wait upon a gentleman, except it be that he may gie ye o're mucke trouble about religion, having had a vera strict education i' the presbytery; gin ye can put up wie that, I sal warrant him honest and vera faithful to his master and that he will take guid care of your horse. He is about thirty years of age and has been a guid deal in service and knows what it is to wait on guid houses in his ain kintra; I dinna ken how he may suit all places in these parts but wie a man of your judgment I think he may do vera weel."

The Captain thanked him for the information. And having conceived a good opinion of Mr. M'Donald's integrity and sense, he was willing to take the young man upon the recommendation he had given.

Accordingly, he being sent for by Mr. M'Donald, the North Briton came and presented himself to the Captain. The wages of his service being agreed upon, he entered on his functions the same day; and in a short time the Captain, having paid his bills in the city, set out with Duncan on the same route with Teague.

[30]

I think it was the fourth day after leaving the city that the Captain, casting up his eyes at a place where there was a considerable length of straight road before him, saw a person trudging on foot,

35. Know. Identifications of other Scottish terms are in the Glossary.

who by his make and gait appeared to resemble the new revenue officer, the quondam bog-trotter. "Duncan," said the Captain, "if that man was not on foot that is before us, I should take him for Teague O'Regan, the waiting man that was in my service and who gave place to you, having obtained a commission in the revenue and become an excise officer. But as I had equipped him with a horse, it is not probable that he could be without one already and have taken to his trotters, after being advanced to be a limb of the government. It would be a degradation to the dignity of office."

"I dinna think," quoth Duncan, "there is muckle dignity in the office. What is he but a gauger? That is of na more estimation in our kintra than a hangman. There is na ane that can live in an honest way without it will take the commission." "Duncan," said the Captain, "it is not so in this country where the government is a republic; and all taxes being laid by the people, the collection of every species is a sacred duty and equally honorable."

"Honor!" quoth Duncan. "Do you talk of honor in a gauger? If that be the way of thinking in this kintra, I wish I were back in Scotland. Everything seems to be orsa-versa here, the wrang side uppermost. I am but a simple waiting man to a gentleman like yoursel and I wad na take the office o' gauger upon me for a' Philadelphia, which is amaist as big as Perth."

By this time they were within a small distance of the traveller, whom the Captain, reconnoitering more perfectly, discovered absolutely to be Teague. The revenue officer, turning round, recognized the Captain and accosted him. "By my shoul and there he is, his honor himself, the Captain, and a new sharvant dat he has trotting on foot as I myself used to do." "And as you seem to do yet, Teague," said the Captain. "What is become of the horse I furnished you? Has he been stolen or has he strayed away from some pasture in the course of your progress?" "By my shoul," said the officer, "neither the one nor the oder of dese happened, but I met wid a good affer on de road and I took it. I swaped him for a watch dat I have in my pocket here. Bless de sweet little shoul of it. It tells de hour of de day and what time of de clock it is, slapeing or waking; and in de night time you have but just to look at de face of it and de sweet pretty figures dat are dare and you will know how long it is before de morning come. Not like de dumb baste that could not answer you a word in de night nor in the day but hold his tongue like a shape and say nothing, while dis little watch, as de call it, can spake like a Christian creature and keep company along de road like a living person. It was for dat reason dat I took it from a country man dat I met wid last night at the tavern, and am now going on by myself and have no horse to take care of and plague me on de road and give me falls over his tail and over his mane, up hill and down hill, so dat I almost broke my neck and thought it safest to ride upon my foot. Dat is truth, master Captain. But who is dis son of a whore dat you have wid you trotting in my place? Does he take good care of your creature at night and clane your boots? I would be after bidding him smell dis cugel here dat I walk wid if he neglect a good master as your honor is."

The blood of Duncan was up at the idea of being cudgeled by an excise officer; and stepping up to Teague, he lifted a cudgel on his part. "Ye cudgel me, sirrah!" said the Caledonian.[36] "If it was na for his honor's presence, I wad lay this rung on your hurdies or gie ye a rap upon the crown, to talk sik language to your betters. I should make ye ken what it is to raise the blood of a Scotchman. You ca' yourself a revenue officer. But what is that but a gauger? Which is the next to a hangman in our kintra. Captain, will ye stand by and see fair play till I gie him his paikes for his impertinence. My lug for it, I sall make this rung rattle about the banes o' his head to some tune."

With that Duncan was making his advance, having raised his cudgel and putting himself in the attitude of a person accustomed to the back sword; which Teague on the other hand observing, accosted him with softer words, not disposed to risk an engagement with an unknown adversary. "Love your shoul," said he, "if I was after affronting you more than his honor my master. Burn me if I don't love you just because you are my master's sharvant and takes care of his baste. I was only joking. It is just de way I would spake to my own dear cousin Dermot if he were here, for in Ireland we always spake backwards. Put up your stick, dear honey, I am sure de Captain knows that I was always good-natured and not given to quarrels, though I could fight a good stick too upon a pinch, but it never came into my head to wrangle with my master's sharvant, especially such a tight good-looking fellow as yourshelf, dat has a good shelelah in your hand and is fitter to beat than to be beaten, by shaint Patrick."

"Duncan," said the Captain, "you have heard the explanation of the hasty words the revenue officer at first used, and it would seem to me that, consistently with the reputation of courage and good breeding both, you ought to be satisfied."

"I dinna ken," quoth Duncan, "it was a very great provocation to talk o' cudgeling, and it may be the custom o' a friendly salutation in

36. A native of Scotland.

Ireland but no in our kintra. While I ha a drop o' the blood o' St.
Andrew in me, I wad na gae up to sik civilities."

Said the Captain, "As far as I can have understood, St. Patrick
and St. Andrew were cousins, and you his descendants or disciples
ought to be on terms of amity."

"St. Andrew a cousin to St. Patrick!" said Duncan. "I canna acknowledge that, Captain. St. Andrew was a guid protestant and a
Covenanter,[37] but St. Patrick was a papist o' the kirk o' Rome and did
na keep the second commandment, but worshipped graven images
and pictures o' saints and tuke the sacrament wie a wafer. I shall never
gie up that, Captain, that St. Patrick was o' kin to St. Andrew. They
might be i' the ministry at the same time, but there is a great different in their doctrine. Did ye e'er read any o' the works o' John
Knox,[38] Captain? Dinna ye ken that the church of Rome is the whore
o' Babylon? If ye had lived in the time o' the persecution ye wad na
hae compared a Scotch saint wie a Irish priest."

Said the Captain, "I have no particular acquaintance with the
distinguishing tenets of the two evangelists, nor do I know anything
of them save just to have understood that the one had planted
Christianity in Scotland and the other in Ireland. But this is not a
point so material to us individually as that we cultivate peace and
have no difference. I must therefore enjoin it on you, Duncan, that
you drop your stick and keep the peace towards the revenue officer
on the highway, that he may not be delayed in going forward to
enter on the functions of his office." Said Duncan, "Since your honor
says the word, I shall lay down my stick, for I ken the law better than
to stand out against the civil authority."

"But, Teague," said the Captain, "how can you distinguish the
figures of your watch so as to tell the hours of the day, you that do not
understand figures?"

"By my shoul," said Teague, "and I never tought of dat. Will not
de figures spake for demselves when I look at dem? I am sure I saw
the son of a whore dat I got her from look at her and tell the hour
o' de day like a pracher at his books, and I am sure and certain dat
such an ill-luking teef as he was could neither read nor write. But by

37. St. Andrew was, of course, one of Jesus' original disciples. Brackenridge is
teasing and playing upon the ignorant enmity between the Scottish and Irish on the
frontier, where the Scots celebrated St. Andrew's Day with libations equal to those
consumed by the Irish on St. Patrick's Day.

38. The Protestant speech of John Knox at St. Andrew's on June 4, 1559, so
aroused the populace that they stripped the cathedral of its ikons and destroyed
the monastic buildings. Thereafter, St. Andrew's was a church of the Covenanters.

my shoul if dat is de way, dat I have to read de marks myself, I will swap her back for a horse or a cow on de road, or for something else dat will plase your honor better; so dere is no harm done, plase your honor, while we are in a Christian country and can meet wid good paple to spake to and take a watch or a colt off our hands when we mane to part wid it, plase your honor."

Such was the conversation at the first interview of the Captain's family, to use a military style, and may be considered as a sample of that which took place in the sequel of this day's travel, as they proceeded together until noon, when they came to dine at a public house and umbrage was taken by Duncan because the Captain had permitted Teague to sit at table with himself, which he did in respect to the office which he held and in order to respect its dignity. "Captain," said Duncan, coming to the hall door and looking in, "d'ye permit an excise officer to sit at the table wie your honor? For silk profanation I never heard o' in a' my born days; if it were in Scotland it wad cause a sight to the whole neighborhood. Does your honor ken that he is an excise officer?" "Duncan," said the Captain, "it is a principle of good citizenship, especially in a republican government, to pay respect to the laws and maintain the honor of its officers. It is for this reason that I make it a point to honor one who was lately my bog-trotter, not that I discern in him any remarkable improvement in talents or manners but simply because the government has discovered something and has seen fit to give him a commission in the revenue. Who knows but it may be your own fortune, at no distant day, to obtain an office; and will you not think it reasonable then that it should be forgotten that you were once in the capacity of a waiting man and that you should receive the respect and the precedence due to your new dignity? It is not with us as in monarchies where the advance is gradual in most cases; though even there an individual, through the favor of the prince or of the queen or of a lady or gentleman of the court, may have a sudden promotion. But in a free state, what hinders that the lowest of the people should be taken up and made magistrates or put into commissions in the revenue? I must insist, Duncan, that you retire to the kitchen and take your dinner and make no disturbance in the house at this time. You will come to understand better the nature of offices in these commonwealths in due time." Duncan retired, but in soliloquy expressing his chagrin at the strange reversion of affairs in America from what they were in Scotland and his mortification at finding himself in the service of a master that could degrade himself by dining with an excise officer.

Teague, on the other hand, though he was silent in the hearing of Duncan, broke out as soon as he had shut the door. "Captain," said he, "plase your honor, where did you pick up dat teef-luking son o'd a whore dat has no more manners dan a shape stealer in Ireland or a merchant dat sells yarn at a fair. By shaint Patrick, if your honor had given me leave in de road, I would have knocked his teet down his throat and if your honor will excuse de table, I will go out and take him by de throat and make him talk to himself like a frog in de wet swamps, de son of a whore, to spake to your honor wid a brogue upon his tongue in such words as dese."

By the brogue Teague meant the Scottish dialect which Duncan used.

"Teague," said the Captain, "the prejudices of education must be tolerated until time and experience of the world have lessened or removed them. He is an honest fellow and I have more confidence in him than I ever had in you, though his talents have not appeared equal, at least if I am to judge from the estimate made of you by these who have a better right to judge than I have. However, I am unwilling to have any disturbance between you, and therefore must insist that you leave him to the reprimands which I myself have occasionally given him and shall continue to give him until he attains a better knowledge of the nature of things in this new hemisphere, so different from those to which he has been accustomed."

This put an end to any altercation between the two, the revenue officer and the waiting man, for the remaining part of that day as they trudged together until they came to the inn at night and, having supped, were about to go to bed. It was what in some places is called an ordinary, that is, an indifferent tavern of but mean accommodations. The house was small and there were but two beds for the reception of strangers; one of these so indifferent as to appear fit only for the servant of a gentleman who might happen to travel the road, though large enough to contain two or three persons. What it wanted in quality of neatness and perhaps cleanliness was made up in dimensions. This bed therefore seemed naturally to invite the reception of two of the company.

"Teague," said the Captain, when about to go to bed, "I think Duncan and you, being the younger men, may pig in together in that large bed and leave the other to me who am an older man and am apt to tumble and toss a little from weariness in my ride and may perhaps disturb you in your sleep."

"Guid deliver me," said Duncan, "frae sik a profanation o' the

name o' Ferguson, as to sleep wi' an excise officer. I am na o' a great
family, but I am come o' a guid family and it shall never be said that
I came to America to disgrace my lineage by sik contact as that. Gae
to bed wi' an excise officer! I wad sooner gae to bed out o' doors or i'
the stable amang the horses."

The revenue officer was affronted at this and gave way to his indignation. "The devil burn me," said he, "if I will be after slapeing wid
you, you son of a whore, you teef luking vagabon wid de itch upon
your back; I am sure all your country has de itch and keep scratching
and scratching as if de ware in hell and could get brimstone for
noting, you son o'd a whore."

"The youke!" said Duncan. "Do you impeach me wi' the youke?"

"You impatche yourself," said the revenue officer. "Did not I see
you scratching as you came along de road? And do you think, you teef,
dat I wish to get leprosy or de scurvy and have to sleep in a bag of
brimstone two or tree weeks before I be fit to travel wid his honor de
Captain again?"

"The deel damn me," said Duncan, "if I can beat that."

"What, swear, Duncan?" said the Captain. "Or curse rather? You
that are a Covenanter, and have religious books in your wallet, the
Confession of Faith and the Catechisms!"

"How can I help it, man," said Duncan. "The deel rive his saul,
but I maun be at him."

Duncan had by this time seized his walking staff and put himself
in an attitude to attack his adversary, who on the other hand had
instinctively ensconced himself behind the Captain and opposed him
as a rampart to the fury of the Scot.

"Duncan," said the Captain, "you are in the wrong on this occasion.
You gave the affront and ought to excuse the revenue officer for what
he has said, which, by the bye, was not justifiable on any other ground
but that of provocation. For national reflections are at all times repre-
hensible. But in order to compose this matter and that we have no
further disturbance, I will take the large, though more humble bed
myself, and sleep with the excise officer, for the reputation of the
government who has thought proper to appoint him to this trust."

"The deel take me if ye shall do that, Captain," said Duncan. "I
wad rather take the stain upon mysel than let my liege be disgraced,
for it wad come a' to the same thing in the end, that I had been the
waiting man o' ane that had been the bed fellow o' a gauger. O!
guid keep us, how that would sound in Scotland. What wad my relation Willy Ferguson, that is professor i' the high college o' E'nburgh,

say to that? But rather than your honor shou'd take the stain upon you, I sal put up wie it for a night, though if the landlady has a pickle strae and a blanket, I wad rather lie by the fireside than contaminate mysel bedding wi' sik a bog-trotting loon as he is, that wad gae into sik an office for the sake o' filthy lucre and to make a living when there are many honest means to get a support other ways."

The landlady gave it to be understood that she could furnish him with a bag of straw and a blanket.

This adjusted the difficulty and saved the delicacy of the Scotchman and embarrassment of the Captain in keeping peace between the bog-trotters, as in reality they both were though the one had obtained a commission and the other remained a private person.

[31]

On the third day, renewing their journey, the conversation between the Captain and his servant turned on the character and history of the present revenue officer, the late Teague O'Regan. The Captain gave Duncan a relation of what had happened in the case of the attempt to draw him off to the Philosophical Society, to induce him to preach, and even to take a seat in the legislature of the United States; that had it not been for a certain Traddle, a weaver whom they had been fortunate enough to substitute for him, the people would most undoubtedly have elected Teague and sent him to Congress.

"Guid deliver us!" said Duncan, "do they make parliament men o' weavers i' this kintra? In Scotland it maun be a duke or a laird that can hae a seat there."

"This is a republic, Duncan," said the Captain, "and the rights of man are understood and exercised by the people."

"And if he could be i' the Congress, why did ye let him be a gauger?" said Duncan.

"This is all the prejudice of education, Duncan," said the Captain. "An appointment in the revenue, under the executive of the United States, ought not to have disgrace attached to it in the popular opinion, for it is a necessary, and ought to be held a sacred, duty."

"I dinna ken how it is," said Duncan, "but I see they hae everything tail foremost in this kintra to what they hae in Scotland, a gauger a gentleman and weavers in the legislature."

Just at this instant was heard by the way side the jingling of a loom in a small cabin with a window towards the road. It struck Duncan to expostulate with this weaver and to know why it was that he also did not attain a seat in some public body. Advancing to the orifice, as it might be called, he applied his mouth and bespoke him, as he sat upon his loom, thus: "Traddle," said he, giving him the same name that the Captain had given the other, "why is it that ye sit here, treading these twa stecks and playing wi' your elbows as ye throw the thread, when thre is one o' your occupation not far off that is now a member of the house o' lords or commons in America and is gane to the Congress o' the United States? Canna ye get yoursel elected? Or is it because ye dinna offer that ye are left behind in this manner? Ye shud be striving, man, while guid posts are gaeing and no be sitting there wi' your backside on a beam. Dinna your neibors gie ye a vote? Ye shud get a chapin o' whiskey, man, and drink 'till them and gar them vote, or ye should gae out and talk politics and mak speeches."

Such was the address of Duncan, meaning nothing more than to amuse himself with the idea of a manufacturer obtaining a seat in the legislature and making laws instead of warping webs. But in the meantime the wife of the mechanic, who had overheard the conversation and was incensed at an attempt to take her husband from his business, seizing a pot-stick and running out and turning the corner of the house, laid a blow upon the posteriors of the orator, accompanying her force with reproachful words to this effect:

"Will you never let the man alone," said she, "to mind his business, but be putting these notions in his head? He has been once constable and twice member of assembly, and what has he got by it but to leave his customers at home, complaining of their work not done? It is but little good that has been got of him these three years, but going to elections and meetings and talking politics; and after all, what does he know of these matters? Just about as much as my brown cow. A set of lounging louts, coming here and taking up his time with idle nonsense of what laws should be made and urging him to be elected, and William Rabb's wife waiting for her coverlet this three months and Andrew Nangle for his shirt cloth. It is enough to put a woman in a passion, that has the temper of a saint, to have her man's head turned so from his own affairs by idle vagabonds that come the way in this manner."

At this she made another effort and, springing forward, was about to impress a second blow when Duncan, retreating and lifting up his stick in his turn, accosted her in these words: "Gin you were a man as ye are a muckle witch, I should be for taking ye wi' this rung across your hurdies. Is it any affront to have it evened to your man Traddle to gae to the senate and to get a post i' the government and no be knotting threads here wi' his shuttle like a tradesman o' Paisly? Ye vile carlin, ye maun be a witch or a warse body to take a stick in your hand, like a driver o' stots, and come pelmell upon a man ahint his back when he is na speaking till ye. Foul fa' me, but if it were na a shame to battle wi' ane o' your sex, I wad break your back with a lunder, before ye knew what ye were about. To keep this honest man here, shut up like a prisoner underground in a dungeon, drawing a reed till him, instead o' throwing out his arms like a Latin scholar or a collegian making his oration to his hearers. Are ye chained there (turning his speech to Traddle) that ye stay sae contentedly yoursel, a man, and dinna break out and escape frae the fangs o' this witch?"

"This witch!" said she, apprehending danger from a second address to the weaver, "this witch! I shall witch you to some purpose, you vagabond." With this she made a hasty step and was nearly on the back of the Caledonian with her pot-stick, having made a stroke at him which he evaded by taking to his heels and retreating speedily. The Captain in the meantime had rode on and left them to complete their dialogue.

[32]

Duncan had affected the wag on the late occasion with the manufacturer and his wife and had like to have suffered some alloy of pain from the blows which were inflicted or were meditated. But at the public house, in a village a little way ahead this day where they halted about noon, a circumstance happened which changed his view a little and disposed him to sadness rather than to play the wag with his neighbors on the road. While the Captain had reclined and was asleep on a sofa, a constable had apprehended Duncan with a warrant, commanding this officer to take the prisoner before a justice of the peace by whom it had been issued. Duncan had taken for granted that it was the weaver's wife who had made complaint and sent after him on account of the threats he had made to chastise her. The bustle in apprehending him had made a noise in the porch and awakened the Captain. "Duncan," said he, "what is the matter?" Lord deliver me," said he, "if I ken. They say I am a prisoner. The bailiff here has ta'en me wi' a warrant. It maun be that witch the weaver's wife that has made a complaint, just because I was jesting a wee about her husband gaeing to the legislature; and she did na take it weel, but amaist brake my back wi' her spurtle; and now she has ga'en awa and sworn belike that I strak her, for this is the way o' these witches, that they turn state's evidence and swear for themselves against honest people."

"Duncan," said the Captain, "this is what comes of your meddling with politics. You must undertake to say forsooth who is qualified to be a representative of the United States; you must insist upon an industrious mechanic to relinquish his occupation; and this not from any opinion of his fitness for such appointment or any principle of love for the public good, but merely for your pastime and in ridicule of a republican government in this country. For though there have been instances of choosing weavers for the legislature and cobblers and coopers, why make a burlesque of this? Have not the people a right to make such a choice? Yet because these things are not common in Scotland, it must be the subject of a laugh here. Had you been serious, there could have been no fault found; but the insult lies in your making a jest of it, which was evident from your manner in turning aside from the highway to address a weaver through the window of a cellar and, in an abrupt manner, to introduce an expostulation with him on the subject of election. No wonder that the termagant, his wife, who did not relish the proposition, even in a serious point of view, was offended and disposed to inflict blows and, on the resistance made on your part and threats probably thrown out, has applied to a justice of the peace and obtained a warrant to commit you to the custody of the law."

"What can they make o' it?" said Duncan.

"I do not know," said the Captain, "what offense it may be in law, but certainly it was a great indecorum to amuse yourself not at the expense of a mechanic but indirectly at the whole body politic of the union; not that I think it unbecoming to send such as Traddle to deliberative assemblies, but that you seemed to think it so because it is a thing not known in North Britain, where aristocratic principles prevail. You might have meant this as pleasantry, but it may be construed a reflection upon a republican government as to destroy the rights of man in the first germ and principles of their existence."

"They canna make high treason o't," said Duncan.

"I do not know," said the Captain, "what a strict judge might make it. I should think it could not be made a hanging matter. However, let us see the warrant and inquire what the justice of the peace has made of it."

"I shall not show the warrant to any man," said the constable, "but to his worship, Justice Underchin, to whom I must carry the prisoner immediately. So come along, come along, the justice will show you the warrant."

There being no help for it, Duncan was obliged to go along, the Captain accompanying him. Being brought before the justice, "Ah, have ye nabbed him?" said his worship. "I am glad ye have got him, a great rascal."

"There is no question," said the Captain, stepping forward and addressing the justice, "but the young man has acted with considerable imprudence, but ignorance of the world and especially of the laws and customs of America has been the principal cause of his intrusion. Though he has not been long in my service, yet I am disposed to speak with some confidence of his civility in general. But may it please your worship, in what shape have you brought the charge? Is it an assault and battery, or what?"

"I make it bastardy," said the justice. "What else would I make it?"

"Bastardy!" said the Captain. "It might be fornication or adultery, but how can it be bastardy in so short a time? It cannot be a rape that your worship means. There was no rape or fornication or adultery in the case. I will engage that.[39] And how can there be bastardy? Some very hot words passed between him and the woman and strokes might have been given, but there was certainly no disposition, as far as I could see, to beget bastards, nor was there time for it. They were not in such a very loving humor when I left them, nor did he stay behind me above twenty minutes on the road."

The justice was a little swarthy man, of a corpulent habit, seated in an elbow chair, with pen, ink, and paper on a stand by him. He threw himself back as he spoke, leaned his head alternately on the right and left shoulder and bridled his lips, as the phrase is, discovering [40] in the affectation of his manner great pride of office and apparent satisfaction in having caught a criminal. Endeavoring to be witty at the embarrassment of the present culprit and the expressions of the Captain, "Why, Mr." said he, addressing himself to this last, "though I do not know who you are that are so willing to assist in the examination of this vagrant, yet I will observe to you that I make no doubt that some hot or at least warm words have passed between them; and stroke, as you call it, might have been given, but as to the time of twenty minutes, or a larger period, it is of no consideration in the law, provided the woman swears, as this one has done, that she

39. Testify to that.
40. Showing.

is with child by him. Nor will his ignorance of the customs of America excuse him. We must commit him or bind him over, if he can find security, to appear at the sessions to take his trial for the fornication."

"Wi' bairn!" said Duncan. "She might just as well have ta'en an oath that I was wi' bairn to her. Was na her man, Traddle, sitting on his loom looking at us a' the time? O the false jade! I get her wi' bairn! I wad get a witch wi' bairn as soon."

"It is extraordinary," said the Captain, "that she could be certain of her pregnancy in so short a time!"

"So short a time!" said the justice. "Do you call six months a short time?"

"It is not six hours," said the Captain, "nor the half of it, since the fracas happened."

"Guid guide us!" said Duncan, who was standing on the background, making his soliloquy. "Guid guide us that I should come to America to be tri'd for getting a woman wi' bairn. What will Mr. Dougal, our minister, think o' this? After ha'ing the Confession o' Faith wi' me and sae mony guid bukes. Standing on the stool is bad enough, but nathing to the way they hae i' this kintra o' taking a man wi' a bum and bringing him before a magistrate, just the same thing as he ware a sheep-stealer. O' the base jade, to swear a bairn upon me; what will my ain folks say when they hear o' it in Scotland? It will be a stain upon a' my kin to the third generation. It was the deel himself put it in my head to stand talking wi' a fool weaver about his election. I wish I ware in Perth again and out o' a' this trouble."

"Six hours!" said the justice, answering to the Captain. "Is it not six months, Sampson," referring to the constable, "since this peddler left this settlement?" "Peddler!" said the Captain. "He never was a peddler, nor is it six months since he left Scotland. He was recommended to me by a gentleman whom I knew very well, Mr. M'Donald, as a lad just come over. So that it is impossible he could have been here six months ago."

"I am no sax months frae Perth," said Duncan.

"Is not your name Ryburn," said the justice, "and are you not that Scotch peddler that was in this settlement two or three months? Can there be any mistake?" referring to the constable. "Is not this Niel Ryburn for whom the warrant calls?" "It is the very man," said the constable. "I knew him by his dialect the moment I saw him in the porch at the public house, talking with the hostler. He has the same brogue upon his tongue and says 'Guid guide us' just in the same manner. Only at that time he used to say also, 'By my fa'th,' and

'By my sa'l' more than he does at present. He has become religious since, or pretends to be so, in order to deceive your worship. But at that time he had not much religion about him and had no 'guid bukes' as he calls them in his pocket but could damn his sa'l and swear like a devil."

"Niel Ryburn!" said the Captain, "That is not the name of my valet. It is that of Duncan Ferguson. But pray who is the woman that he is said to have got with child? The weaver's wife is the only one that he has had a conversation with to my knowledge; and as I said before, they were not much in the way of making love when I left them."

"A weaver's wife!" said the justice. "No, Mr. M'Radin, or whatever else they may call you, it is no weaver's wife. It is Kate Maybone that has made oath against him. He had carnal knowledge of her about six months ago, when he was in this settlement peddling and got her with child."

"I perceive," said the Captain, "we are all at cross purposes and under a mistake in this business. This North Briton——"

"Stop," said the justice. "If you are to give your testimony, Mr. with the cocked hat," speaking to the Captain, "we shall take it by yourself and not let the peddler hear it to enable him to frame his story to the same purpose."

Accordingly, Duncan being withdrawn in the custody of the constable, the Captain was examined and related the particulars on oath of all that he knew respecting the prisoner; and now being ordered to withdraw, the prisoner was called in and interrogated.

His story was to the same effect with that of the Captain and would seem to distinguish him from his countryman named in the warrant, but his Scottish dialect founded the presumption of identity so strongly that it was difficult, if not impossible, to get over it.

"I see," said the justice, "that they have framed their stories by collusion. They are a couple of ingenious rascals, though the one of them, the peddler, affects great simplicity, and the other vouches for him that he is ignorant. I believe I must commit them both, the one for bastardy and the other for horse-stealing. For the circumstance of having but one horse between them is extremely suspicious and renders it probable that they must have stolen that one. The story which they tell, of having come in company with a revenue officer whom they have sent ahead on foot, is absurd, especially when you add what the one who is called Captain tells of this officer having been once his servant, or passed for such, under the name of Teague O'Regan and bog-trotting, as he calls it, in the manner that this Duncan, which he pretends is the name, does now; and yet even then being likely to be taken from him to preach, to go to Congress, and the Lord knows what. It is impossible; it must be a falsehood; and the probability is, that this fellow, this Captain, is the head of a gang of horse thieves, and this Scotch peddler and the Irish revenue officer are under-strappers with him in the trade."

This being signified to the Captain who was now called in, he addressed the justice to the following effect: "Mr. Justice," said he, "what I have related to you upon oath, however improbable it may appear, is the fact; and as to your surmises of horse stealing, they are groundless; and you may commit, if you think proper, but you shall answer for the consequences. It is no small matter to deprive a citizen of his liberty, and I am not so much unknown to the government as not to obtain redress against an ignoramus like you who disgrace the commission by your stupidity, as many of the same office do. The utmost of your power is to commit, but it may come in my turn to impeach for your abuse of power. What proof or presumption have you that I have stolen horses? Is it that of having a servant on foot rather than having one mounted? If I had stolen one horse, could I not as well have stolen two? The presumption is the reverse of what your worship states. As to the North Briton who is charged with bastardy, by the name of Niel Ryburn, with a certain Kate Maybone, where is the woman? Cannot she be brought face to face with the man and confronted? Let her then say if this is Niel Ryburn, and that this simple lad is the person who begot a child with her six or eight months ago. I am persuaded he was on the east of the Atlantic at that time, and if she could become pregnant by him, she must have been on that side also. Let this matter be examined."

From the sedate and firm manner with which the Captain had expressed himself, the justice began to be apprehensive of having been mistaken and was intimidated. He was willing therefore to send for the woman who had made the oath. Being in the village, she was in a short time brought before his worship by the constable who had been dispatched for that purpose. "Kate," said the magistrate, "is not this the Scotch peddler, the father of your child and against whom you have made oath?"

"The father of my child!" said Kate. "Does your worship think I would let such a servant-looking son of a bitch as that get me with child? Does your worship mean to affront me by having him taken up in the place of the moving merchant, Mr. Ryburn? No, no, he is not the father of my child. I never saw the clumsy-looking dunce in my life before."

Duncan was well pleased to be relieved from the charge of bastardy but at the same time a little hurt at the undervaluing of the witness. "Young lady," said he, "I wish you muckle joy o' your big belly but I dinna envy the peddler o' his guid luck o' ha'eing you wi' bairn. If I was to stand i' the stool, it should be for anither sort of luking lassie and no sik a brazen fac'd ane as ye are."

Kate was about to make reply; but the justice, not thinking it comported with the dignity of office to suffer an altercation in his presence and being chagrined at not finding this to be the real culprit, released the arrest with ill humor, desiring Captain, prisoner, Kate, and constable to be gone about their business.

[33]

The second day after this, in the afternoon of the day, as the Captain and his man Duncan were advancing on their journey, they perceived a person ahead coming towards them with a long slouching walk, as if in considerable haste, and a stick in his hand. "If that man had not his face the wrong way," said the Captain, "I should take him for the revenue officer, Teague O'Regan. He has a good deal of his appearance, both in his person and his gait. But he cannot have mistaken his direction so much as to be coming this way instead of going to his district."

"I dinna ken," said Duncan. "These Irish ay put the wrang end o' their speech foremost and why not put the wrang end o' their course now and then?"

As they were debating, the person approached, and it was discovered to be Teague.

He had advanced to a pass of the mountain, where he was met and opposed by two men of an athletic personal appearance who forbade him, at his peril, to proceed farther. They were armed with clubs and presented a very choleric countenance. The revenue officer had thought it not advisable to encounter them, being two to one, and proposed rather to fall back and join himself to the Captain and the Scotchman, who might support him in his march.

These two men were of the name of Valentine and Orson, so called either from the fierceness of their nature or from their superior strength, resembling the two champions of that name of whom we read in books of romance.[41] They had been born and bred in these mountains.

Valentine had the advantage of some education with a Welsh school-master who passed his native language upon the young man for Latin; so that conceiving himself to have acquired the rudiments of this tongue and therefore qualified to enter on the study of some one of the learned professions, he had deliberated whether he should plead law, preach, or be a physician; but, happening one day to see a member of Congress riding along with a boy behind him carrying a portmanteau, he had taken it into his head to be a member himself and had canvassed frequently for that delegation, but had been disappointed, one person had another coming forward and taking off the votes. He had made up his mind for some time past to make an experiment of personal force to intimidate competitors. For this purpose he had taken to his assistance another young man of the name of Orson, whom he found in the neighborhood and with whom sallying out as a kind of squire or armor bearer, he could knock down any fellow that had the impudence to set up against him in the district. Orson had not actually been suckled by a bear, like his namesake in romance, but he was a rough, stout man and well qualified to bear a part in this mode of canvassing.

The rumor had prevailed by some means that Teague was coming forward to stand a trial in that district, whether propagated by some wag who passed him on the road and was disposed to amuse himself with the apprehensions of the two rustics or . . . [through] some mistake on the part of travellers who had come through the village in the neighborhood.

The Captain, however, and the revenue officer himself had resolved their menace into a dislike of the excise law and a wish to intimidate, or prevent by force, the opening an inspection office in that district.

Under these impressions, advancing to the pass, they were met by the young men, who made a show of battle, though on their part not a little disconcerted at seeing Teague return with a reinforcement and with the advantage of cavalry.

41. *Valentine and Orson* is a romance of the Charlemagne cycle written during the reign of Charles VIII and first printed in 1495 at Lyons. Valentine and Orson were twins born in a forest. Orson was carried off and reared by a bear. He became rough and uncouth. Valentine was taken by his uncle, King Pepin, and became a knight. Many years later the twins recognized each other in the forest.

The Captain placed himself in the center, on horseback and a little in advance of the two wings on foot, Duncan and Teague. The North Briton preserved a composed manner and showed a steady countenance. The Hibernian, on the other hand, willing by an appearance of great rage and much valor to supersede the necessity of battle or blood-shed, stood with his right foot before the left, flourishing his cudgel and grinning like an angry person who was impatient for the onset.

As in the manner of heroic men, the Captain thought proper, before the commencement of hostilities, to accost the adverse combatants to see whether it might not be in his power to remove or at least allay their prejudices against the obnoxious law and induce them to suffer the officer to pass. Accordingly, he addressed them in the following words:

"Gentlemen," said he, "the law may be exceptionable on general principles or locally unequal in its operation to you in this district. Nevertheless, it is the law and has received the sanction of the public voice, made known through the constitutional organ, the representatives of the people. It is the great principle of a republican government that the will of the majority shall govern. The general will has made this a law, and it behoves individual minds to submit."

"I wad na sleech and prig wi' them," said Duncan, stepping forward and flourishing his cudgel. "I wad na hae many words about it. But just see at once whether they will dare to stap the high road. Gin they persist, I can tak ane o' them, and ye and Teague can tak the ither; and my lug for it, I sal gie the ane that fa's to my lot a weel payed skin, I warrant him. Sae dinna ye tak up time fairlying about the matter, but gae on and try our rungs o'er the hurdies o' them. I sal gar this stick crack o'er the riggin o' the loons in a wie while."

Teague in the meantime was in the background, endeavoring to look sour, making wry mouths, and grinning occasionally, all this with a view to support the threats of the North Briton.

"Duncan," said the Captain, for he had not attended to Teague, "put up your cudgel. Policy oftentimes avails more than force. The law in question may be odious, and great allowance ought to be made for the prejudices of the people. By soft measures and mild words, prejudices may be overcome. These appear to be but young men, and rashness is a concomitant of early life. By expostulation we may probably have the good fortune to be able to pass on without being under the necessity to attempt battery or shed blood."

The two young men were not to be intimidated by a show of

cudgels or grinning and wry mouths. But still conceiving that the object of the Captain was to force an election in favor of his precursor, the Hibernian, and not understanding the scope of his harangue but supposing him to speak of the law of election where the votes of the majority, that is, the greater number of votes constitutes the representative, they were as much disposed to use force as at first, and, advancing, appeared ready to sustain the shock.

An affray must have ensued, for the Captain having taken every possible measure to avoid blows was now resolute to force the pass even at the risk of battle. But just at this instant a grave man, coming from the village, who had known the character and had been frequently a witness of the conduct of the young men, addressed them: "Young men," said he, "will you be eternally running into errors of this kind? Have you interrogated these gentlemen and understood from themselves whether any of them are candidates and mean to disturb you by setting up for Congress in this district? It is possibly the humor of some wag, coming up the road and knowing your disposition, that has created the surmise."

The fact was that some wag who had passed Teague on the road and who had known the apprehensions of Valentine had given rise to the report. For he thought to amuse himself by it, knowing the extravagancies into which it would of course throw the two young men. For the whole country, not long before that time, had heard in what manner they had mistaken individuals for public candidates. On one occasion they had fought with a mason and his barrow-man and abused them considerably. On another occasion they had knocked down a potter with a bag of earthenware and broke several of his vessels. For this reason, the grave man of whom I spoke, who had got a hint by some means of what they were about, had traced the young men and, coming up at the critical moment, addressed them as I have before said, exhorting them to make inquiry first whether their apprehensions were well or ill founded and not to take it for granted that either of these personages were competitors for Congress before the fact had been ascertained and their pretensions considered by an amicable expostulation.

"Candidates for Congress!" said the Captain. "What could have put that into the young men's heads? It is true, this bog-trotter, who is now an excise officer, was on the point once of being a candidate or at least of being elected a representative of the union; but having escaped that, though with some difficulty, he is now in the executive department and has received an appointment to the collection of the revenue of a district beyond this, to which he is now on his way and is far from having any thoughts of an election of any kind whatever."

The two young men, at this, were relieved from their fears, and their minds seemed dilated with unusual joy. Stepping forward, they shook hands with Teague and invited him to drink with them; but the Captain apologized, alleging the necessity on the part of O'Regan to press forward as speedily as possible and to be on the spot where the functions of his duty called him. This apology seeming to suffice, they all three made obeisance to the young men and to the grave-looking man, and passed on.

[34]

The Captain and the two on foot journeyed from hence together without any material incident falling out or anything to attract the attention, save what arose from the sparring of the bog-trotters. This took place on the ground of irreligion in Teague and disregard for the covenants, but more especially on a difference of opinion with regard to the desert of their respective services in the late rencounter with the highway-men, as they were disposed to call them, Teague alleging that he had intimidated them by grinning and wry mouths, Duncan claiming the credit by the display of his cudgel. The Captain had a good deal of trouble in parrying a decision of their respective pretensions or adjusting them in such a manner as to satisfy both. They were likely sometimes to come to blows. He was relieved, however, by the approach of the revenue officer to his district, into which they now began to enter.

After some days' peregrination through it, having made choice of a central situation, it was thought proper to open an inspection office, which was done by hiring a house and writing over the door, "Inspection Office of Survey, No. etc."

Suspicion had existed on the part of the government that opposition would be made in this district to the opening an office or at least to the collection of the revenue. These were founded not only in reports of threats of that nature but, in some instances, of actual violence clandestinely committed on deputies. It was for this reason, among others, that the President had made choice of O'Regan, a stout and resolute man, as he thought him, with a shelelah in his hand, who could repel occasional insults. So far these suspicions appeared to be without foundation; the officer having conspicuously traversed the district and opened an office without molestation.

The Captain was now about to return home, having seen the establishment of his ward in an office under government. But before he parted with him, he thought it not amiss to give him lessons with regard to the discharge of his duty in his present appointment. With this view, drawing him into a walk the second day, a small distance from the village, he began his lecture in the following words:

"Teague," said he, "for I am still in the habit of giving you that appellation, not having yet ascertained whether you are to be styled your worship, your honor, or your reverence, or at least not having yet been accustomed to add these epithets, Teague, I say, you are now advanced to great dignity, a limb of the executive of the union. It is true, your department is ministerial. Nevertheless it requires the wisdom of the head to conduct it. But the integrity of the heart is the great object to be regarded. Keep your hand from bribes and, by a delicate impartiality towards all, even from the suspicion of taking them. I should regret indeed, after all the pains I have taken in fitting you for an office and contributing to your appointment, to hear of an impeachment against you for a misdemeanor in that office. By conducting yourself with a scrupulous honor and pure morality in your present trust, the way is open to a higher grade of advancement; and there is no kind of doubt but that in due time it will be attainable. The President of the United States, from whom you have received your commission, is said to have the virtue, or rather the excess of one, never to abandon the person whom he has once taken up or at least to carry his attachment to an extreme of reluctance in that particular, whether owing to great slowness in conceiving unfavorably of anyone or to pride of mind in an unwillingness to have it thought that his judgment could be fallible. You will have an advantage here, but at the same time there is an ultimate point in this, as in all things, beyond which it is impossible to preserve a man. Bear this in mind and be honest, attentive, and faithful in your duty. And let it be said of you that you have shown yourself a good citizen."

Just at this instant a noise was heard, and, looking up, a crowd of people were discovered at a considerable distance advancing towards them but with acclamations that began to be heard. They were dragging a piece of timber of considerable length, which appeared to be just hewn from the woods and was the natural stem of a small tree cut down from the stump and the bark stripped off. At the same time a couple of pack-horses were driven along, which appeared to be loaded with beds and pillow cases.

The Captain was led to believe that these were a number of the country people who, having heard of the revenue officer coming to his district, had come forward to pay their respects to him and to receive him with that gratulation which is common to honest but illiterate people in the first paroxysms of their transport. Having understood that country to be chiefly peopled with the descendants of the Irish or with emigrants themselves, he had supposed that, hearing the new officer was a countryman, they had been carried forward with such zeal to receive him, with huzzaing and tumult. On this occasion he thought it not amiss to turn the conversation and to prepare the mind and the manners of the deputy for this scene, which, being unusual, might disconcern and embarrass him.

"Teague," said he, "it is not less difficult to preserve equanimity in a prosperous situation than to sustain with fortitude a depression of fortune. These people, I perceive, in a flow of mind are coming forward to express with warmth the honest but irregular sallies of their joy on your arrival among them. It was usual in the provinces under the Roman republic when a questor,[42] of whom a favorable impression had preceded, was about to come among them. It is a pleasing but a transient felicity, and a wise man will not count too much upon it. For popular favor is unstable to a proverb. These very people in the course of a twelve-month, if you displease them, may shout as loud at your degradation and removal from dignity. At the same time this ought not to lead you to be indifferent, or at least to seem so, to their well-meant expressions of favor at present, much less to affect a contempt or even a neglect of them. A medium of ease and gracefulness [is necessary] in receiving their advance and answering their address, whether it be a rustic orator in an extempore harangue or some scholar of the academy or school-master they may have prevailed upon to draw up a speech and read it to you. There is no manner of doubt but the President of the United States may have been a thousand times embarrassed with the multitude of addresses delivered or presented to him, and it required no small patience and fortitude to sustain them. Yet it has been remarked that he has received them all with complacency, showing himself neither elevated with the praise nor irritated by the intrusion. And it is but reasonable and what a benevolent man would indulge, for it is a happiness to these creatures to give themselves the opportunity of being distinguished in this manner."

42. Under kings of the early Roman Republic, questors were judges at certain criminal trials. Later they had a degree of military power, acting as chief assistants to military commanders and governors.

Duncan, who had heard a rumor in the village of what was going forward, had in the meantime come up and, understanding from the last words of the Captain what had been the drift of his conversation with Teague and discovering his mistake, interrupted him at this place. "Captain," said he, "ye need na be cowshuning him against applause and popularity and the turning o' the head wi' praise and guid usage, for I doubt muckle if it comes to that wi' him yet. I wad rather suspect that these folks have na guid will towards him. I dinna ken what they mean to do wi' him, but if a body might guess frae the bed ye see there on the pony's back, they mean to toss him in a blanket. But if it were to be judged frae the tree they hae trailing after them, I wad suppose they mean to make a hanging matter o' it and take his life a' the gether. There is na doubt but they are coming in a mob to make a seizure o' the gauger, and the talk o' the town is o' a punishment I dinna understand, o' tarring and feathering. I have heard o' the stocks and the gallows and drowning like a witch, but I never heard o' the like o' that in Scotland. I have heard o' tarring the sheep to keep them frae the rot, but I never heard o' tarring a human creature. Maybe they mean to put it on his nose, to hinder him frae smelling their whiskey. I see they got a keg o't there in their rear, drawn upon a sled; at least, I suppose it to be whiskey they hae in that keg, to take a dram as they gae on wi' the frolic, unless it be the tar that they talk of to put upon the officer."

This last conjecture was the true one. For it was tar; and the stem of a tree which they drew was what is called a liberty pole, which they were about to erect in order to dance round it with hallooing and the whoop of exultation.

The cavalcade now approaching, they began to cast their eyes towards the group of the three as they stood together.

"By de holy faders," said Teague, "I see de have deir looks upon me. De look as wild as de White Boys, or de Hearts of Oak in Ireland.[43] By de holy apostles, dere is no fighting wid pitch forks; we shall be kilt, and murdered into de bargain."

"Teague," said the Captain, "recollect that you are an officer of government, and it becomes you to support its dignity, not betraying unmanly fear but sustaining the violence even of a mob itself with fortitude."

"Fait, and I had rader be no officer at all," said Teague, "if dis is

43. Militant Irish agrarian groups who destroyed property on nightly raids in protest against conditions imposed by their landlords.

de way de paple get out o' dair senses in dis country. Take de office yourshelf; de devil burn me but I shall be after laying it down as fast as I ever took it up, if dis is to come of it; to be hooted at like a wild baste and shot and hanged upon a tree like a squirrel or a Paddy from Cork when de foolish boys hang him upon the 17th of March [44] wid potatoes about his neck to make fun o' de Irish. I scorn to be choaked before I am dead; de devil burn de office for me, I'll have none of it. I can take my Bible oath, and swear upon de holy cross dat I am no officer. By shaint Patrick, and if dere are any Irish boys amongst dem I would rather join wid dem. What is de government with offices to a son o'd a whore dat is choaked and cannot spake to his acquaintance in dis world. By de holy apostles, I am no officer; I just took it for a frolic as I was coming up de road, and you may be officer yourself and good luck wid de commission, Captain; I shall have noting to do wid it."

At this instant the advancing crowd raised a loud shout, crying, "Liberty and no excise, liberty and no excise; down with all excise officers!"

Teague began to tremble and to skulk behind the Captain. "By de holy vater o' de confession," said he, "dey are like de savages. Dey have deir eyes upon me. I shall be scalped; I shall be kilt and have de hair off my head, like a wolf or a shape. God love you, Captain, spake a good word to dem, and tell dem a good story, or by de Christian church I shall be eat up like a toad or a wild baste in de forests."

The bog-trotter was right, for this moment they had got their eyes upon the group and began to distinguish him as the officer of the revenue. An exact description had been given them of his person and appearance, for these people had their correspondents even at the seat of government; and travellers, moreover, had recognized him and given an account of his physiognomy and apparel.

"There he is, there he is," was the language, "the rascally excise officer. We shall soon take care of him. He is of the name of O'Regan, is he? We shall O'Regan him in a short time."

"The devil burn me if I am de excise officer," said Teague. "It is all a mistake, gentlemen. It is true I was offered the commission, but the Captain here knows dat I would not take it. It is dis Scotchman that is the officer. By my shoul, you may tar and feather him, and welcome."

"No," said the Captain, stepping forward, "no, gentlemen, for so

44. St. Patrick's Day.

I yet call you, though the menaces which you express and the appearance of force which your preparations exhibit, depart from the desert of that appellation. Nevertheless, as there is still a probability of arresting violence and reclaiming you from the error of your meditated acts, I address you with the epithet of gentlemen. You are not mistaken in your designation of the officer of the revenue, though he has not the candor to avow himself but would meanly subject a fellow bog-trotter to the odium and the risk, an act of which, after all the pains that have been taken of his education to impress him with sentiments of truth and honor, I am greatly ashamed. No, gentlemen, I am unwilling to deceive you, or that the meditated injury should fall on him who, if he has not the honor of the office, ought not to bear the occasional disadvantage. I am ready to acknowledge and avow, nor shall these wry faces and contortions of body which you observe in the red-headed man, prevent me, that he is the bona fide, actual excise officer. Nevertheless, gentlemen, let me expostulate with you on his behalf. Let me endeavor to save him from your odium, not by falsehood but by reason. Is it not a principle of that republican government which you have established that the will of the majority shall govern, and has not the will of the majority of the United States enacted this law? Will——"

By this time they had sunk the butt end of the sapling in the hole dug for it, and it stood erect with a flag displayed in the air, and was called a Liberty Pole. The beds and pillow cases had been cut open and were brought forward. A committee had been appointed to conduct the operation. It was while they were occupied in doing this that the Captain had without interruption gone on in making his harangue. But these things being now adjusted, a principal person of the committee came forward just at the last words of the Captain.

"The will of the majority," said he, "yes, faith, the will of the majority shall govern. It is right that it should be the case. We know the excise officer very well. Come, lay hands upon him."

"Guid folk," said Duncan, "I am no the gauger, it is true; nor am I a friend to the excise law, though I came in company wi' the officer; nevertheless I dinna approve o' this, o' your dinging down the government. For what is it but dinging down the government to act against the laws? Did ye never read i' the Bible that rebellion is warse than witchcraft? Did ye never read o' how many lairds and dukes were hanged in Scotland lang ago for rebellion? When the government comes to take this up ye sal all be made out rebels and hanged. Ye had better think what ye are about. Ye dinna gie fair play.

If ye want to fight and any o' ye will turn out wi' me, I shall take a turn wi' him, and no just jump upon a man a' in ae lump, like a parcel o' tinklera at a fair."

The committee had paid no attention to this harangue but had in the meantime seized Teague and conveyed him to a cart in which the keg of tar had been placed. The operation had commenced amidst the vociferation of the bog-trotter crossing himself and preparing for purgatory. They had stripped him of his vestments and, pouring the tar upon his naked body, emptied at the same time a bed of feathers on his head which, adhering to the viscous fluid, gave him the appearance of a wild fowl of the forest. The cart being driven off with the prisoner in this state, a great part of the mob accompanied with the usual exclamation of "Liberty, and no excise law. Down with all excise officers."

[35]

· · · · · · · · · · · · · · · · · · ·

The evening the outrage had been committed on him, he had run several miles—naked as he was, if a man may be said to be naked that is invested with a layer of viscous fluid and the adhesion of birds' feathers to cover him—through much danger from the country people who were ill affected to his office. He had at length gained the recesses of a forest where he thought himself safe for the night, until near morning when the barking of wolves at no great distance, as he thought, led him to apprehend the being devoured by these animals, who might take him for an object of their prey. To escape this, he had thought it advisable to climb a spreading beech tree, and there remained until after sunrise when two hunters, coming along at that early hour, descried him among the branches, and not without much surprise and astonishment. At first they took him for a bear; but, seeing the feathers, it was decided that he must be of the fowl kind. Nevertheless his face and form, which appeared to be human, made him a monster in creation or at least a new species of animal never before known in these woods.

They at first hesitated whether to take him down by a shot or to pass on and leave him unmolested. But at length it was determined to pass on for the present as if they had not seen him and to rouse the settlement to take him with dogs and the help of men. It would be a valuable acquisition to have such a creature to carry to the great towns for a show. It might be a fortune to a man. This being resolved on, one of the hunters was dispatched to rouse the settlement, while his comrade in the meantime had taken his station on an eminence at no great distance to watch the motions of the wild creature and give information of his change of situation. The officer in much melancholy of mind had descended from the beech and was sitting on the point of a rock, looking about him like a bald eagle, when a couple of stout fellows came suddenly behind him with the folds of ropes and entrapped his body so that he could not move his arms, which they took to be wings but were as tightly laced as a ship's yard arm when the sails are furled to prepare for a tempest.

A cage having been made and put into the bed of a wagon, he was conveyed to the capital, [where] the proprietors, after having published an advertisement, began to exhibit him as a curiosity for the sum of a quarter dollar to each grown person and an eighth of a dollar to the children of families whose parents brought them with them.

In a short time this uncommon creature, as it was thought to be, became the subject of general conversation, and the Philosophical Society had heard of it. Having called a special meeting, they dispatched two members to ascertain and report the nature of the animal in a memoir to be inserted in their transactions.

The two members accordingly requested of the proprietors an opportunity of a leisurely examination of the animal and paid them a quarter dollar each extraordinary [45] for this indulgence. The proprietors were disposed, as was natural, to assist with some particulars of fiction [about] the singular qualities of the animal they had in charge. They related that when they first saw it, in its flying from the mountain, it was just alighting on the tree top; that having taken it, they had at first offered it boiled and roasted flesh but this is refused; but that at length it had come to eat flesh both roasted and sodden, with considerable gout and sometimes even with rapacity. This was false, by the bye, for they had tried the officer with raw flesh at first, which he had refused, and would eat only roasted or boiled.

The proprietors informed that when first taken, its cries or voice was of a mixed sound between that of a wild cat and heron, but that it had come to have some imitation of the human voice and even articulation and might, from that circumstance, be probably a species of the parrot.

45. Extra.

The philosophers noted all this, and doubtless made a proper use of the particulars in determining the genus of the animal. For the last thing that a virtuoso ought to question is the truth of facts. It is by taking facts as granted that an hypothesis is most easily established.

. . . .

The Society expressed their approbation of it, and it was proposed to make a purchase of this animal for the purpose of examining it more fully in their own hall and possibly of sending it to the societies abroad for their examination also. This proposition was adopted, and the same members [were] appointed to drive a bargain with the proprietors for the subject of their show.

When the deputation came forward and began to traffic with the keepers, proposing a purchase of the curiosity in their possession, the revenue officer in the cage just by raised what is called the Irish howl in a most pitiable manner, recollecting what the Captain had told him on a former occasion with regard to the use to which they would apply him when they should have him in their power.

"God love your shouls, my dear masters," said he, "that have taken me in the wild woods. I care not fat you made o'd me, a wild baste or a turkey buzzard or a fish o'd de vater while I gat good mate to ate and clean straw to lie down upon, but for the sake o'd de holy fathers do not sell me to dese filosophers that will cut me up as you would a dead cat and put my skin upon a pitchfork just to plase deir own fancies; rader let me stay where I am and show me to de good paple dat gape and stare but keep deir teeth in deir mouths and luke foolish but don't affer to bite."

The philosophers assured him that his apprehensions were without foundation, having not the least intention of dissecting, at least until he died a natural death. Doubtless it might be an object to ascertain from the internal structure of his body to what genus or class of animals he might belong. Nevertheless they were persuaded the society would content themselves with the observations drawn from external structure, at least for some time. On this, turning round to the proprietors, they resumed the conversation relative to a purchase, the supposed animal continuing to vociferate and roar horribly.

. . . .

The Society, after having retained the curiosity a year or so and ascertained its structure and properties, proposed sending it to some of the foreign societies who had expressed a wish to have an ocular examination of it also. The preference was given to the societies of

France, and it was accordingly shipped in a brig of Blair M'Clenachen that was bound to Nantes. At this place, on coming ashore by rolling and tumbling in it [the brig] having worn off the tar and feathers from his back-side, he was mistaken for a *sans culotte;* and the mob, rising, broke the enclosure and let him out. I have not heard whether he joined the army of the patriots, or is on his way home again to this country.

[*End of Volume Four (Philadelphia, 1797). Chapters included are the original "A Chapter to be Referred to the Third Volume at the Conclusion," and Book I, 1, 5, 8, 9, 10, 12, 16.*]

from *Incidents of the Insurrection in Western Pennsylvania in the Year 1794*

[*The excise tax became a rallying symbol of Western opposition to the Federalist policies of Washington and Hamilton. Dissension had been smoldering for years. The settlers resented the Spanish rights to navigation of the Mississippi, the government's apparent disinterest in protecting them from Indians, and its failure to settle western land disputes equitably. Although Brackenridge had denounced the excise tax in print, he did not wish to oppose his government with force. When the insurrection occurred, he was caught between the conflicting demands of his conscience—sympathy with the cause of the insurgents and loyalty to his country. This conflict led him into the role of mediator, which earned him the distrust and scorn of both sides.*

Although Hamilton exonerated him from suspicions of treason, Brackenridge set down the record of events, persons, and emotions that comprised the insurrection, hoping to show how he had been drawn unavoidably into the swirl of activity and how he had maintained a consistent role of mediator. The insurrection was the major crisis in his life, and his account of it was a major turning point in his literary production. It is at once a suspenseful drama of individual and mob psychology, a realistic portrait of social movement, and a story of individual sensibility (a word that appears frequently in the narrative). Often his sensitivity to the play of psychology at the center of his drama brings to mind the literary approach of Henry James. His literary aim is to show the situation in which the man acted and to reveal the psychological, social, and philosophical motives for his action.

The Incidents of the Insurrection *combines characteristics of his early and late writings. Under intense stress, the narrator calls upon his classical knowledge to guide him. And in the midst of terror he cannot resist the touch of satire: "Hearing that I had been considered as a leader of the insurgents, I thought I must endeavor to support the appearances, as I would be a good deal looked at." But the light strains of satire never disturb the serious mood. They are matched with strains of sensibility, particularly in scenes portraying the insurrectionist Miller and Mrs. Brackenridge. The whole is realistic in describing character and action. Brackenridge reports what he hears and sees and how his mind reacts. And for the first time, he renders frontier speech without satirical intent.*

Near the end of the narrative, Brackenridge declares a separate peace with

266

society, much in the manner and circumstance of Frederic Henry in Hemingway's
A Farewell to Arms. He abandons the social responsibility that is dictated by his
classical guide, Solon: "If the like scene should happen again, I will not conduct
myself on the principle of Solon's law . . . let the executive and insurgents settle
their own negotiations; I will have nothing to do with them."]

[1]

What I write is with a view to explain my own conduct, which has not been understood. It is possible I may not be able to remove the misconception of everyone. I am aware how difficult it is to change opinion, even with the best cause on my side. But I may support those who have undertaken my defense in conversation, and it may satisfy others who are disposed to find men innocent rather than criminal.

On the evening of the 14th of July, David Lenox, marshall of the district of Pennsylvania, was introduced to me at my house. I had heard that he had been, on his way, serving process on delinquent distillers in the intermediate counties from Philadelphia to the Western country, and in the Western country itself. The conversation turned on this subject and the marshall expressed, with great sensibility, his satisfaction in having met with no insult, much less injury, in the execution of his duty. My impression was that of surprise that he should have apprehended any. For, though the people had been in the habit of thinking it no inconsistency with the reputation of a good citizen to insult or abuse an excise officer, yet I had considered them as distinguishing between these and other officers of government. For though outrages had been committed on excise officers, yet no sheriff nor constable had been opposed in arresting the offenders. They had been brought in upon process and prosecuted at the court. There was no reason in the distinction, but it was made. It was owing to this, that the excise law was odious and the public voice [was] against the officers; but the office of sheriff or constable carried with it the authority of the law, which the people had been in the habit of respecting, and the opposing [it] would be considered infamous in public opinion. I had supposed they would have considered the marshall in the light of a sheriff or judicial officer and would not molest him. However, it so happened that I was mistaken in my confidence of his security; for the evening of the next day, having been out in company with the inspector of the revenue of the district, John Neville, serving some remaining writs upon distillers in the county of Allegheny, he returned with an unfavorable account of his

reception. He had served the last writ he had to serve in that
quarter, and had just quitted the house of a distiller of the name of
Miller when a number of men were observed to be in pursuit of
them, and a gun was discharged. The marshall, conceiving it not to
be with a view to injure but intimidate, turned and expostulated. But
observing a fullness of countenance and advised by the inspector, who
knew their disposition better, he thought proper to ride off and escape
them and had come to town. The inspector had gone to his own
house, about seven miles from Pittsburgh and about the same distance
from the house of Miller.

The next morning after day-break the inspector, having just got
out of bed and opened the door, discovered a number of armed
men about the house; and demanding of them who they were and
whence they came, the answer was such as induced him to consider
their intentions to be hostile. And on their refusing to disperse, he
fired on them. The fire was returned, and a contest ensued. The
Negroes from some adjoining small building fired upon the flank of
the assailants and they were repulsed with six wounded, one mortally.
The inspector or his family received no injury. His house, which was
a frame building, was perforated with the balls.

Towards the middle of the next day the son of the inspector,
Presley Neville, who resided in the town of Pittsburgh, read a letter
from his father written at his house in the country, informing that a
large number were said to be collecting at a place known by the name
of Couche's fort, about four miles distant from his house. The son
expressed to me his apprehensions for the situation of his father. It
was asked by me, what he understood to be their object. It was
answered, to demand of his father to deliver up his commission.
"Deliver it," said I. It was answered, "No."

My idea was to put by the tempest for the present, until the
civil authority could interpose and bring to account individually
those who had disturbed the peace. If the mob who burned the
house of Lord Mansfield in the riot in London [1] could have been put
off by his delivering his commission, I presume he would have delivered it. Another could easily have been made out for him.

It may be said that it would have occurred to a good citizen to
give assistance to the inspector and to help him to defend his house,
and that the gallant and successful defense which had been made the

---

1. Probably during the Gordon riots of 1780, protesting repeal of the Catholic
Relief Act of 1778. As speaker of the House of Lords and chief justice, William
Murray, Earl of Mansfield, became a symbol of repeal.

preceding morning gave ground of resolution to attempt defense against a farther force. But I easily distinguished between the surprise of an unexpected resistance and the deliberation where it is expected. It was also understood, from the letter of the inspector, that a much more considerable force, perhaps five hundred men, were said to be collecting. I easily conceived that, as the disaster of the first attack had brought a second, the repulse of a second would bring a third; and the numbers and the rage would increase. I am not a fighting man; and it was most natural for me to think of policy and the giving the rioters the piece of paper which they had their mind upon and let the justices of the peace, the constables, the sheriffs, the grand juries of the courts, settle it with them afterwards. It may be said, they could not have been brought to justice. That might have been the case, but I thought at the time they could.

In the afternoon of the day John Wilkens, Jr., of Pittsburgh, brigadier general of the militia, calling upon me, informed me that a demand by Neville the younger, on behalf of his father, had been made of John Gibson, major general of the militia, and of himself as brigadier general, to call out the militia in order to suppress the rioters; and [he] wished to have my opinion as to their authority to call them out. Having given the question a short consideration, I thought they had not the power. The governor, under an article of the constitution, has constructively the power: "He shall take care that the laws be faithfully executed." And by an act of the legislature of April 11th, 1783, he is expressly empowered "to call into actual service, whenever it may be necessary, part of the militia, in case of rebellion or of an actual or threatened invasion." But it appeared to me that the constitution and the act constitute the governor the judge of the occasion, and that it is not in his power to delegate this discretion or constitute another the judge of it. But if he could, on inquiring of General Wilkins, I found the fact to be that he had not delegated this discretion or constituted those officers the judges of the occasion of calling out the militia; no provisional instructions, as in the case of an Indian invasion, having been given that respected an opposition to the laws or a rebellion.

General Wilkins returned to me a short time afterwards and said that Neville the younger had called upon John Gibson and himself, as judges of the court, to raise the posse of the county, and he wished my opinion with respect to their power in this case. Giving it a short consideration, I was of opinion that they had not the power. By the constitution, the judges of the court [are] justices of the peace so

far as relates to criminal matters. A justice of the peace, on information given, can direct his warrant to the constables or apprehend
offenders or, on an affray in his presence, can command assistance
to suppress it. But it did not appear to me that he could raise the posse
of the county. "But," said I, "the sheriff can. He is in town; let him
be called upon."

Judge Wilkins [*General Wilkins*] left me, and in a short time
returned and said the sheriff doubted his authority. Judge Wilkins
wished me to explain it to him. I said I was ready. He left me, and
in a short time I received a note from him requesting my company at
the public house, whence the note was dated. I attended instantly
and found there Judge Gibson, Judge M'Dowel, and the sheriff of the
county. I was requested by Judge Wilkins to explain to the sheriff
his authority. I did so, fully. The sheriff appeared alarmed at the
talk of raising the posse and thought it not practicable. I was asked
my opinion. I do not recollect from [whom] the question came. I
gave it decidedly, that it was not practicable. All concurred.

"But," said I, "this can be done; ride out without arms and
address the people. Persuasion will avail more than force. If this is
adopted, I will be one to go." It was agreed; and in a few minutes,
I had returned to my house, was on horseback, and at the river to
cross with the company who were all ready with the same expedition.

At the moment we came to the river, we fell in with Neville the
younger, Marshall Lenox, and a young man of the name of Ormsby,
a son of John Ormsby of Pittsburgh, a family for whom I had regard
but knew the young man to be inconsiderate and rash, and was
persuaded that on this occasion he acted without the knowledge or at
least the approbation of his parents. All three were armed, which I
thought imprudent. I felt concern for them and, taking that liberty
with the young man which I could not take with the others, I
addressed him abruptly: "What!" said I, "armed?" "Yes," said he.
"You will not ride with us armed." "You may ride as you please,"
said he, "I am armed." Neville the younger, who was mounted on a
gray horse, with pistols in his holsters, spoke: "We are not all born
orators," said he. "We are going to fight; you to speak." I thought
him a better chevalier than a judge of the occasion.

But I did not know at the time that arrangements had been made
on their part for a defense, that Major Kirkpatrick and ten or a
dozen soldiers from the garrison of Pittsburgh had gone to the house
of the inspector.

At the river we found two boats. They took one, and [we] took the other.

Crossing the river, being many in the boat and crossing rather high, we stranded the boat on the bar, the water being low; and this circumstance being likely to give some delay, to lighten the boat, I leapt my horse overboard and rode the remainder of the bar and swam the channel on the other side. One or two of the gentlemen in the boat followed me. I mention this circumstance as marking our anxiety to reach the people.

Ascending the hill on the other side of the river, I reflected that I had heard that the roads to Pittsburgh were guarded and that persons that day had been stopped and interrogated who were on their way to the town or from it. It struck me that we might be thus stopped or delayed or prevented altogether from going forward. Mentioning this to the sheriff, who was some distance ahead with me, I inquired of him if, riding through the country in the execution of his office, he did not know of any less public road, equally near or not much less so than the main road, which we could take and avoid the out parties of which I spoke. The sheriff said he knew the old road to Couche's fort, which was the place, and that he frequently took it going that course. It was equally near or not much less so than the new road. We waited at the fork of the road for the company; and suggesting these reasons, it was agreed to take the old road. It may seem trifling to mention this circumstance, but it becomes material when it is known that it has been alleged that we quitted the main road with a view to avoid the very object which we proposed, which was that of falling in with the body of the people.

Couche's fort was about nine miles distant. As we rode, which was with all the expedition possible, we observed the harvest fields deserted by the men, women only to be seen. Stopping at a house and inquiring with a view to gain intelligence of the movements of the country, the woman of the house, as we took her to be, appeared alarmed at seeing us, and knowing the sheriff, asked him, "Are you of Neville's party?" This impressed me as showing the popular idea that the country was on one side and the revenue officer on the other.

Reflecting on the best means of introducing our intention to the body, who were supposed to be in arms, it struck me that seeing the sheriff and the judges of the court coming forward, the first impression would be that it was with a view to take cognizance as civil officers of what was done, and this might make our situation dangerous. It was proposed and agreed, therefore, that these gentlemen should remain and that I, who was the only one of the company who was not a civil officer, should ride forward and acquaint them with our views in coming; that it was to dissuade and prevent, and not to take cognizance.

Coming to the house of a certain Hulse, where these gentlemen had proposed to stop and which was half a mile off Couche's fort, we were informed that the body had marched for Neville's house.

We set out to overtake them and rode with haste. Coming within a mile and a half of Neville's, at the house of a Dr. Adams, we learned from some who had been spectators that all was over and the house burned, that the people were returning and in great rage at the loss of their leader. This was a James M'Farlane,[2] who, it seems, commanded on that occasion. It was not thought advisable for us to go forward as things now were; nor even safe to remain and be in their way, as they would misconstrue our intention in coming and supposing it to have been with a view of assisting the excise officers, make us objects of their passion. We set out therefore for Pittsburgh, and rising the hill above the house where we had been, we saw the failing flame of the burning and heard the firing and the shouts of the parties on their way home from it.

Riding about two miles, we stopped at a public house kept by a man of the name of Shockan, and understood that the tavern keeper had rode towards Neville's house to learn or observe what was to be done. After some time he returned; but having observed only at a distance, he could give us no particular information. We had intended to remain at his house until we received some farther account; but the people appearing, the women especially uneasy at our being there lest it should be heard afterwards and injure them, we set out and came to Pittsburgh. I mention the uneasiness of these people as showing the fear which was impressed of seeming to have anything to say to anyone that might be disposed to take a part [on] behalf of the excise officer. And as officers of government and from the town, that suspicion might lay against some of us.

·   ·   ·   ·   ·   ·   ·   ·   ·   ·   ·   ·   ·   ·   ·   ·   ·   ·

[2]

On Monday, the 21st of July, being the fourth day after the burn-

2. Major James McFarlane, who had been an officer in the Revolution. He was a leader of the Mingo Creek society which Brackenridge called "the cradle of the insurrection."

ing of the house of the inspector and the second after the departure
of the marshall, in the afternoon of the day, a young man came to
my office and delivered me a note from David Hamilton,[3] informing
me that the committee was to sit at the Mingo meeting-house on the
Wednesday following and expressing a wish that I would be present.
I conceived that it was with a view to the object he understood me
before to have in proposing to go to the committee; viz., the explaining to the people the effect of the return of the writs and inducing
them to be satisfied and not to arrest or detain the marshall. Nevertheless, I was greatly alarmed at the idea of having correspondence with
one involved in the guilt of treason. I tore the note and threw it in
the lower part of a closet in my office, among useless papers, meaning
never to make further mention of it.

The next day Neville the younger came to my office and asked
me if I had not received a note from David Hamilton? "I have," said
I, "but how have you come to the knowledge of it?" "The young man,"
said he, "that brought it mentioned it." "I had never intended to have
mentioned it," said I, "but here it is," opening the closet and taking
up the pieces and putting them together and giving them to him to
read. I wished to have him as a witness of the contents. "Do you mean
to go?" said he. "No," said I. "This is high treason that has been
committed; and in treason there are no accessories before or after the
fact. All are principals. And I am aware of the delicacy of having anything to say to people in the predicament in which these are. I have
reflected on the subject and think it not safe to go." "I would wish
you to go," said he. "It might answer a good end." Connecting in my
mind his engagement on behalf of the marshall, who had gone, and
his responsibility in that case, I understood him to wish me to go to
reconcile the people with the circumstance as far as might be and
also to counsel moderation in general. Not a word passed with regard
to my object in going, but I conceived it to be sufficiently understood
what the object was. I was still disposed to decline it but was solicited
and finally said, "I will go, provided you will vouch with what sentiments I go." "I will," said he. "And provided," said I, "some person
can be got to go with me to bear testimony of what I shall say or do
on the occasion." It was agreed that I should speak to some and he
should speak to others. He did speak to some, and I spoke to others.
The persons that agreed to accompany me were the chief burgess,

3. A successful lawyer from Washington, Pennsylvania, the most active leader
of the insurgents.

George Robinson; the first assistant burgess, Josiah Tannehill; one of the regulators [4] of the town, William H. Beaumont; [and] Peter Audrain and Colonel William Semple, formerly of Philadelphia, merchants.

Setting out on the day and arriving at the meeting, I was struck with finding, not a committee, as I had expected, of those persons who had been concerned in burning the house of the inspector but a large convention of others with these. . . . I conceived that those persons had come with the view of counselling moderation and devising the best means of healing what had been done. Yet, from the delicacy of the situation, there was a distance and silence among all of us as we reclined upon the grass or strolled about prior to the assembling of the meeting. I was upon terms of intimacy with many and yet do not recollect to have exchanged a single word with a man. Every countenance discovered [5] a strong sense of the solemnity of that occasion, those who had been involved not more than those who were afraid to be involved. It will be asked me, "How came any there who were afraid to be involved?" I have accounted for my being there; but how came David Bradford,[6] James Marshall,[7] Edward Cook,[8] and Craig Richey [9] there? I select these as instances. As to Marshall and Bradford, I am at a loss to say anything by way of opinion or deduction. I can only state what I have understood from others or what is within my own knowledge. Not having had the least communication by word or writing with Marshall or Bradford prior to that day or on that day relative to the subject, I have nothing of my own knowledge. I have understood from others that after the first attack upon the house of the inspector, when the adjacent country was about to be roused to a second attack, persons went to the town of Washington and called on Marshall and Bradford to come forward on that occasion. They declined help. The expression of Bradford reported to me is "I cannot act; you may do as you think proper." He alluded, as was understood, to his being the prosecuting counsel for the Commonwealth, and in that case not at liberty to do what others might.

After the destruction of the house, persons went to Marshall and

4. Town councilmen.
5. Showed.
6. A rising lawyer from Washington, Pennsylvania, who had served as a delegate to the Mingo Creek society meetings that organized opposition to the excise.
7. Prominent member of the Mingo Creek society.
8. Associate judge of Fayette County.
9. Prominent man of Canonsburg and member of the Mingo Creek society.

Bradford, demanding of them to come forward and support what was done, or they would burn their houses. They had a claim upon them as having been conspicuous in the deliberative committees with regard to the excise law and alleged that Bradford had encouraged them to what they had done by his words when urged to take part before the burning. "I encourage?" said he. "Good God! I never thought of such a thing." "Yes, you did encourage," said they, "and if you do not come forward now and support us, you shall be treated in the same or a worse manner with the excise officer." He found himself under the necessity of coming forward; and that being the case, he would seem from that time to have adopted the most violent counsels. Marshall was obliged also to come forward and thought it necessary, having come forward, to adopt violent counsels. I am of opinion that both these men acted, in the first instances, under a subordination to popular influence. Be this as it may, it is not from a solicitude to make an apology for them that I state this but from the wish that I have to show the truth of the transactions. Edward Cook also came forward, probably at the solicitation and under the fear of the people. Craig Richey and many others I know did. They had, with great difficulty, avoided the going to the burning the house of Neville but could not avoid at least the appearance of being with the people now. I have introduced the names of these persons because they were conspicuous at this meeting. It was opened by putting Cook in the chair and making Richey secretary.

A letter was produced and read from Neville the younger, which had been sent by a gentleman of our company, stating that his father and the marshall had left the country, that the marshall had not considered himself bound by that part of his engagement which was to surrender himself when demanded and of which engagement he (Neville) had become sponsor, because, after the engagement made and the marshall dismissed upon it, he had been again arrested and was indebted to himself for his escape. I did not think Neville had been so good a casuist. However, the people thought it subtlety, and were not satisfied.

.   .   .   .

On the whole, the letter of Neville was not well couched to answer the occasion. It gave great offense and was considered an insult.

This and other letters being read and discussed a little, Benjamin Parkinson [10] addressed the chair: "You know," said he, "what has been

10. A hot-headed, irresponsible man of the people from Washington, Pennsylvania.

done. We wish to know whether what has been done is right or wrong and whether we are to be supported in it or left to ourselves." These were the words. They impressed me with an agony of mind. There was silence for some time. Marshall, coming forward, observed that it was not necessary to say whether what was done was right or wrong but what is now to be done? I was relieved at this and thought him in the right train.

Bradford now spoke and, to my great astonishment, declared his approbation of what had been done and called upon the meeting to pledge themselves to support it. His declamation was of considerable length and extremely violent. Yet from my knowledge of the man, I doubted whether he spoke according to his wish or harangued according to the humor of the people and from a fear of them.

After he had spoken there was a dead silence. The question would be taken; support or not support? My situation was delicate. There was but a moment between treason on the one hand and popular odium on the other, popular odium which might produce personal injury before I left the ground. To withdraw would be the same thing as to oppose.

Marshall came to me, a thing which I suspected from him or someone else, and solicited me to speak. I had been planning the scheme of an harangue. Having settled some outlines in my mind, I addressed the chair.

I gave them a narrative of what had taken place at Pittsburgh since Hamilton and Black [11] had been there; that the marshall with the revenue officer had left the country and, as was supposed, had ascended or descended the river; that the inspection office was shut up [and] the label [12] which announced it taken down. And here I related the circumstances of Craig [13] taking it down, painting it with some humor, and making them laugh at his expense. This with a view to impress the idea that I was diverted with the catastrophe of the office, and this as a substitute for saying anything directly to approve what had been done. Putting them in good humor, I ventured to touch

11. David Hamilton and John Black headed the party that called on General Neville to ask his resignation as tax inspector.

12. A notice advertising the excise office.

13. Major Isaac Craig, an engineer and son-in-law of the inspector, had insisted that the notice advertising the excise office should remain on the door, until he heard the rumor Brackenridge had started that five hundred men from Washington were coming to burn Pittsburgh because the excise office was still open. Then Craig rushed to the office, ripped the notice from the door, and called upon a bystander to watch him tear it into bits.

upon the subject more seriously. To avoid the giving any vote upon the question, I stated that we were not delegated for the purpose of giving a vote but simply to give a narrative of what had taken place there with respect to the excise office, in order to calm the minds of the people and render it unnecessary for any force to come and take it down. It will be seen that I introduced the idea of a delegation as an apology for not giving any vote.

As an individual, however, I was willing to give advice: "What has been done might be morally right, but it was legally wrong. In construction of law it was high treason. It was a case within the power of the President to call out the militia." I saw this struck them greatly. They had entertained no idea that it would be cognizable otherwise than in the county courts. "But," said I, "the President will reflect upon the difficulty of getting the militia to march. They will be reluctant from the midland parts of Pennsylvania, from the upper parts of Maryland and Virginia. It will probably be necessary to bring them from Jersey and the lower parts of the states. For this reason the President may be disposed to give an amnesty." Here I stated the amnesty which had been given by the state of Pennsylvania in the case of the riot at Wilson's house in Philadelphia in 1779,[14] as an example.

I continued to observe that, in order to obtain amnesty, an application must be made to the executive; that it would come with a better grace and with more support from those not involved, on behalf of those that were, than from those that were involved; that it was not the interest of those involved to involve others but to let them remain as they were, in order to act as mediating men with the government. Here I discovered rage in the countenance of Benjamin Parkinson and others. They considered me as evading the support which was more agreeable; viz., the coming fairly in with them in the transaction and making it a common cause. I saw that they distrusted the certainty of an amnesty and did not relish the idea of asking it. I had therefore to impress two things strongly, the necessity of asking an amnesty with the probability of obtaining it.

In order to impress the first, I enlarged upon the want of power to support what was done; the small basis on which they had to stand, a small part of a small country, not even the whole country

14. In 1779, James Wilson was commissioned advocate general for France, and in this capacity he represented Louis XVI in all claims rising out of the French alliance until the close of the war. The riot was presumably started by dissatisfied claimants.

west of the mountains with them, unprovided at the same time with arms, ammunition, and resources of war.

In order to impress the last, the probability of obtaining an amnesty, I [offered] the evidences which the executive had already given of a disposition to avoid war, even to a degree that was blamed or perhaps blamable, in the case of the spoilations on our commerce by the British and in the case of the Indian tribes.[15] Here I introduced the countermand of the Presque Isle establishment at the interference of the executive of the United States, in consequence of threats from Cornplanter, a Seneca Indian.[16] And in order to put them in good humor and at the same time lead to the point I had in view, the practicability of obtaining an amnesty, I indulged a good deal of pleasantry at the expense of the executive on the subject of Indian treaties. I introduced General Knox [17] on the one side and Cornplanter on the other, and made them make speeches. "Now," said I, "if Indians can have treaties, why cannot we have one too?" Returning gradually to seriousness, I concluded by proposing a larger meeting, perhaps co-extensive with the survey, and sending delegates to the executive on the subject of an arrangement with regard to what had been rashly and, in legal construction, criminally acted; that if this measure was adopted, though it would be inconvenient for me and [not] agreeable in the heat of that season to take such a journey, yet I was willing to be one to go to the executive.

I have been the more particular in giving the substance of my speech on this occasion, and the clue to understand it, because it has been misconceived and the pleasantry, which I indulged on the subject of Indian treaties, [has been] construed into a contempt of the executive. If the President himself had been present, perceiving my drift, he would have excused me. However, depositions were taken of

15. In "Thought on the Present Indian War," *National Gazette,* Feb. 2, 6, 1792, Brackenridge states that the British have an eye to commerce with the Indians and thus incite Indian attacks on the American settlements. "It is not a war, therefore, with the Indians merely; it is a war with the British king under cover." He strongly condemns Washington's government for its leniency toward the British, and the evidence of this leniency is the government's failure to defend the western settlers from Indian attacks. The government, he claims, is too interested in establishing good relations and commercial credit with the British.

16. Cornplanter, the Seneca chief, refused to join the Delawares, Shawnees, and other hostile tribes in their war against the United States. Instead, he settled his Senecas peacefully on Presque Isle, opposite the present city of Erie. When Pennsylvania planned a settlement on Presque Isle in 1790, Cornplanter went to President Washington and complained. As a result, the executive vetoed the act establishing the settlement.

17. General Henry Knox, Secretary of War.

this part of my speech and considered as an evidence of *male mens,* a bad disposition towards government.

In the course of my speech, I had perceived different impressions on the different descriptions of those present. Those not involved were greatly relieved and satisfied, and manifested this by the countenance and by the nod of the head. Those involved, the more discerning of them, were dissatisfied and manifested this by the countenance and by the shaking of the head.

After I had done speaking there was a total silence, and the greater part left their seats. A considerable part left the house. I went out and walked about, waiting to learn what the general impression was. My company from Pittsburgh communicated to me that numbers of the people were dissatisfied, and there appeared to be a murmuring among them. Daniel Hamilton,[18] who had been at the burning of Neville's house, but who was personally well disposed to me, came to me and informed me that there was a considerable dissatisfaction at what I had said. . . . "Benjamin Parkinson and that man," said he, pointing to a man in a blue coat with a black scarf on his arm and who, I have since been told—whether truly or not I do not know —was a brother of M'Farlane that had fallen,[19] "are stirring up the people against you." On this I stepped in to observe what was doing there. I observed the chairman, Edward Cooke, James Marshall, David Bradford, and others in a knot or globe in the center of the house, conversing with their heads together in a low voice. I passed by in a slow walk along the entry of the meeting house. I was not asked to stop or join in the deliberation. I walked back and, as I passed, just spoke to James Marshall and asked what they were concluding on. He said he did not know. I thought myself not trusted and withdrew.

I have since engaged Alexander Addison [20] to make inquiry and to find from Marshall or Cooke what was the subject of deliberation at the time. He informs me that they cannot recollect that there was anything material. I can only say that the language of James Marshall, on the motion of Parkinson and the conduct of Cooke in nodding from the chair with an appearance of assent to me in my proposing that those not involved should remain so, had impressed me with an

18. Cousin of David and John Hamilton. The three of them led the aggressions against the excise officer, Robert Johnson. On September 6, 1791, they tarred and feathered him.

19. Andrew McFarlane, brother of James, who was killed at the burning of the Neville house.

20. District Judge; later a bitter enemy of Brackenridge.

idea [that] they were averse to violent measures. However, I was so alarmed with what I then saw and what I had heard out of doors that I immediately went out and found some of my company and gave the hint to get off as speedily as possible. They collected and set off. Mixing among the people, I made an apology that my company were going and, not wishing to lose my company, I was about to go. I set off and met John Cannon, who wished me to stay. I said it was immaterial, for that not being delegated I could give no vote on any question. Getting off to some distance, we were called upon but we hastened our pace. Coming to the house where we had left our horses and having got them from the pasture and dined, which might take up an hour, it was suggested by some of the company that we had come off abruptly, and we might be accounted spies, and it might be well if I would go back and show myself and make some apology. I had felt an impression of the kind myself, and taking my horse, I rode back and dismounting and, leaving him in a bottom at a stream at some distance, I walked up as if I had not been at all away. I found that a great number of the people had gone and some were going away. Those remaining were engaged in hearing some man, who was making the *amende honorable* [21] or explaining some conduct or some expressions which had indicated a disposition to comply with the excise law.

Having just shown myself, I withdrew, returned, and joined my company. Before we set out, the master of the house where we were, an old gentleman, returned and informed [us] that nothing had been done but a large meeting agreed upon at another day.

.   .   .   .

[3]

The post was interrupted on the 26th of July, on the way from Pittsburgh and near Greensburg. The packet from Washington and Pittsburgh was taken out. It was carried by Benjamin Parkinson to Washington, and from thence it was accompanied by Bradford and Marshall and others to Canonsburg, a village seven miles distant. It was there opened: no letter on the late affairs from any individual of Washington. There were letters from individuals of Pittsburgh. These letters gave great offense and made the writers objects of resentment.

The result of the convention at Canonsburg, at the opening of the mail, was the issuing circular letters to the officers of the militia,

21. A full acknowledgment of error and an apology.

proposing a rendezvous at Braddock's field for the purpose of a march to Pittsburgh. The object of the march was the taking the magazines of the garrison and any military stores that might be found in the town. It was also contemplated to take the writers of the letters and imprison them in the jail of Washington. These were the objects contemplated, according to the information given me. It may not be correct.

What was the object of intercepting the mail is questionable. Bradford was a weak man, but yet it seems hardly probable that he could be so weak as to think it any object to know what people would think of what had taken place. He might easily know what individuals would write from his town, knowing what they were used to speak in it. Knowing characters, he might know opinions. It is more probble what has been suggested by men of that town; viz., that knowing what some would write if they wrote at all and expecting these might write and being an enemy and wishing an advantage, he hoped to have it in his power to turn the rage of the people on them. If this was his object, he was disappointed in it; nevertheless, he was sufficiently incensed against the writers of the letters; and whether it was this resentment that gave rise to the idea of a march to Pittsburgh for the purpose of arresting these men and this drew with it the idea of taking the magazine, or whether the taking the magazine was the primary object and this incidently brought in, I am not sufficiently informed. It would seem probable that the march to Pittsburgh and the taking the magazine would have been, at all events, attempted as a necessary act to furnish means of defending what had been done, the intercepting the mail. For it is to be presumed, if we suppose the actors in this affair to have had reflection, that they had made up their minds to set the government at defiance; in that case, it became them to arm themselves with the means of war.

The circular letter was dated the 28th of July, and the rendezvous was ordered the 1st of August. It was directed to the officers of the militia in the same manner as an order would issue from a proper authority, and it was obeyed with much greater promptitude. When an officer disapproved of it, he did not dare to conceal from his battalion or company that he had received such a notice; and when communicated, it was the people commanding the officer, not the officer the people. "Call us out, or we will take vengeance on you as a traitor to your country." The whole country was an inflammable mass; it required but the least touch of fire to inflame it. I had seen the spirit which prevailed at the time of the stamp act and at the commencement of the revolution from the government of Great Britain, but it was by no means so general and so vigorous among the common people as the spirit which now existed in this country.

. . . .

Knowing that the government could not possibly overlook the outrages committed and finding the disposition in the people to support them, I saw my situation perfectly and canvassed in my mind the practicability of lying by and remaining a spectator or the necessity of abandoning the country. I thought also of taking part, but the cause was not good; at the same time [it was] hazardous and nothing [was] to be got by it. A revolution did not suit me nor any man else that had anything to lose or was in a way of making something. A secession of the country from the government presented nothing that could be an object with me. The repealing the law by an exhibition of force might be the only thing in view with the people at the moment, but I knew they would not stop there. The opposing one law would lead to oppose another; they would finally oppose all and demand a new modelling of the constitution; and there would be a revolution, or they would be suppressed. For my part, I had seen and heard [more than] enough of revolutions to have any wish to bear a part in one. But to lie by was impossible; no man would be suffered to remain neutral. I thought therefore of emigrating.

. . . .

Nothing but the suddenness with which the march to Braddock's field came upon us prevented my being out of the way at that time. It was impossible to make arrangements in so short a time. When that came, I thought of nothing but weathering the blast for the moment and then making my escape.

. . . .

Whether my sentiments were communicated to James Marshall or not, the sentiments of others were, both to him and Bradford, and with such effect as to alarm them at the rashness of the steps they had taken and induce them to issue orders of countermand for the rendezvous. These were actually sent to some quarters and received, and the march of the battalions arrested.

. . . .

The countermand of the rendezvous produced dissatisfactions in the town of Washington and the adjacent country, and the people rushed in from every quarter and demanded that the business should go forward. . . . To show their disapprobation of the apostasy of

Marshall, the door of his house was tarred and feathered that night. Threats were also thrown out of personal injury and he was under the necessity of declaring his readiness to go forward. Threats were also thrown out against others. Indisposition, lameness, pressing business was affected; many yielded to their fears and thought it safest to go. Others were disposed to go, with a view of endeavoring to moderate the multitude and prevent outrages. Of this last description there were numbers of the principal officers of the militia, who came with battalions or companies to humor them and keep them from mischief. The common language of the county at the time was [that] they were coming to take Pittsburgh; some would talk of plundering it, others of burning it. It was an expression that Sodom had been burnt by fire from heaven, but this second Sodom should be burned with fire from earth. I believe plunder was an object with many. The shopkeepers were told at their counters, by persons cheapening their goods, that they [customers] would get them at a less price in a few days. The very women coming in from the country would say, "that fine lady lives in a fine house, but her pride will be humbled by and by." Persons were coming to the blacksmiths with old guns, that had laid by a long time, to have them repaired. Others were buying up flints and powder from the stores. There were many that were supposed to be from distant parts, no one of the town knowing them. I saw some, whom I took for spies, who had been sent to look at the state of the garrison or of the town. I traced some without appearing to do it and found them lounging from place to place without seeming to have anything to do.

We had seen copies of the order of march; and now it was understood from various accounts that the people were on their way to Braddock's field. Major Butler [22] had been industrious to improve the defense of his garrison; Major Craig had removed his family into it; Colonel Neville had prepared to defend himself in his own house. It was thought advisable to have a town meeting to consider what was best to be done. Notice was given of a meeting in the evening.

[4]

The ground where Braddock fought is on the east side of the Mononga and on the same side with the town of Pittsburgh. The militia from Washington had therefore to cross the river in order

22. Major Thomas Butler, Commandant of Fort Fayette. His letter to Secretary of War Knox was among those intercepted in the robbery of the mail, July 26.

to come upon the ground. They had crossed in great numbers at the same ford where he did and were now upon the ground. They were dressed in what we call hunting shirts, many of them with handkerchiefs upon their heads. It is in this dress they equip themselves against the Indians. They were amusing themselves with shooting with balls at marks and firing in the air at random, with powder only. There was a continual discharge of guns and constant smoke in the woods and along the bank of the river. There appeared a great wantonness of mind and disposition to do anything extravagant. We had advanced within the camp, as it was called, when the [*Pittsburgh*] committee halted and waited for General Wilkins, at the head of the Pittsburgh militia, to come forward. I saw him march by us and discovered in his countenance sufficient evidence of a sense of danger. Though I knew him to be a man of great personal intrepidity, yet I did not wonder at his apprehensions. Nothing but his appearing at the head of the militia, who were now to be considered as friends of the cause, could have saved him. I was thinking of his danger, when I turned my head a moment and was struck with the very man I was most afraid of, Andrew M'Farlane, just by me. He was dressed in a blue coat, with dark visage, lowering countenance, and a rifle in his hand, looking at me. I eyed him in my turn but did not venture to speak. I trusted to his fear of the people, as he did not know perfectly how I stood with them. After some time he turned about and went away.

The next object that arrested my attention was Bradford walking before a number of battalions that had just crossed the river and were ranged upon the bank to be viewed by him. I was solicitous to know what my reception would be. I know that from his going on to the intercepting the mail and the procuring of this movement of the people, without my knowledge, he had not expected assistance from me; and his not communicating his intention of it discovered [23] a mistrust of me. But I found our proceeding at Pittsburgh had satisfied him, for he advanced and spoke to me. The usual questions by him and everyone else were, had we sent away those men? Was there no danger of their coming back? Our usual answer was, they were gone; they would not be suffered to come back. Epithets of indignity were sometimes used with respect to them, to mask our sentiments the better. It was said by them that more must go. Everyone from Pittsburgh that I heard speak at all assented to everything that was said,

23. Showed.

for it was a part of the system adopted and we trusted to the arrangements that could be made to soften all matters and prevent injury to anyone in proportion as we ourselves could acquire confidence with the leaders of the multitude.

Having been some time upon the ground, I fell in with Benjamin Parkinson, the other person of whom I had been personally apprehensive. He was in a group of men whom I knew to be warm in the cause. I advanced with great appearance of confidence and frankness of manner and saluted them. I was received with cordiality and thought myself very fortunate. All or most of those had been at the conflagration of the house of the inspector and had heard me at the Mingo meeting. . . . My appearance on the ground, now to join them, had effaced the unfavorable impressions.

They sat in a group upon the ground, each with his rifle in his hand or lying by him. I sat with them. The conversation turned upon the burning of the house; and they expressed great rage against Kirkpatrick [24] who had been the cause, as they said, of the burning it and the death of James M'Farlane, by his [*Kirkpatrick's*] refusing to let the house be searched for the inspector's commission and his papers. They expressed resentment [toward] Major Butler for sending his soldiers to the house of the inspector. They had inquired for Ormsby, who had accompanied Neville the younger and the marshall from Pittsburgh. I said he was upon the ground but was scarcely worth inquiring after. He was an inconsiderate young man that would go anywhere. He had gone there and he had come here and it was little matter what he did; that we had heard in what manner they had treated him when they had him a prisoner; that they had taken his horse and pistols and hanger from him and put him on the bare back of a colt to ride, as a steed congenial with his years and discretion. I had heard something like this. But whatever might have been the case, I was disposed to give them the impression that I was diverted with the circumstance . . . therefore [I] put them on the relation of it and laughed immoderately, but concluded that he had been sufficiently punished by his apprehensions on that occasion and, as he had gone there without the knowledge of his parents and had come with their approbation here, it was not worth while to mind him. It was agreed it was not.

I did not know that in the meantime the young man had been on the point of assassination.

24. Abraham Kirkpatrick, Neville's brother-in-law.

Fifteen men had painted themselves black, as the warriors among the Indians do when they go to war. They had gone in search of Ormsby. Zedick Wright of Peter's Creek had discovered it and, having a good will for the family or from motives of humanity, made haste to give him intelligence of it. He had escaped but a few minutes, not a quarter of an hour, when they were seen to pass by openly in pursuit of him. He made his way to Pittsburgh in the course of the day by devious routes and lay concealed in the barracks of the old garrison until the whole cavalcade was over.

I was greatly disconcerted on one occasion in the course of this day by James Ross of Washington.[25] It was the first time I had seen him on the ground. . . . Sitting with two or three others at the root of a tree, [as I was] passing by, said he to me with a smile, "You have got a great deal of subtlety, but you will have occasion for it all." I was alarmed and looked about to see who must have heard him. There were none near me but those just with him, whom I knew and who were wearing the mask also. But I gave him to understand that he had alarmed me, for he could not know the characters of those [with] me; he said he did and considered that before he spoke. Talking of the arrangements made, he thought the business well managed on part of the town and that nothing else could have saved lives and property.

People were coming in from every quarter all that day, generally armed, but some without arms. It was impossible to know the real sentiments of almost any one among the multitude; how far they were there from necessity or from choice. Every man was afraid of the opinion of another. Sometimes a word dropped, if not well taken, would lead to a confidence. The great bulk of the people were certainly in earnest, and the revolutionary language and the ideas of the French people had become familiar. It was not tarring and feathering, as at the commencement of the revolution from Great Britain, but guillotining, that is, putting to death by any way that offered. I am persuaded that if even Bradford himself, that day, had ventured to check the violence of the people in any way that was not agreeable to them and had betrayed the least partiality for the excise law or perhaps even a remission of his zeal against it, he would have sunk in an instant from his power and they would have hung him on the first tree. Yet he was weak enough not to have foreseen this; it had been an argument used . . . in [attempts at] dissuading him from a

25. Lawyer; most important political figure in Washington County.

perseverance in the measure undertaken that no man could calculate the consequence of putting the mass in motion with arms in their hands. His answer was that he could say to them, "Hitherto shalt thou go and no further." Certain it is that his influence was great. I saw a man wade into the river, lift cool water from the bottom of the channel, and bring it in his hat to him to drink. Applications were made to him that day for commissions in the service.

Nevertheless, whatever his idea might have been, he would have been at the extent of his power if he had ventured to tell the people that they should return without going on to Pittsbugh. It was the object of all men who were apprehensive of the consequence to dissuade from this, but it appeared very doubtful through the whole day whether or not it was practicable. It was afterwards found that it was not.

Towards the evening there was a council of the Pittsburgh committee. It had been represented to them and was the fact that the people from the town, not expecting to detain that night, had brought no provisions with them. It was suggested that they might be suffered to return to town and be at the place of rendezvous early in the morning. It was thought expedient and orders were given accordingly.

I had seen General Wilkins but little through the day; he had remained close with the Pittsburgh people and ventured little through the multitude. On his first coming he had gone up to Bradford, apprehensive that he [*Bradford*] might denounce him, and addressed him: "Sir, have you anything against me?" "No," said he. This resolute behavior probably prevented him having anything to say.

On its being known that the people of Pittsburgh were going home for the night, there was a great clamor in the camp. It was said they were about to desert the cause and, in fact, never had been sincere in it.

The fact is there were of them [some] shrewd enough to discover this. Some would say, pleased with our address but who had rather have had us all in earnest, "You have acted well, but we understand you. We give you credit for your management." It would be answered, "What! Do you doubt our sincerity?" They would say, "We do not dispute your good policy."

Finding the effect of the departure of the Pittsburgh people, it was thought advisable to countermand the leave given. I rode after them with great haste and turned them to the field with orders not to leave it, let their want of food be what it might, rather than produce a dissatisfaction with the people on the ground and bring them irregularly and in bad humor to the town. It will be asked, whence had I this authority? And how was I obeyed so readily? I was of the committee to whom the power had been entrusted of conducting all affairs upon the occasion.

On my return with the Pittsburgh people, I saw James Marshall for the first time upon the ground. I saw he was greatly hurt in his mind at the trouble he had brought upon us and had great solicitude with regard to the event. I explained to him the dissatisfaction that had taken place at the departure of our people and wished him to ride through the camp and give information that he saw us all returned. He mounted his horse, with his rifle in his hand, and set out to do it.

In the course of the day, a great subject of conversation had been the taking the garrison. It would seem to have been the original object of the movement but had been laid aside. On what principle I do not know, whether on account of the difficulty of accomplishing it or the projectors of the enterprise hesitating to make war so immediately on the United States. I should rather think it was the danger of the enterprise that operated on the mind of Bradford, for he would naturally reflect that he could not avoid taking a part in the attempt himself; and I have no idea that he was a man of courage under certain danger. The reason ostensibly assigned, at the relinquishment of this object, was that it was found the military stores in the garrison were intended for the campaign against the Indians and it would be improper to derange the operation of that campaign by seizing them. This part of the enterprise had been abandoned by the projectors of it, but the rumor had gone abroad, and it was not generally known to the people that it was abandoned. Their query everywhere was, "Are we to take the garrison?" I answered always that we were. The query then was, "Could we take it?" It was answered, "No doubt of it." "But at a great loss?" "Not at all; not above a thousand killed and five hundred wounded." This loss, to the more thinking part, appeared very serious.

Various modes were proposed of taking it. Some thought of providing stakes with sharpened points and rushing up with those and putting them in the port holes to obstruct the firing from them while others were cutting away the pickets. In the meantime, others with their rifles [would be] taking off the men at the guns in the block-houses of the bastions, as the Indians took off the artillery men in St. Clair's expedition.[26] I was asked, what was my plan of taking it? I

26. Indian sharp-shooters picked off all but one of Major General Arthur St. Clair's artillerymen during his expedition along the Wabash river in 1791.

suggested the undermining and blowing up a bastion. "But they would fire upon the diggers; besides, it would waste powder."

To some complaining that, called out so hastily, they were not well furnished with provisions, I proposed starving out the garrison; but these were apprehensive they would starve out themselves.

After night I had a great deal of conversation on this subject in the bushes and at the sides of fences, laying our heads together and whispering. I was for the most desperate measures but admitted that much blood must be lost.

About midnight I rode through the camp where the people were lying at the fire in their blankets or without. I made a pretense of inquiring for the Pittsburgh battalion; and this with a view, at the same time, to let them know that the Pittsburgh people were upon the ground. My principal object was to ascertain the determination of the people with regard to their coming to Pittsburgh. I found the universal sentiment to be that they would see the town. There was little sleep in the camp. The firing and shooting had ceased; but there was a continual conversation.

Coming up to a fire, a person to whom I was known accosted me: "Is Kirkpatrick gone?" said he. "He is gone." "And why the devil did you let him go?" said a person starting up behind him. The question came so suddenly upon me that I was a little struck with it; but recovering, I replied that it was no fault of mine that he went away. I would rather have kept him here and punished him by law. This was the truth, for I was prosecuting him at that very time for misdemeanors. The enrage, or the enraged man as I may call him, made no reply; but the person who first spoke to me gave me a touch in the side and said, "Come, take a dram. We will not detain you." This I understood to be a hint to go away. I give this incident because . . . having mentioned it afterwards, it was used by some as proof that I had endeavored to inflame the people against Kirkpatrick by talking of punishing by law. It is true the man deserves my resentment; nevertheless, I had too much regard for my own feelings and the opinion of the public to avail myself of that occasion to do him any injury. But my expression in the case mentioned was equivocal and was understood; viz., as relating the circumstance which was the ground of their resentment, the defending Neville's house. My insinuation was that this was punishable by law. The thought was new to the man and it occupied his mind for the moment.

Passing on to a range of fires, I found Hamilton's battalion. This had arrived late in the evening; it had been long expected and was called the bloody battalion. The greatest part of it had been at the burning of the inspector's house. We expected desperate measures when these came. It was commanded by John Hamilton,[27] a man very moderate and reasonable, and who was disposed to restrain the people from violence and with that view had come with them.

Daniel Hamilton, his cousin, was the first that accosted me; and wishing to serve me with the people, [he] called out, "This is a true Whig. But what do you think of that damned fellow, James Ross? He has been here and all through camp, persuading the people not to go to Pittsburgh." I saw now that it was in vain to oppose the going, and it was better to acquiesce and say they should go. In that case there would be more management of them than if they came in spite of opposition. I saw this and took my part decidedly. "Damn the fellow," said I. "What business has he with Pittsburgh? The people of Pittsburgh wish to see the army, and you must go through it and let the damned garrison see that we could take it if we would. It will convince the government that we are no mob but a regular army, and can preserve discipline and pass through a town, like the French and American armies in the course of the last war, without doing the least injury to persons or property." There was a general acclamation, and [they] professed a determination to molest no one.

Returning to a farm house just by the camp, where some of our committee were, I communicated the result of my observations. Some of them had been through the camp in the same manner and had the same impressions that I had with regard to the impossibility of preventing the people coming to town.

In the morning, having convened in the camp and held a council of principal officers, it was proposed to form a committee to consist of . . . three deputies from each regiment, who should deliberate on what was to be done. Deputies being chosen . . . the committee met, of which I was one, as representative, with General John Wilkins and Captain John M'Masters [28] for the militia of Pittsburgh. In order that our deliberations might be more free, it was proposed to withdraw to some distance. We withdrew and occupied a shady ground in the wood. Edward Cooke was appointed chairman. Bradford opened the meeting by stating the cause of their assembling in arms; viz., in order to chastise certain persons who had discovered sentiments friendly to the excise law, that their sentiments had come to light

27. One of the tarring and feathering Hamiltons. He was also sheriff of Washington County in 1783. (See note 18, p. 279.)
28. A tavern owner of Pittsburgh.

through the vigilance of some persons who had intercepted the mail and found their letters, that these letters would speak for themselves. Here, taking out the letters from his pocket, he read them and commented on them; that from Major Butler of the garrison, giving some account of the outrages committed and his sense of the atrocity; [29] that from Neville, the son of the inspector, alluding to the authors of the disturbance and giving them the epithet of rascals; [30] that from Edward Day, suggesting a project of carrying the excise law into operation; [31] that from General Gibson, stating a motion by Bradford at the Mingo meeting to support the outrages committed; [32] that from the prothonotary Brison to the same effect.[33] At the authors of these two last letters, he [Bradford] appeared particularly enraged, as distinguishing him at the Mingo meeting and representing him as making such motion. Addressing himself to me, "Were you not there? Did I make such a motion?" I looked at the man with astonishment. Is it possible, thought I, that you did not know the scope of your harangue? You did not make the motion, but you supported it, and that is all the inaccuracy in the statement of the letter. But is it possible that you would regard [object to] being distinguished to the government as supporting violent counsels when you have distinguished yourself so effectually in the very act of obtaining these letters? However, it was no time to explain; it would involve myself and put it out of my power to serve others, to enter into an altercation with the Robespierre of the occasion by stating, as the fact was, that if he did not make the motion, he supported it. I therefore evaded it by saying that the statement in the letter was not accurate, but that might be the fault of the information given to the writers. It was answered that it became them to be more cautious in giving credit to information; and at all events it evinced a disposition unfriendly to the people, to be communicating information to the government of what they were about. There was no answering this.

Having read the letters and put them up again, said he, "There is another person that is an object of resentment with the people, Major Craig. He has had the insolence to say that if the inspection office is shut up in the town of Pittsburgh, he will open it in his

29. Written to Secretary of War Knox.

30. Written to General Daniel Morgan, commander of the Virginia Volunteers and young Neville's father-in-law.

31. Written to Secretary of the Treasury Alexander Hamilton.

32. Written to Governor Thomas Mifflin of Pennsylvania.

33. Prothonotary James Brison had also written to the governor.

own house." Calling on the deputies from Pittsburgh, "Have any of you," said he, "heard this?" It was answered, no. It was stated by me particularly that I heard nothing of it. . . . I knew no better way than to turn it to a laugh and make the man an object of ridicule for the moment; besides concealing thus any partiality for the man on his own account, or ours, I could, with the less suspicion, parry what might be proposed against him by substituting something of less effect. It was with this view I went on and introduced several other incidents respecting Craig; viz., that so far from saying that he would keep the inspection office in his house, it was himself that took down the label on the inspection office in the town; and having torn it in several pieces, presented it to a certain Captain Lang to carry it to the country to convince the people that it was torn. This incident I painted in such a manner as to make the people laugh. I represented it in the engineer [*Craig*] to be the effect of vain fear, and that, though at first he affected to be a bloody man and would have had a few of the town to fight the whole country, yet on a report prevailing that the people were coming to the town to pull down the inspection office, he ran and took away the obnoxious signature himself. Bradford was asked by someone where he had received the information. . . . He said it was the talk of the camp.

It was now the question, what resolution should be taken with regard to these men? It was proposed and adopted that the question with respect to them should be taken singly. The case of Major Butler was considered first. His offense was two fold; the interfering with the civil authority of the people by sending a military force to the house of the inspector and by corresponding with the government.

There was no man so rash as to question the illegality of these acts. But it was observed by me that, being an officer of the United States, he was amenable to the executive for anything unconstitutionally done, and on a representation to the President there could be no question but that he [*the President*] would remove him at least from the command in this country. It would be therefore most advisable to take no order with regard to him at that time, but postpone the consideration of his case until the meeting at Parkinson's ferry and then remonstrate to the executive and obtain his recall. It was agreed.

The case of Craig was taken up next. It was observed by me that there was certainly ground of suspicion of his being overzealous in behalf of the excise law; nevertheless, it might be bad policy to order him out of the country at this time. In his capacity of quartermaster, he had the care of the military stores that were sent forward occasionally and intended for the campaign at that time carrying on against the Indians. . . . It might derange these operations and give offense to the people of Kentucky, who were also against the excise law, to disturb the quartermaster in his arrangements and prevent the forwarding these stores. But he [was] also an officer of the United States, appointed by the Secretary of War, General Knox, and that the same steps might be taken with regard to him [*Craig*] as [to] Major Butler; a representation could be sent from the meeting at Parkinson's ferry to the Secretary with information that he was proscribed by us and a demand that he should be superseded in his office and proscribed by him also.

. . . .

These being disposed of, the case of Gibson and Neville was taken up. On their behalf I spoke also and with regard to Gibson observed that he was a man of an inoffensive disposition, not much harm with him; could do little injury, go or stay; was a man in trade, and the being disturbed would affect him in making remittances to his merchants; and the fraud, in that case, would be theirs, not his; that it was no object to banish him. With regard to Neville, he had used harsh expressions, it was true, but it was under the influence of passion and in a private letter to a relation.

It was discoverable that it did not go down well to pass over all. There were many that discovered ill humor; there were sundry speakers for and against. In the case of Neville, there was a man, leaning on one knee with his chin upon the head of his staff and a slouched hat upon his head, who spoke softly but with great eagerness for Neville. But at this moment, a man whom I afterwards understood to be a Captain Murray, with great liveliness of manners came forward, dressed in a light blue camblet coat, leather overalls, buff waistcoat, and a cutlass by his side. He had not been present until that moment. The fact was that fresh battalions of militia were every moment arriving; and as they arrived, they chose deputies to the committee. Murray, wishing to make up for his lost time, was very active now; and understanding the question was with regard to the banishment of certain individuals, he was strenuous for the banishment. If it had been for hanging, it would have been the same thing; for the man had no resentment, politically or personally, but simply wished to distinguish himself and become conspicuous in the revolution.

I felt little or no concern in the case of Neville, for I did not see it to be of any consequence to him whether he was to go or stay. I rather thought it was his interest to be sent away, and I had understood that it was his wish to get out of the country. He actually expressed himself to that effect to the messengers from Washington, who came with the intercepted mail, and applied to them for a passport, mistaking their authority. I had seen him the morning of our march to Braddock's field; and with as much anxiety of countenance as a man could discover who conceived his life to be in danger, his expression was, "The only thing I think of is to escape assassination." Well, I thought of nothing but this, the saving his life and property. For Gibson I was concerned; not that I thought it would ultimately be of any damage to him to be banished, but I supposed his feelings would be hurt for the present and he might think it of consequence to be sent away.

I was standing by Bradford at this time. Turning to him, I observed with some warmth, "The sending away the people is a farce; it will be the best recommendation they can have to the government; they will get into office and be great men by it. It is better to let them stay and be insignificant where they are. You could not have done a better thing to those that are gone than to have sent them off." My language was candid, and his answer was equally so. "But," said he, "the people came out to do something, and something they must do." I now saw that, whatever his theory might have been with regard to the extent of his power over the people, his feelings for his own safety corrected his vanity; and he saw the necessity of giving a tub to the whale. He had heard the declamation of Murray; viz., that we must be firm and clear the country of disaffected persons, etc.; and conceiving that Murray, just fresh from the camp, had brought its sensibilities with him, he was unwilling to relax in his disposition with regard to the expulsion. "We ought to be firm," said he, "and unanimous."

At the first withdrawing of the committee and taking their station in the wood, we were followed by numbers who wished to hear the deliberation. The committee being opened, it was moved and the chairman directed to inform the people that it was our wish to deliberate in private. The chairman addressed them to this effect. Some went away, and others did not; some came again, and others with them. There was a constant intercourse between the committee and the camp. It was frequently told them that we wished to be by ourselves; but in spite of all that we could do, we had a gallery of riflemen. Just at this moment about a dozen came up fresh from the camp; and having listened a little, leaning over a log with their rifles on it, as we were deliberating on the case of Neville and Gibson, "Gentlemen," said one of them, "we do not understand your counseling in mystery. Do something speedily or we will go to execution ourselves." This, with the disposition that had been discovered in the committee, induced us to think it not advisable to delay the determination in the case of Neville and Gibson, lest the multitude should go on and the committee of course break up without any determination at all; and in that case, no resolution having been taken and announced with regard to these persons, they would be left to any resolution of the mob. Under these impressions, our Pittsburgh members, consulting aside, were of opinion [that] it was best to say at once that they should be sent away and that we ourselves would engage to have it done, but requested eight days for them to be ready. Before this ground of the question, it was proposed by some one of us that the consideration of their case should be postponed to the meeting at Parkinson's ferry. But that did not consist with the idea of doing [it] effectually and at once, and it was rejected.

Bradford now moved that the troops should go on to Pittsburgh. "Yes," said I, "by all means, and if with no other view, at least to give a proof that the strictest order can be preserved and no damage done. We will just march through and, taking a turn, come out upon the plain of the Monongahela's banks; and taking a little whiskey with the inhabitants of the town, the troops will embark and cross the river."

James Ross, at this moment stepping from another part of the committee and passing by me, said, "The veil is getting too thin. I am afraid it will be seen through." But the committee had now risen and were going away.

"It is well for you," said Benjamin Parkinson to me, "that the committee has broke up in such a hurry. You would have been taken notice of, you gentlemen of Pittsburgh. Give us whiskey! We don't go there for your whiskey." This was said grinding the teeth and biting the lip. I considered his umbrage at these words as no more than a pretense of a quarrel and was alarmed, but made in the softest manner an explanation that I meant no more than we should drink together and not any offense whatever, and that it would affect me in the most sensible manner if anything inadvertently said by me should interrupt harmony and injure the cause. I got him to seem satisfied, but I rather suppose that he had begun to suspect me of not being in earnest in the cause and that this was the real ground of resentment.

A number of the Pittsburgh committee having met, it was proposed and thought advisable that some individuals, in whom Major Butler would have confidence, should ride in before the multitude and inform him of the state of things; that there was no intention of disturbing him, and this lest he should mistake the case and fire upon the people, and they might suppose the town in collusion with him and make this a pretense of injuring it. Some members set out and went into town for this purpose. Others were dispatched who undertook to have the boats ready at a proper place to transport the people, and water and whiskey on the ground where we should halt, that there might be no pretense of leaving the ranks in order to obtain refreshment.

Several members of the committee and other inhabitants of the town, alarmed at the idea of the people coming, had gone home to put out of the way some of their most valuable articles. Some of them buried their books and papers. I had sent orders the preceding day for my papers to be carried out of the town, and they had been carried out.

Officers in the meantime having been appointed, Edward Cooke and Bradford generals and Col. Blaenay officer of the day, the drums began to beat and the line of march was taken up. By the direction of our committee I went forward to the advanced guard and undertook to conduct by the proper road to Pittsburgh.

[I conducted] the militia by what is called the Monongahela road; the route was at a distance from the garrison, which is built on the bank of the Allegheny river. Entering the town and marching to the main street to satisfy the people and wheeling to the left and leaving the town, the whole body was halted on the plain to the east of the town. By the best estimate I have been able to collect, the numbers were about 5,400. About a fourth of the whole numbers, at Braddock's field, had turned from thence and not come to town. So that at the place of rendezvous there might have been in the whole about 7,000 men.

By the order of the committee, every possible provision had been made for them on the ground that the short space of time could allow; and as soon as the Pittsburgh militia, who had marched in the road, could be dismissed from the ranks, they were employed in carrying water to the plain. Members of the committee set the example by carrying water and whiskey to these whiskey-boys, as they have since been called. I was employed among the rest, very busily. I thought it better to be employed in extinguishing the fire of their thirst than of my house. Most other persons thought in the same manner, and every man had at least a hut that he could not afford to have plundered or burned down. In spite of all that could be done, straggling companies left the ground and came into the town and were extremely insulting and troublesome. By order of the committee the taverns had been shut up, but the tavern-keepers were under the necessity of distributing gratis.

Great activity was used by well-disposed men to preserve order. General Bradford left all to his officers and gave himself little trouble. I did not see him through the whole afternoon. He had retired to a bower to cool himself in the shade. There he was expatiating to those who had accompanied him on the object accomplished, the expulsion of the obnoxious characters.

It was an object of moment for the safety of the town to have the multitude thrown across the river as speedily as possible. There were but three or four boats that could be collected from the ferries, and it would take a long time to transport so great a number with these. But it was recollected that the horse, which might be a third of the number, could ford the river. Knowing the ford which is at the confluence of the Monongahela and Allegheny rivers, I rode down and attempted it; it was found to be practicable. Returning and lading down a few squadrons, they crossed. When it had been announced that the river was fordable, the whole of the multitude that had come on horse-back came down and crossed the river. [Those on] foot in the meantime, the greatest part, had crossed, and we had the prospect of having the town clear that night.

But notwithstanding all exertions, a . . . hundred or two had remained in the town; these were in concert with some of those who had crossed the river and who were to burn some farm buildings belonging to Kirkpatrick on the hill opposite the town [and] to set on fire his house in town. It was also said that the house of the company whose clerk Day had been, and Gibson's house, Neville's, and that in which Brison had lived, were to be consumed. The burning these, from their situation, would have burned the quarter part of the town. But if they had begun to burn at all, the whole would [have] been burned.

A company commanded by a Captain Riddle, dressed in yellow hunting shirts, were seen in the evening parading the town, as having something in view. They appeared bent on mischief. About nine o'clock at night the alarm was that these and others were about to burn the house of Kirkpatrick. The inhabitants were called upon to defend it. I found General Wilkins and a number with arms rushing down. I addressed them, "This will not do; it is contrary to the system we have hitherto pursued and which has been successful. Return and lay down your arms. If a drop of blood is shed between the town and the country, it will never be forgiven. It will be known that there is a tumult in the town between the inhabitants and the country people; and those that have crossed the river, many of them, will return and we shall fall a sacrifice. If the house is to be defended, it must be by the people of the country themselves."

In fact, a number of the people of the country were at this time in arms to assist in defending the house. James Marshall and Edward Cooke and a brother of M'Farlane, that had fallen, had gone down. He had been called forward on the principle that, being supposed to have the greatest cause of resentment against Kirkpatrick, if he should oppose the burning no other could with a good grace insist.

It was on the same principle (an incident which I had forgot in my narrative) that the committee of Braddock's fields had sent for Andrew M'Farlane; and represented to him our apprehensions of injury to the property, even of one by whom his family had been injured, that he would express his sentiments in the camp and make it as public as possible. His answer was that he had no wish to injure the property and would declare it publicly; but that if ever Kirkpatrick and he should meet, one of them should die.

Those in arms with General Wilkins rested where they were. Going forward, I addressed myself to the people that were going forward for the purpose of burning the house. Said I, "Gentlemen, you cannot burn that of Colonel O'Hara [34] that is near it; he is a good man, and he is absent. If it is to be destroyed, let it be pulled down, not burned. I will be the first to pull a board off myself. But what necessity to take the trouble now, or to give yourself the trouble at all? The people of Pittsburgh will pull it down and throw it in the river."

These desisted to go forward. There had been some at the house and were preparing to set fire when Cooke, Marshall, and M'Farlane came forward and prevented it. A mistake of Cooke was fortunate. Thinking those he saw before him at the house to be of the persons

34. Colonel James O'Hara.

that were there to defend it, said he, "Boys, are your guns loaded?" "Yes." "Then put in a second ball; and the first man that puts fire to the house, shoot him down." Some affected to be there to defend the house, and some went off.

In the meantime, intelligence had been brought that the people were about to destroy the buildings of Kirkpatrick on the south side of the river; I fell in with David Hamilton and Thomas Stokely,[35] about to cross for the purpose of dissuading from it. I crossed with [them] to direct the ferry boats to be sent over to the town side of the river, in order to prevent any part of those already over from recrossing to the town. Having ordered the boats over, I was returning when the flame of a building of Kirkpatrick's on the hill began to illuminate the river. It was a barn with the produce of the harvest in it. This had been the signal agreed upon for the inflammation of the house of Kirkpatrick in town or other buildings. This had been prevented by the measures taken.

I have been minute in my relation of the incidents that respect Kirkpatrick's house and my concern to save it because it has been insinuated that I had a wish to have it burned. I do not affect a regard for the man, for I have none; and it is no presumption of my regard for him that I wished to save his house, but rather the contrary, for I well know that, if burned, he would make five times the value of it out of it. It was in some degree for the sake of the people themselves that I wished to save them from doing mischief. How would Kirkpatrick make five times the value by the destruction of his property? It would be considered as destroyed in the cause of the government and therefore liberally repaired. The being the brother-in-law of the inspector would establish a connection between his loss and that of the officer.

That plunder had been an object with many of the multitude is certain. Among other proofs of this, I saw a man on Braddock's fields put his hat, an indifferent one, on the muzzle of his rifle and, twirling it about, say, "I have a bad hat now, but I expect to have a better one soon." On the day the people marched into Pittsburgh, a number of women on the hills opposite the town, from a considerable distance, collected to see the destruction of the town and to share in the plunder. The day succeeding, a body near a thousand at the distance of four or five miles halted and deliberated and with difficulty were prevented from coming back to plunder. On their way on another

35. A state senator.

road by the farm house of Neville the younger, where a tenant lived who had been a deputy under the inspector, they deliberated on the plundering and burning the house, and presented their pieces to shoot the wife of the deputy.

. . . .

[5]

Had the denounced persons left the country immediately, before it became known extensively that they were obnoxious, they could have got out of it without difficulty; but it was no easy matter afterwards. The cause of their proscription was not distinctly known, and it was thought to be some great state crime that had come to light. The people had an idea that it would be no harm to shoot them down, at least to arrest and imprison them.

Kirkpatrick was to have had an escort of two men, but one only had been able to join him; the other had been detained by the people who, not knowing the measures of the committee, were lying in wait to apprehend him. With the person that had been able to join him, he escaped by a circuitous route on the frontiers of the country as far as the Allegheny mountains and then ventured to take the road.

Prothonotary Brison had been detained a night at the house of the deputy attorney for the Commonwealth at the distance of some miles from Pittsburgh. It was rumored in the neighborhood that he was there still. A party of about forty persons had collected in the night and surrounded the house. They demanded of the attorney to give them entrance that they might search for the culprit. It could not be refused. The lady of the attorney had fainted with the fright; a mulatto woman had been dispatched to the spring hastily for a glass of cool water; and mistaking her complexion in the dark, she was taken for the prothonotary making his escape in the disguise of a night cap. She was pursued; and supposing herself obnoxious, she left the glass and took to the woods. It was thought that the prothonotary had escaped, and the resentment fell on the attorney for harboring a criminal; and it was with great difficulty and not until the mulatto woman, recovering herself, had come back that he could convince them of the truth.

Edward Day had taken the safest route and descended the river to Fort Washington.[36]

36. In Ohio.

The inspection offices through the whole survey, comprehending
five counties, had at this time been burned down with the dwelling
houses of the deputies. Liberty poles with inscriptions and devices
[were] raised everywhere. Inscriptions such as, "an equal tax, and no
excise"; devices such as a snake divided, with this motto, "united we
stand, divided we fall." I met with no man that seemed to have
an idea that we were to separate from the government or to overthrow it, but simply to oppose the excise law; and yet the people
acted and spoke as if we were in a state of revolution. They threatened
life and property familiarly. They talked of not suffering Alexander
Addison, the district judge, to return to the country. He was at that
time in Philadelphia.

A report that, on his way down, he had met the marshall and
encouraged him to come forward with the writs had rendered him
obnoxious. They proceeded to acts of violence among themselves,
every man avenging his own injury. Persons consulted me on the
expediency of coming to town to shelter themselves there. I dissuaded
[them] from this measure, as dangerous to them and to the town
both. We could not defend it; and if we could, yet whence our
provisions? It was better to conceal and lie by a little, until it could
be seen what arrangements could be made for the restoration of
order; or if, in the meantime, any man was apprehensive of injury
to himself personally, he had better cross the Ohio and be absent for
a while under the pretext of discovering and improving vacant land.
I was consulted by many, supposing me to have a knowledge of the
times; and when I thought myself safe, I gave my real sentiments. . . .
My sentiments were that the people must be brought to order by
arrangements among themselves, or the government would reduce
them. When I thought myself not safe, not knowing the persons or
suspecting myself to be watched, my answers were evasive or equivocal.

The most delicate conduct was necessary in order to avoid giving
offense. Some days after the cavalcade at Braddock's fields, I was reading an advertisement, by one who had been there, put up at a public
house in Pittsburgh and laughing with some persons present at the
singularity of the phraseology and orthography. Looking around, I
saw two or three from the country who discovered [37] by their countenances strong emotions of resentment; they had conceived our
merriment, at the expense of the advertisement, to indicate an undervaluing of the writer and his service. I turned it off suddenly by

37. Showed.

saying that it was no matter; he did not spell well but he might be a good soldier and fight well. This restored their good humor.

. . . .

I canvassed my situation fully and began more seriously to think of emigration; but in that case, I would be considered in the light of a deserter and my property become a sacrifice. I thought of disposing of my house, which was perishable, to some individual less conspicuous and under his name save it. But that would be suspected or discovered. I thought of being absent on some pretense that might be plausible; and it struck me to prevail with the people of Pittsburgh to appoint me as an envoy to the executive, to state the motives of their conduct and explain their situation. I mentioned this to James Ross, who approved of it and at my request [agreed to] sound General Wilkins to get him to favor it. Mr. Ross did so, but informed me that General Wilkins was not willing that I should leave the town. He was in the same situation himself and did not like to lose company. I have learned since that there were more in the same situation and with the same reflections elsewhere who had planned the getting out of the country by pretending to go below to purchase powder. . . .

I made up my mind now to wait the result of the meeting at Parkinson's ferry. My object was a pacification of the country by means short of force. With a view to this, I wished the government to have a just idea of the situation of the country, the magnitude and extent of the opposition. In that case, the executive might be disposed to adopt conciliatory measures. On this principle, having received a packet containing some papers from Tench Coxe [38] of Philadelphia on agricultural subjects to be communicated to the people of the country, it struck me to communicate to the government by writing to him my impressions with regard to the disturbance. This letter was misunderstood and considered as proof that I was engaged in the insurrection. Some expressions led to this misconception, which [expressions] I had used to save myself with the more violent of the people of the country, if it should fall into their hands by the intercepting the mail, a thing constantly expected. In writing to Tench Coxe, I considered myself as writing to the government, understanding him to be in an official situation near the President.

A term had come into popular use before this time to designate the opposition to the excise law; it was that of Tom the Tinker. It

38. Alexander Hamilton's supervisor of the revenue.

was not given, as the appellation of Whig originally was, as a term of reproach by adversaries,[39] but assumed by the people who were active in some of the masked riots which took place at an early period. A certain John Holcroft was thought to have made the first application of it. It was at the time of the masked attack on a certain William Cochran, who rendered himself obnoxious by an entry of his still, according to law. His still was cut to pieces; and this was humorously called mending his still; and the menders of course must be tinkers; and the name, collectively, became Tom the Tinker. Advertisements were now put up on trees on the highways, or on other conspicuous places, under the signature of Tom the Tinker, threatening individuals or admonishing or commanding them in measures with regard to the excise law. . . . It was not now, "Are you Whig or Tory?" But, "Are you a Tom the Tinker's man?" Every man was willing to be thought so; and some had a great deal of trouble to wipe off imputations to the contrary. Advertisements appeared in the gazettes, from individuals, appealing to the public and averring the falsehood of aspirations upon them as favoring the excise law.

· · · · · · · · · · · · · · · · · · · ·

I had frequently heard it said by the people of the country, since the introduction of the excise law, that it were better for them to be under the British, and at this time such language began to be very common. But I cannot say that I ever heard any person of note breathe the idea. It was said that arms and ammunition could be obtained from the British.

· · · · · · · · · · · · · · · · · · · ·

Reports from the east of the mountains were that the people on that side were as violent as those on this, that they had proceeded to outrages. This was alarming. I saw before me the anarchy of a period, a shock to the government and possibly a revolution—a revolution impregnated with the Jacobin principles of France, and which might become equally bloody to the principal actors. It would be bloody unavoidably to them, and to the people, destructive. Let no man suppose that I coveted revolution. I had seen the evils of one already, the American; and I had read the evils of another, the French. My imagination presented the evils of the last strongly to my view and

39. The term Whig was probably abbreviated from Whiggamore, a nickname for the Presbyterian peasantry of the Western lowlands of Scotland. Originally a term of reproach, Whig was meant to imply that those designated were no better than the Presbyterian rebels of Scotland.

brought them so close to probable experience at home that, during the whole period of the insurrection, I could scarcely bear to cast my eye upon a paragraph of French news. This is not a statement of sentiment invented now; they were my expressions at the time. [40] It was not the excise law alone that was the object with the people; it was with many not the principal object. A man of some note, and whose family had been at the burning of Neville's house, was seen on horseback in Pittsburgh the day of Braddock's field, riding along with a tomahawk in his hand and raised over his head: "This is not all that I want; it is not the excise law only that must go down, [but] your high offices and salaries. A great deal more is to be done; I am but beginning yet."

.   .   .   .

There was an accidental circumstance which, independent of fixed and permanent causes in the minds of the people, contributed to the inflammation of this period. It preceded the election of sheriff and members of assembly; and without meaning anything more than to be elected, the candidate was clamorous against excises and salaries, and was for taking arms, not having the least expectation of fighting, but willing to make other people think that he would fight. This class of men were numerous and greatly vociferous. Strange as it may seem, it never once struck them that if things went on in that manner there could be no election.

I have given the state of the country previous to the meeting at Parkinson's ferry.

[6]

The meeting was opened by placing Edward Cooke in the chair and making Albert Gallatin [41] secretary . . . there appeared to be members from Ohio county in Virginia and five counties of Pennsylvania. In the whole there [were] two hundred and sixty. Our hall was a grove and might well be called the mountain, for we were on a very lofty ground overlooking the river. We had a gallery of lying

40. For views of Brackenridge on the French Revolution, see "Oration of July 4, 1793," pp. 147–50.

41. Gallatin had been chairman of county delegates to earlier anti-excise meetings in 1792. On October 14, shortly after the Parkinson Ferry meeting, he was elected to Congress.

timber and stumps, and there were more people collected there than there was of the committee.

. . . .

Several persons spoke on the subject of constituting magazines of arms and ammunition and seemed to wish resolutions pointedly to this. . . . Gallatin was laboring hard to divert this by attacking it in front. . . . I affected, as before, to oppose Gallatin and made an apology for those who were for providing means of war. Said I, "It may not be amiss to talk of these things and to hold out the idea of fighting with a view to avoid it, just as a general displays columns, meaning by that display to avoid engaging. This idea of our being about to fight may induce the government to accommodate with the country.[42] But enough is done. These things will be left to the direction of the standing committee."

The apology saved the pride of the speakers and satisfied the hopes of the violent; and there was no more said. I was thought to be for war, if it should be necessary. I was applauded by the gallery, and it was said I had gained what I had lost at Mingo creek.

. . . .

I lay that night at a farmhouse in the neighborhood, with a hundred or more of the gallery or committee about me. The whole cry was war. From the manner in which they had understood me, I was greatly popular with them. "Stand by us," said they, "and we will stand by you."

I felt my situation with extreme sensibility. I had an attachment to the people because they had an attachment to me, and I thought of the consequence: . . . suppose that, in the prosecution of the plan I have in view, arrangements cannot be made to satisfy them and that a war must ensue; what shall I do? I am under no obligation to honor, to take part in supporting them, for I have no way contributed to produce the disturbance. And though, on principles of conscience, it may be excusable in them to make war, for they think they are right, yet it would not be so in me, for I think them wrong. But on the score of self-preservation and personal interest, what am I to do? It is a miserable thing to be an emigrant; there is a secret contempt attached to it, even with those to whom you come. They respect more the valor, though they disapprove the principle, of those that stay at home. All I have in the world is in this country. It is not in money;

42. Come to terms with the Western country.

I cannot carry it with me; and if I go abroad, I go poor; and [I] am too far advanced in life to begin the world altogether.

But as to these people, what chance have they? They may defend the passes of the mountains; they are warlike, accustomed to the use of arms, capable of hunger and fatigue, and can lie in the water like badgers. They are enthusiastic to madness, and the effect of this is beyond calculation.

The people on the east of the mountains are, many of them, dissatisfied on the same principle and will be little disposed to disturb the people here if they should mean to defend themselves. It is true, the consequence of war, supposing the country independent of the United States, will be poverty and a miserable state of things for a long time; but still, those who stand by the country, where they are, have the best chance and the most credit in the end. Should I emigrate and the country be reduced, I cannot live in it again for a thousand reasons. I am in a quandry, and in either case the election is painful. The only thing that can suit me is an accommodation and having the matter settled without a civil war. But is there any prospect of this? Will the executive be disposed to act with mildness or rigor in this instance? The excise law is a branch of the funding system, which is a child of the Secretary of the Treasury,[43] who is considered as the minister of the President. He will feel a personal antipathy against the opposers of it and will be inclined to sanguinary counsels. The President himself will consider it as a more dangerous case than the Indian war or the British spoilations and will be disposed to apply more desperate remedies. He will see that here the vitals are affected, whereas there the attack was upon the extremities. Nevertheless, the extreme reluctance which he must have to shed the blood of the people, with whom he is personally popular, will dispose him to overtures of amnesty. These were my reveries as I lay, with my head upon a saddle, of the flooring of a cabin.

In the morning, the committee of four having met, we proceeded to the arranging and mending the resolutions. Bradford was not satisfied with the indefinite expression of the power given to the standing committee but wished to have it in plain terms, probably with a view to get something to pass the committee that would involve all equally with himself in the treason committed. I wished to evade it, and endeavored to divert his attention by keeping him laughing. I dispensed with Craig on this occasion and made use of Herman Husband.

43. Alexander Hamilton.

I endeavored to amuse Bradford with him, as a person would a boy by playing bear.

I had heard of this extraordinary character many years ago, when [he was] a principal of the insurgents known by the name of Regulars in North Carolina. I had seen him in the year 1778, when he was a member of the legislature of Pennsylvania. I was present when a Quaker lady was introduced and preached before the house. Herman, who was a divine as well as a politician, thought her not orthodox and wished to controvert; but the house, willing to avoid religious controversies, would not suffer him.

I had visited him in the year 1780 at his residence in the glades of the Allegheny mountain on my way from Philadelphia to Pittsburgh. He had then just finished a commentary on a part of the prophet Ezekiel. It was the vision of the temple, the walls, the gates, the sea of glass, etc. Loggerhead divines heretofore had interpreted it of the New Jerusalem, but he conceived it to apply to the Western country, and the walls were the mountains, the gates the gaps in them by which the roads came, and the sea of glass the lake on the west of us. I had no hesitation in saying that the commentary was analogous to the vision. He was pleased and said I was the only person, except his wife, that he ever got to believe it. Thought I, your church is composed, like many others, of the ignorant and the dissembling.

It was to this topic I drew him [*Bradford*] at present, and wished him to explain his reveries. But Bradford was too intent on getting the resolution amended to an explicit provisional declaration of war; he complained of my laughing and wished me to be serious. Gallatin, not perceiving my drift, said cynically, "He laughs all by himself. . . ."

[7]

I have mentioned James Ross as a commissioner on the part of the United States. The others were William Bradford, Attorney General of the United States, and Jasper Yates, a judge of the Supreme Court of Pennsylvania. The two last had arrived at Parkinson's ferry a short time after the adjournment of the meeting; from thence they came [to] Pittsburgh. Being known to the Attorney General and the judge, I waited on them at the public house after their arrival. I found Major Craig giving them a tragical account of the cruel treatment of Kirkpatrick, Neville, and the others by the people of Pittsburgh in sending them away. I felt great indignation and addressed him before the commissioners. Said I, "The representation is not just. You are imposing upon these gentlemen. You are leading them to suppose that the people of Pittsburgh expelled these men; it was the country. We acted as their guardians in sending them away; the act was for them more than for ourselves." Here I gave a detail of the circumstances. He was silent and withdrew.

I had discovered in the commissioners unfavorable impressions towards me; I was at a loss whether to attribute them to what they had heard on the way or to the account of Craig. An expression of the Attorney General struck me much. In my observations on the account of Craig I had said that I had never considered myself as an insurgent. I was employed to negotiate for those who were, but that did not involve the fact that I was one myself. Said the Attorney General, "That will be a subject of future consideration." I was with the commissioners but a short time, finding the point of view in which I conceived myself to stand with them. The expression of the Attorney General had hurt my mind and, with the language of Craig, became the subject of very serious reflections. I considered Craig but as an automaton, and that his impressions but [to] be those with which Colonel Neville went away. That being the case, I had reason to suppose that this representation would be the same which Neville would make to the executive. The people of Pittsburgh, and in particular myself, could be held up as insurgents. After all my labor to get matters settled, this family [*Neville's*] would consider me as having injured them; and when they returned, I should be insulted by them. I had found it hard enough in the village before to support myself against them, but it would be worse now. I began to consider whether it would not be better to stand with the *sans culottes* of the country and keep these men away while they were away. But was it practicable? I could not reconcile it to myself to disturb the union; that would be a wickedness beyond all possibility of contemplation. But this country might secede from it. That is a right that is never given up in society. A part of a country, as well as an individual, may quit a government; and no doubt this country will quit the United States in due time. That may be by a consent of the union or without it. But at the present there would be no consent. The example would be dangerous to give. Common interest would not suffer it. We are bound to the union for our proportion of the public debt. We must discharge demands against the partnership before the firm, as to that, can be legally dissolved. The United States have land beyond us; they cannot suffer us to shut them out from these by an independent government between.

But is it practicable to establish and support such a government? Perhaps it might claim these lands to the westward and invite all the world to take possession of them. Collect all the bandits on the frontiers of the state to help us to fight for them; tell the Spaniards to come up to the mouth of the Ohio and give us a free trade; let the British keep the posts and furnish us with arms and ammunition; get the Indians of the woods to assist us; tell them that the people on the east of the mountains want our whiskey and their lands. We might wage war, and perhaps succeed. It is true we should succeed to misery for a while and poverty at last. But even this would be more tolerable to me than to live under any circumstances, suspected by the government and treated with contumely by these people when they had returned loaded with the favors of the government, as having been the great defenders of it.

These were the thoughts of a night. When I saw James Ross in the morning, I explained to him my chagrin of the preceding day and my reflections in consequence of it; and gave him to understand that I had half a mind to become an insurgent. He took it more seriously than I intended it. His expression was, "The force of genius is almighty. Give them not the aid of yours."

I told him that nothing but self-preservation would lead me to think of it, or the being unjustly suspected. He soothed my mind by assuring me that no suspicion could possibly fall on me, that the commissioners the preceding day were perfectly satisfied with the explanation I had given in the presence of Craig, and that what he had said had not left the least impression.

.   .   .   .

The point was now gained to which I had always looked forward, the point where the foot was to be fixed in order to make an open stand against the insurrection. This was my expression to James Ross. . . . "The point is gained," said I. "There is a basis now laid from which we can act." To this point I had always looked forward, not expecting commissioners from the government but propositions from it to commissioners . . . holding out an amnesty, which I took to be the great secret of composing the disturbance. Until that appeared, the disposition of those involved would lead them to cut throats to support themselves; and the whole country, conscious that every man had in some degree contributed by words or by actions to produce that mental opposition to the law which had terminated in actual force, could not reconcile it to their feelings to abandon those who had acted with precipitation in the late instances. But an amnesty being given, these could say to their countrymen, "You are now on a ground with us; stop, we will go no further."

I considered the appointment of commissioners on the part of the executive as a pledge of amnesty, though I had yet no information of their powers. I therefore saw the way clear for the country to get out; and now the conduct ought no longer to be a concealment of intentions and a half-way acquiescence, but an explicit avowal of opinions.

On this principle I took the first opportunity I had with Bradford and Marshall, and it was in the presence of one of the committee before any conference with the commissioners, to inform them of my real sentiments with regard to the violation of the laws which had taken place, and particularly with regard to those in which they had been implicated—the intercepting the mail and the rendezvous at Braddock's fields. Bradford looked red and angry, Marshall pale and affected.

.　.　.　.　.　.　.　.　.　.　.　.　.　.　.　.　.　.　.

My system from the commencement had been to take the business out of the hands of the multitude as speedily as possible by instituting an extensive committee. [It was] not to take a final question but, having enlightened that committee and rendered them moderate, to make use of them as evangelists among the people when they went home to disseminate the proper doctrines. It was on this principle that I had suggested the Parkinson's ferry meeting. The fury of the people at that meeting led me to see the necessity of reducing the country into still smaller bounds by a committee extracted from the first. It was on this principle I approved and supported the appointing of a standing committee. Even this committee was too large with which to break the business, and therefore I wished the smaller committee of twelve to be the body with which we should begin to act. Having instructed and enlightened these and gained their assent, we should come forward with them to the standing committee as so many disciples, not wounding the pride of others by having it upon them, without their concurrance, to judge, but deliberating, as if not having judged at all.

Having instructed and converted the standing committee, we should send them home to disciple as many as they could; and come forward in the original and extensive committee in order to govern the result. In the meantime . . . the gazettes and handbills [would] reach the body of the people with reasonings on the subject. If this system could have been adopted, it might have succeeded. For it is a great mistake to suppose that Bradford or Marshall or others led the people. It was the people led them. It was the mass of the people that commanded, and it was the fear of them that operated on the minds of the more conspicuous individuals. Even Bradford was the most obstinate because he was the greatest coward. He had no reach of thought to see the danger from the government, but the danger from the people was just before his nose.

. . . .

The conduct of the people below contributed to deprive us of that time that was necessary to bring the public mind, among ourselves, to a proper sense of interest and duty.

In drafting [the report] which had been committed to me on the part of our committee, I had introduced our statement, at least the statement made by me, of our general grievances in this country. It was with a view to show the people that we had made the most of our case and of course must be supposed to have got the best terms that could be given; and if we, who had been thus impressed, had yielded, they might. The commissioners thought it might rather strengthen opposition in their minds, and it was struck out.

I had stated strongly, on the part of the commissioners, the sense they had expressed of the outrages committed, the burning, the expulsions, and especially the intercepting the mail and the march to Braddock's field. It was with a view to bring these strongly before the minds of the people that, sensible of the atrocity, they might the more appreciate the value of an amnesty. But I am disposed to believe that this gave offense to Marshall and Bradford, who had been implicated in the last acts. For I cannot otherwise account for the dissatisfaction they discovered towards me from this time. I cannot believe that Marshall, especially, was at all dissatisfied at being relieved from the extremely hazardous situation in which he had been involved.

Concluding the report, I added some reasons which had been suggested, at least by myself in the committee, as grounds of conceding to the propositions of the commissioners. They were such as I thought would have weight with the people. Albert Gallatin, in his speech in the legislature of Pennsylvania on the subject of the insurrection, speaking of these reasons, says, "They are, I suppose, such as, in the judgment of the author, would make the most impression upon the people. On that head, however, I think he was mistaken." I think now, as I did then, that they were the most likely to impress. But that is a matter of opinion. I am not going to dispute about it. The true democratic principle on which it should be put doubtless was that "the will of the majority should govern. The national will had made the law, and it should be obeyed." However unequal and oppressive on this part of the community we might suppose it, yet the good of the whole demanded our submission.

It is an abstract argument that must satisfy the understanding but can never reconcile the heart. It is precisely the same with the theological argument of the divines; the good of the whole requires that some should be damned, and a man cannot be a saint until he feels a disposition to be reconciled to the divine will, in this particular, even if it should fall to his lot to go to hell. A man regenerated may come to this, but a natural man never will. So an enlightened politician may comprehend and acquiesce in the principle of submission to inequality of burdens when the nation dooms him to it; but the common mind revolts, and nothing will quiet him but the consideration that he cannot help himself. My argument, therefore, chiefly contemplated the want of power; and sometimes, by introducing an idea of postponement on the ground of existing circumstances, I endeavored to get an acquiescence for the present. Using the argument with one, his answer was, "The people never can be roused again." I knew that, and it was on this principle I suggested it. It was quite safe to talk of another day, for if the devil had been once laid it would be difficult to raise him again. The people would begin to look back and be made sensible of the precipice on which they had been standing. Let the law be put in operation, and they would not find it the evil they had conceived it to be.

At the request of the commissioners, it had been urged to call a meeting of the standing committee at an earlier day than appointed. They were called to meet on the 28th of August.

[8]

Our committee of conference met at Brownsville on the morning of the 28th of August. Brownsville is on the Monongahela, at the mouth of a stream known by the name of Redstone.

The first thing that struck us was a party of men, perhaps seventy, armed with rifles, who had marched from the upper part of Washington with a view, as we understood, to take the person and burn the buildings, mill, dwelling house, etc., of Samuel Jackson, near that place, who had given offense by an expression disrespectful to the committee. Pains were taken to dissuade [them] from outrage, informing them that, by the arrangements made at Parkinson's ferry, all complaints against offenders were to come before the committee, who were to decide upon the criminality and upon the punishment. They were prevailed upon to be contented with having him brought before the committee and tried in form, but insisted upon going with a file of men to bring him.

The committee of sixty having met, which was under a shade of boards constructed for the occasion, Edward Cooke was constituted chairman and Albert Gallatin secretary.

Samuel Jackson had been, by this time, brought up and was before the committee. He was of the denomination of the people called Quakers, a tall man with a broad brim to his hat. He preserved a grave demeanor and stood with an appearance of composed submission to the sufferings that might await him.

The charge against him was that, speaking of the committee, he had called it a scrub congress. The charge was proved by two witnesses. The question now was what punishment should be inflicted if he was found guilty, in the language of scripture, of "speaking evil of dignities." By the Scottish law it was what is called "leese-making," and subjects [one] to transportation. By the common law of England, which is our law, it might be construed sedition, indictable and punishable as a misdemeanor. In the delicate situation in which the country then was, it was thought to be a dangerous language, tending to lessen the respect due to the newly constituted authorities and evincing a bad disposition towards the cause of the people. A general and sincere concern was felt for the man because it was made a serious matter by the country and especially by the body of armed men who had marched a distance of twenty or thirty miles to do execution on his person and property. There were of the committee [those] who must be supposed incensed and of course resentful of the insult.

I had recourse to my usual expedient in desperate cases, pleasantry. "I recollect," said I, "to have read that in the time of Oliver Cromwell, lord protector of England, when he was in the height of his glory, a person came to him and gave him information of words used by another, greatly contemptuous of his dignity; viz., 'he has said that your excellency may kiss his ————.' 'You may tell him,' said Oliver, 'that he may kiss mine.' This Quaker has called us a scrub congress; let our sentence be that he shall be called a scrub himself."

The story of Cromwell had produced a sudden, involuntary, and loud laugh and [had] thrown a light upon the affair of Jackson, introducing a proper sentiment with regard to him; viz., that there was more magnanimity in disregarding his expressions than in punishing them. The troop that had brought him laughed and took him off to give him the epithet. He got a bucket of whiskey and water to drink with them and we heard no more of it.

The report was now about to be read; and a number of copies having been struck off, they were distributed among the members. While it was reading, there appeared great agitation in the committee; at some sentences, a rumor as in a church at the response—not "Lord help us to keep this law," but that of "Good Lord deliver us."

The popular mind had by this time gone far beyond that idea of an amnesty and they rather thought of giving an amnesty than of taking it, passing by the injuries of government on condition that it did not repeat them. They had expected a suspension of the law or, at least, a promise of a repeal of it.

I was a good deal alarmed and saw that it would not do to come forward immediately. It would be necessary to give them time to reflect a little and to prepare the way by a general conversation out of doors. Findley, Smiley,[44] and other popular men were on the ground and might contribute to inform the people.

It had struck Gallatin and others in the same point of view, and it was moved to adjourn until the next morning. It was with a view to give the members time to consider the report. An adjournment took place, and I heard Bradford calling for the Washington members to convene by themselves.

I had crossed the river that night and lodged at a farm house on the west side, and this not only with a view to convenience but also to be out of the way if, in consequence of dissatisfaction with our report, any personal violence to the committee of twelve, or any of them, should be meditated, a thing which I thought not at all improbable, for what avails popularity in such times as these? It is but the turning of the hand, the palm up or down, from the height of favor to the lowest point of obloquy and persecution. Was there any man in Pennsylvania more popular than John Dickinson at the commencement of the American revolution?[45] He was to be opposed to a

44. Assemblymen from Westmoreland and Fayette Counties who were political enemies of Brackenridge. Findley wrote his own account of the events: *History of the Insurrection in the Four Western Counties of Pennsylvania* (Philadelphia, 1796).

45. Called "the penman of the Revolution," John Dickinson opposed the Declaration of Independence and lost favor. But later (1787–1788) he wrote a series of papers under the pseudonym Fabius which promoted ratification of the Constitution.

declaration of independence and became obnoxious. James Wilson was at the height of political fame among the people but he had disapproved of the form of constitution they had adopted in the Commonwealth and they were about to murder him in his own house.[46] I possessed, at this present time, the best kind of popularity; viz., that obtained after much obloquy through a series of years, suffered to correct itself; a popularity obtained, doubtless, by failing a little with the popular gale, at least not opposing it, but chiefly by a steady and upright demeanor in my profession. The popular mind, though passionate, is generous; and if it becomes sensible that it has wronged a man, will repair it. I mean to explain this more fully, as far as regards myself, in the conclusion of this narrative.

But though possessing at this time a solid popularity, I knew that a breath on the subject of the excise law would put it to a temporary death. However, I had no thought now of the loss of popularity but so far as it would produce permanent danger on the ground. Gallatin was in his own country, among a people more moderate, and he might be in less danger; nevertheless, he was not without apprehensions and had reason.

In the morning, crossing the river and coming into the village, I was led to understand that at the private meeting of the Washington members the preceding evening a great warmth and talk of guillotining was heard and the clapping of hands. I met Gallatin and James Lang, a member of the committee of twelve and who was of that village [47] and was greatly alarmed from what he had seen and heard. It was early, and the committee of sixty had not yet collected; and the gallery, of which great numbers were from the neighborhood of the Mingo meeting house, had not yet convened. I had conversed with some the preceding evening before I left the village and found strong prejudices against me, as having made use of my talents as a lawyer to persuade the committee of conference to the acquiescence with the propositions of the commissioners. It was insinuated that we had been bribed, and [I] was told myself that attorneys would take fees. I hestitated, therefore, whether I should remain or not. It might be safest to return to Pittsburgh. I thought of this, more especially as I had observed that Bradford had preserved [48] a distance from me and

46. On August 4, 1794, this same James Wilson, now a justice of the State Supreme Court, issued a certificate stating that the laws in Western Pennsylvania were being obstructed by forces too powerful to be suppressed.

47. Brownsville.

48. Stood off.

appeared to be dissatisfied. I knew that the example of arresting members in the French Convention, the knowledge of which was familiar here, might lead to the arresting me or others that were obnoxious; and between an arrest and putting to death, as there so here, there would be but little interval. Gallatin acknowledged himself not insensible of the delicacy of the situation and that insult, at least, might be offered, but observed that we had bound ourselves in honor to the commissioners to come forward and support the propositions. I reflected with myself that, nevertheless, in this undertaking of our committee of conference with the commissioners it was not understood that we were to run a risk of life or even indignities in recommending their own interest to the people. However, as Gallatin was disposed to try it, I was willing. It was then considered what should be the order of our speaking; there was a reluctance with each of us to break the business. I proposed that we should get James Edgar, a member of the committee of twelve, to begin. He was an associate judge of the court of Washington and a king or a rabbi in the Presbyterian churches of the Western country, had been a presbytery or elder from his youth, had been a member of committees in the early period of the American revolution, and of legislative assemblies, executive and censorial counsels, or deliberative conventions ever since. His head was prematurely hoary with prayers and fastings and religious exercises; his face thin and puritanic, like the figures of the old republicans in the time of the long parliament in England. He was a man of sense and not destitute of eloquence. It was agreed that he should open the way for us. It was proposed by him, but he appeared reluctant, I know not on what principle. It was imposed, therefore, upon Gallatin.

The committee having convened with a formidable gallery, as the day before, Gallatin addressed the chair in a speech of some hours. It was a piece of perfect eloquence and was heard with attention and without disturbance. I shall not undertake to give the scope of this speech as I could not do it justice and probably may have misconceived and might mistake some part of it.

. . . .

It was a difficulty with me to find anything new that could be advanced, and I spoke more for the sake of showing that I had courage to speak than from an idea that I could add to the argument or improve the impression that had been made. However, I exerted my invention to vary the light of the argument and to add something new. Gallatin had addressed himself chiefly to the patriotism of the audience. I addressed myself to their conscience and fears. I confess that it was in their fears that I had most confidence. Gallatin had been didactic and deliberate, though animated. I became more impassioned and declamatory. My observations were to the following effect:

"It seems to be an idea entertained by the people that we can remain a part of government and yet wage war against it. That is impossible in the nature of the case; we are known to the government by representation only and not by force. We must therefore either overthrow it or it must overthrow us. But we have sworn to support it. If we contemplate the overthrowing it, where is our oath of allegiance? But can we overthrow it? We might as well think of tossing the Allegheny mountain from its base.

"But we may obtain a repeal of the law by an exhibition of force, by possessing the mountain and making a show of arms. That is not probable after the steps taken by the President. On principle of example it would so vitally affect the safety of the government that it can never be countenanced. We are told by the commissioners, and we have no reason to doubt it, that the whole force of the union will be exerted to crush such a precedent.

"But cannot we secede from the union? Not, and remain part of the government at the same time. We must dissolve our connection with Pennsylvania before we can cease to be under the government of the United States. But have we a right to dissolve our union with both? An individual may emigrate from society and a part of a society may separate from the whole, but an individual cannot leave a state in war because he owes service for the benefits he has enjoyed in peace. He cannot leave it without discharging debts he owes to individuals or to the public. How then can a part of the community separate before it has discharged the obligations contracted by the whole?

. . . .

"But is it our interest to secede? Having no sea coast, we are at the mercy of the imposts of all around us, even for the necessaries of life. If the weight of the Union, in the scale of nations, cannot procure us the surrender of the western posts, peace with the Indians, and the navigation of the Mississippi, how shall a half uninhabited, uncommerced extent of a hundred and fifty miles square command it? There is no manner of question but the time will come when the Western country will fall off from the Eastern, as North will from the South, and produce a confederacy of four; but surely it is our mutual interest to remain together as long as possible, to bear with inequalities or local and partial grievances while we enjoy general advantages and avoid general evils.

. . . .

"But are you able to secede? Can you fight the United States? Can you beat the 15,000 that are in requisition by the President? Grant it. Perhaps 30,000 in the passes of the mountains, for a heat. What of that? Are you able to beat a second 15,000 or a second 30,000? . . . I know your spirit but condemn your prudence.

"But do you know that you are mistaken in your support at home? Do you think that all are sincere who have been clamoring for war? Some clamor because they are cowards and wish to be thought brave, because they [are] ignorant enough not to expect a war. Others because they have not estimated the fatigues of campaigning and do not consider how soon they will be tired. Others because they have contracted for the sale of their lands, are about to remove to Kentucky or elsewhere. Others—and this class numberous—because they have nothing to lose and can make their escape by the floods. If you depend upon these, you will, by and by, have to take the same course and descend the current with the frogs.*

"But men affect to be for war because they are afraid to speak their real sentiments. I have my [eye] upon those here present and could name them who are thought to be strenuous for the most violent measures, and yet in the course of our committeeing have acknowledged to me what they really think, and it is their earnest desire to get out of the scrape upon almost any terms. After what has happened, any terms short of life ought to be accepted.

"The outrages have been grievous, wanton, and useless; in construction of law, amounting to high treason. Having had no privacy with these transactions or concern in the perpetration but disapproving when and where I could speak with safety, nevertheless, for the sake of those involved, I have labored hard to bring them out and have ever looked forward to that amnesty which is now before you. If I, who have nothing to apprehend for myself, have been ready to embrace it, surely those in a different predicament well may.

"I have heretofore felt myself embarrassed in [not] knowing what to do. I considered the feelings of the country with partiality of heart, knowing the ground of them to be the unequal law in question. I

* This expression escaped me in the hurry of the speech and gave great offense. [H.H.B.]

made excuses for the breaking into acts, knowing it to be the error of judgment, not distinguishing between what feelings are and what acts ought to be. I was impressed with the reflection that the disapprobation of the law having been general in the country and expressed by almost every one, no man could tell how far by words he might have contributed to that current of resentment which, at length, swelled beyond the constitutional banks of representation and remonstrance and broke out into outrage. He must, therefore, have a disposition to repair the mischief and save those who have gone to an excess not contemplated. . . . If these terms are not accepted, I am done and consider myself as discharged in honor and in conscience from all further concern in the business. It is, therefore, the last and only advice I have to give, that you acquiesce with the propositions of the commissioners and accept the amnesty offered you. It is the expedient left to save the country, which has been already impaired and reduced by your late history It was improving in agriculture, replenishing with buildings, becoming an object of emigration from abroad, and is now dejected from this height to a considerable depth from what it was. The value of property is reduced from what has happened. I do not consider what I possess at this moment as of more than one half of the value of what it was three months ago, but it will be still worse unless the evils that are impending are prevented by an immediate acquiescence. . . ."

Edgar followed me, with great earnestness and with the solemnity of an evening sermon, in a discourse of great length.

Bradford now rose to speak; and contrary to his engagements with the commissioners personally and his agreement with the report of the committee, he opposed the acceptance of the propositions in direct and violent terms. Speaking of the resources of war, arms, ammunition, etc., said he, "We will defeat the first army that comes over the mountains and take their arms and baggage."

"Not so easy neither," said a man in a blue coat who was in the gallery. This, I understood afterwards, was a Colonel Crawford,[49] a brave Indian warrior of the frontiers. He had some experience of what fighting was and an idea there might be fighting; Bradford had none. . . .

Gallatin spoke a little and moved to take the vote on the proposi-

49. On June 11, 1782, Colonel William Crawford was tortured and killed by the Indians at Upper Sandusky, Ohio. On the expedition which led to his death were Colonels John Crawford, his son, and William Crawford, his nephew. Brackenridge may be referring to either man.

tions of the commissioners. Objections were made to the taking any vote at all. The question was then put, "Shall a vote be taken?" This was negatived, not a single person rising but the committee of twelve who had made the report. It was again moved on our part to take a vote by ballot on the propositions, presuming that an unwillingness to let their sentiments be known on the subject was the reason of objecting to the taking the vote publicly. The question was put, "Shall a private vote by ballot be taken?" It was negatived, the twelve only, as before, rising.

Here was a moment of delicacy indeed. The taking no vote was rejecting the propositions. And what the consequence? Measures must have been taken instantly to prepare for war. Bradford would have come forward with the schedule, baffled at Parkinson's ferry, with his heads of ammunition, arms, money, provisions, etc. Gallatin and myself would have been arrested upon the spot. For the example of the terrorists, as they have been called, was in the public mind, especially with Bradford, who had some light, wandering information of French affairs as he had of other subjects, and had heard of their arresting one another after their debates and cutting off heads; and coupling the successes and the executions together, he would conceive the idea that the executions produced the successes.

Gallatin, with great presence of mind, seized the moment and proposed that we should take a final vote by ballot; not to be made a part of our answer to the commissioners but simply in order to know our own minds.

There was hesitation even at this, for every man was afraid the hand writing, even of his ballot, would be known, and by some means it might transpire in what manner he had voted.

At this instant, a member of the committee rising and having a scrap of paper in his finger with the word yea written on one part and the nay on the other, held it up and proposed that sixty scraps with the words yea and nay written in the same manner should be made out by the secretary, and a scrap given to each of the members; and let every one divide the scrap in two parts, with the yea on one and the nay on the other; and let him chew or tear the yea or the nay as he thought proper, and [put] the other piece into a hat held by the secretary. When these were drawn out, it would be seen what the private sense of the committee was, without the possibility of anyone knowing how another voted. This mode was thought sufficiently safe and adopted.

It struck me greatly to observe the carefulness of every one in dividing or putting in his yea or no. All having been put in and the tickets drawn out, there were found 34 yeas and 23 nays.

It verified what I had stated, that the sentiments of a great part were not privately what they publicly avowed. . . .

Bradford appeared struck on finding that the majority was with us. His countenance became dark and dismayed, for I remarked [50] him with attention. The members that had been for war were pretty easily discoverable by the dissatisfaction they evinced by the countenance or by language. There were some of them considerably enraged. But the gallery were the most explicit in showing satisfaction or dissatisfaction with the vote. It was in general not a popular one.

However, it had changed the face of things; and, there appearing a majority in favor of adopting the propositions, it remained for the committee to go on and make up their answer to the commissioners. But having sat a long time, it was thought proper to adjourn and meet again for the purpose. During the adjournment, Bradford went home. . . .

No gallery, or little, had attended in the afternoon. On going out I saw clubs and clusters of those who had been the gallery in private and close conversation in different places. Passing by some of them, I spoke with confidence, as if I suspected nothing, but was received with silence and with looks of indignity. These were persons who were at that time my clients in causes of moment and with whom I had been long in habits of attachment; yet notwithstanding every lien of amity, they behaved to me in this manner. A man whom I had brought with me from Pittsburgh to carry the copies of the report, a few hundred of which had been printed, gave me to understand that, from what he could overhear, there was something on foot. I gave him money to discharge my bill at the public house and, as speedily as I could without seeming to be in haste, crossed the river. My horses had been left in a pasture on that side. I assisted a lad in driving them up, bridled them and had them saddled, and was ready to mount, when the man whom I had left had got over. Some persons had crossed over with him; among these were four of the Allegheny members of the committee. It was then dark. We rode eighteen miles that night and got through the bulk of the Mingo creek settlement.

I have learned since that nothing but a want of decision prevented them from arresting me after my speech in the forenoon. It was in agitation, but they wavered in attempting it. The going away of

50. Observed.

Bradford also discouraged them. They had talked of arresting Gallatin, but his speech had been more abstract and guarded and had not given so much offense as mine. It was in agitation, some days after this, to take him; and a body of men had actually collected at Fredericktown on the west of the Allegheny for that purpose. They were dissuaded by persons who went over from Fayette County and who endeavored to remove their misconceptions.

In our company that night, of the four Allegheny members that were along, was one of the name of Miller. When he first joined us I was suspicious of him knowing that he had been a principal in the two attacks upon the house of the inspector and commanded a company upon Peter's creek in a settlement through which we had to pass. I did not know but he might have been dispatched with orders to arrest me as I went through. I communicated this to some of the other members in the company, and we took care to ride fast enough not to put it in his power to be much ahead of us. He lodged with us where we halted a few hours and slept on the planks at the house of a German.

In the morning when we had set out, which was early, on our way I kept close by him and fell into conversation. He had been in the American service during the war with Great Britain, had been employed chiefly in the Western country in the war against the Indians. [He] had distinguished himself for fidelity, activity, and bravery on every occasion. I led him to talk of his services, and he gave the history of a variety of incidents. Sliding gradually from thence, I touched upon the present affairs of the country, the coming of the marshall, the opposition to him, the attack upon the house of the inspector, etc. I knew he had been one of the delinquent distillers and that it was on leaving his house, after having served a writ, that the marshall had been fired upon, which was the first opposition he had met with in the service of process. Miller gave me, with frankness, a relation of the whole circumstances. "The federal sheriff," said he, "was reading the writ, and General Neville was on horseback in the lane when he called to the sheriff to make haste. I looked up and saw a party of men running across the field, as it were, to the head of the lane. The people fired upon them." "Do you think," said I, "they fired balls and meant to hit them?" Said he, "I believe they meant to hit them; they pursued them and would have killed them.

"That night," continued Miller, "it was concluded that we would go on to Neville's and take him and the marshall. I felt myself mad with passion. I thought 250 dollars would ruin me; and to have to go to the federal court at Philadelphia would keep me from going to Kentucky this fall, after I had sold my plantation and was getting ready.*

"I felt my blood boil at seeing General Neville along to pilot the sheriff to my very door. He had been against the excise law as much as anybody. When old Graham,[51] the excise man, was catched and had his hair cut off, I heard General Neville himself say they ought to have cut off the ears of the old rascal; and when the distillers were sued [52] some years ago for fines, he talked as much against it as anybody. But he wanted to keep in the Assembly then. But whenever he got an offer of the office himself, he took it. I am a relation of Kirkpatrick. His mother and my mother were sisters. I was always for General Neville in his elections, and it put me mad to see him coming to ruin me."

I desired him to give me the particulars of the attack upon Neville's house the first day. He did so; he said they had about thirty men with fifteen guns, six only in order. They found the general just got up. After some words, he fired first. It was from the windows. A horn was blowing in the house the time of the firing. "Was the door open?" said I. "It was," said he. "Why then did you [not] rush into the entry?" "We were afraid," said he, "that he had a swivel or a big gun there.

"The Negroes," continued Miller, "by this time fired out of their cabins upon our backs and shot several, and we got off as well as we could."

"Well, what now? Are you for war?" "No," said he, "I voted for peace, but if I was to acknowledge that, I need never go home. I will have to deny it, and I will have to do whatever my company will insist upon me doing now. But I expect to get away soon and to be clear of it."

* This was one of the men that was thought might be depended upon in case of a war. [H.H.B.]

51. Because of the prejudice, Westerners could not be appointed to collect the excise, and apparently few Easterners relished the position. In 1783, William Graham, a bankrupt tavern-keeper of Philadelphia, was sent to collect the taxes in Fayette, Washington, and Westmoreland Counties. Unable to collect, he accepted small bribes offered by the farmer-distillers to get rid of him. Graham became the butt of practical jokes and pranks. The people amused themselves by singeing his wig, cutting the tail of his horse, putting coals in his boots. In 1784 he was besieged in a public house in Westmoreland County through the whole night. When he finally escaped to Washington County, some hundred persons got hold of him, cut off his hair, and forced him back across the Monongahela into Westmoreland.

52. Twelve of Graham's attackers were brought to trial in 1785. Brackenridge acted as their attorney.

By this time we had arrived at his house, about eight miles from Pittsburgh. As we came up, three pretty children presented themselves in the inside of the fence that enclosed the cabin; and one of them said, putting his fingers between the rails, "Daddy, I have got a little brother." *

I was sensibly affected with the reflection that possibly that daddy might come to be hanged and that brother fatherless before it could know that it ever had one. . . .

Such was the state of things when the commissioners, both of the United States and the state of Pennsylvania, having done all that was in their power to do, left the country.

.   .   .   .

[9]

Just after the commissioners had left the country, a certain John Galton, calling on the printer of the *Pittsburgh Gazette,* presented him with a note which he had received, signed Tom the Tinker, commanding him to have it inserted in the *Pittsburgh Gazette.* In the situation of the country, even then, the printer thought it prudent for his own personal safety to insert it. It shows the sentiments of the violent, at this time, on the question of submission:

> Poor Tom takes this opportunity to inform his friends throughout the country that he is obliged to take up his commission once more, though disagreeable to his inclination. I thought when I laid down my commission before that we had the country so well united that there would have been no more need for me in that line, but my friends see more need for me than ever. They chose a set of men whom they thought they could confide in but find themselves much mistaken, for the majority of them have proved traitors. Four or five big men from below has scared a great many, but few are killed yet. But I hope none of those are any that ever pretended to be a friend to poor Tom; so I would have all my friends keep up their spirits and stand to their integrity, their rights, and liberty, and you will find poor Tom be your friend. This is a fair warning; traitors take care, for my hammer is up and my ladle is hot. I cannot travel the country for nothing.

> From your old friend,
>
> TOM the TINKER

John Galton, the person who brought Tom the Tinker's letter to the printer, was a client of mine in an enactment brought for him

---

* The woman had been brought to bed in his absence. [H.H.B.]

against a certain M'Clure. He called upon me at my office and, with a freedom which he thought he could take with his lawyer who would not suspect him of personal ill will, he inveighed against me much for having consented to the propositions of the commissioners. "What?" said he, "five men scare seventy-five?" The court being at hand, he was led to inquire when his cause would come on. "Not at all," said I. "How so?" said he. "Why," said I, "the government is gone to the devil; the courts are overthrown; all law is at an end; there can be no justice now. The strong hand must manage all things. Is this M'Clure a stout fellow? Has he any sons? Cannot you and your sons beat him? Take the cudgel and drive him off." "Ah," said he, "that will not do." "It may be," said I, "there is no help for it; that is all that can be done now, at least until some other government and other courts of law are set up in the place of those that are overthrown." He did not appear sensible of the scope of my observations but thought it a play of fancy on my part and laughed; and, after inveighing another while against the committee of conference, he would return to the question, "When will my cause with M'Clure come to trial?" I mention this incident to show the indistinct conception on the part of the people of the connection between the state government and the federal. Though laws of the state are not the laws of the union, yet the laws of the union are the laws of the state. I scarcely ever met a man that I could get to comprehend this. . . .

[10]

I had now set out to attend the court of Westmoreland at the seat of justice at Greensburg. The state of the public mind in this county was, as elsewhere, unfavorable to submission. The same charge, with additions, was delivered by Judge Addison here as at Pittsburgh, but I recollect no reply or approbation of the grand jury. The election for a member of Congress and for the state legislature was approaching, and the people talked familiarly of resisting and yet electing. The tide of popularity had not ebbed so far against me in that quarter, being remote from Brownsville, where I had declared myself. Applications were made to me to let my name run for Congress in that district, as they were dissatisfied with Findley on account of his recommending it to them to submit to the laws. They considered it as strangely inconsistent that he should have been speaking and writing against the law [53] and should all at once turn around and be in favor of it. Having had a political difference with Findley, which had become personal,[54] I might have been disposed on a less delicate occasion to improve the prejudice against him, and it might have been amusing to have taken advantage of the adverse gale to sail by him in a popular vote in his own district. But it must have been at the expense of the people and myself in an essential point of allegiance and fidelity to have availed myself of this error of the people at the time; I had therefore to justify Findley in his recommendation to them to submit. This had a good effect; for if so strong an adversary of Findley as they conceived me to be, and with an offer of a seat to Congress against him, nevertheless supported the same sentiments which were rendering him unpopular, these sentiments must be right and for their interest.

During the sitting of the court, great pains were taken to inform the people and persuade them. The second evening, all that were attending were convened and harangued by Findley and by gentlemen of the bar of that county. The disposition appeared to have become general to submit, that is, to make a declaration of committing no outrage for the future upon officers of the revenue. But there was reluctance at the idea of signing the words in the form of the commissioners.

In the evening of the third day I understood that a young man by the name of Parker, who resided in Westmoreland, was about setting out from Greensburg to his father's family near Parkinson's ferry in the county of Washington in order to inform them of the general disposition to submit in his county and induce them to sign and to take advantage of the amnesty, as several of his brothers had been involved in the affair of Neville's house. It struck me at the moment that it would be rendering an essential service to humanity and to the object of composing the country if that settlement from which the insurrection sprung could be brought to submit. I reflected that my apprehensions at Brownsville might have been, in some degree, imaginary. But if not, by this time the public mind might have cooled a little and reason have begun to take place; and that this young man, coming from Westmoreland and informing them of a

---

53. In 1787, William Findley led the opposition to the adoption of the Federal Constitution in the State Assembly. When a vote was to be taken, he and nineteen western members absented themselves in order to avoid a quorum.

54. Over the adoption of the Constitution. The object of ridicule in Brackenridge's Hudibrastic satire is William Findley.

disposition in that county to submit, the fear of being left by themselves would take place and reduce their violence. I felt a passion at the moment of risking my own safety to assist in accomplishing this object, and proposed to the court to excuse my attendance and I would ride into the Parkinson's ferry settlement. The distance to Parkinson's ferry was about twenty-five miles. Having set out and crossed the Youghiogheny river in the night, we halted and went to sleep for some hours in the ferry house. Setting out, we arrived at the Monongahela opposite Parkinson's ferry early in the day. Inquiring of the keeper of the ferry, of the name of Devore, with regard to the sentiments of the country, he referred us to a Major Scott, who was standing by loading his rifle. "I was over," said Major Scott, "the other day on Mingo creek when there were about two hundred present, and they all to a man pledged themselves not to sign and to shoot any man that will. I am going to the meeting in the forks of the river, and I will take care that nobody shall sign there."

I was silent and crossed the river.

. . . .

It was suggested by the young man to ride on to the house of Benjamin Parkinson, about a mile ahead. I hesitated, informing him that I knew of but two men in the settlement who had any predisposition to assassinate me and that Benjamin Parkinson was one of them, Andrew M'Farlane the other. He urged me with great earnestness and pledged himself to lose his life before I should lose mine. I rode on.

Coming opposite to the house and having leapt over a small pair of bars into the yard, I was struck with [the sight of] a horse standing saddled and a rifle at the door. I took it that Benjamin Parkinson was setting out for the place of meeting for the purpose of taking the sense of the people that day, and the taking his rifle with him was no good symptom of a disposition for submission.

Alighting and entering the house to an inner apartment, I was all at once appalled with the sight of Benjamin Parkinson and Andrew M'Farlane together; Andrew M'Farlane with a rifle standing by him. I was shocked; but concealing my sensations, I addressed Parkinson with an appearance of perfect confidence. He spoke frankly and with a countenance of pleasure. Stepping out with young Parker, he left me with M'Farlane, to whom I had bowed but not yet spoken. I was sitting just by him, within a step in the small room. I kept my eye upon his hand and his rifle, and thought if I saw him move to seize his rifle I could perhaps by a sudden spring gain the door. I cast a glance at a window in the room and thought of springing head foremost through it, if I saw him move. My fear was that the young man [*Parker*] would not have the resolution to offend the country by interfering to defend me after what Parkinson might communicate to him out of doors. I thought my situation precarious and the chances against me. While these were my sensations, I turned around with an open and direct countenance to M'Farlane. "Mr. M'Farlane," said I, "these are disagreeable times." "Indeed they are, Mr. Brackenridge," said he. The expression and the manner relieved me from my apprehensions in a moment and left me only at a loss to account for his seeming cordiality. "For," continued he, "I have been for these two days afraid of my life because I recommended submission. I have been afraid to sleep at home, and I am obliged now to go with my rifle." Ah hah, thought I, I shall not be shot yet.

Benjamin Parkinson in the meantime came in and expressed himself extremely happy at the information he had received from young Parker and much obliged to me for my intention of coming over to serve the settlement, that, for his part, he was heartily disposed to submit and was going to the meeting for the purpose. I asked him if he had a form of the submission; that if not, I had a number of them in my pocket. He said he had one. On inquiry I found that the district he had to attend lay up in Monongahela and out of my way to Pittsburgh. Young Parker and Parkinson urged me with great solicitation to ride there in order to assist in persuading the people; but, judging from their apprehensions, I did not think it advisable to run the risk. I answered that Parker's family doubtless credit their brother, and that he could give the same information that I could and state my solicitude in riding all night to serve them, that if I went to any meeting at all it would be to the Mingo meeting which was on my way, and to that of Peter's creek district which was on my way also. The only question was whether it would be advisable to go to the Mingo meeting. M'Farlane, with candor and good will towards me, gave his opinion that it was not advisable, that the rage of the people against our committee at Pittsburgh, and me especially, was violent, that, for his part, he was under apprehension of going himself to the Mingo district, though among his neighbors, and meant to go to David Hamilton's, about four miles distant in a lateral direction, in order to find out whether it would be safe to go to the meeting. On this I declined going but purposed writing, by him to Hamilton, an open letter which might be read at the meeting or elsewhere, as containing information from me. The letter was as follows:

David Hamilton:

Sir,

I have rode all night from the court at Westmoreland with a view to come to the meeting of the Mingo creek district but, from what I hear, do not think it safe; but I state my sentiments by letter, which you may consider as written to you and to others. It is to inform them that the greater part of Allegheny county will submit and all Westmoreland will and, I presume, Fayette. You will then be left alone. Surely you would not wish to give the excise officer the satisfaction of having you hanged. For this reason, all those that have been involved in any violence ought especially to save themselves. It is from motives of humanity that I have taken this trouble. If there could have been any doubt of a force coming before, after the propositions of the commissioners, if the people would persist, there can be no doubt; and it will come with a rage against the country, after having rejected what is so reasonable.

I took the road now towards Pittsburgh but not the direct road, as it would have led me by the Mingo Creek meeting house. As I rode I fell in with numbers crossing my course in a direction to the meeting, and all of them armed. Stopping at a cabin to inquire the way, I was struck with the appearance of John M'Donald, the secretary of the Mingo Creek society, stepping out. I was not afraid of him, having had a conversation with him in Pittsburgh and knowing his sentiments to be moderate. His advice also to me was not to go to the meeting; his expression was, "Let them go to the devil their own way."

Inquiring the way to Pittsburgh, he directed me by the house of John Holcroft. "This is the very man," said I, "that I am the most afraid of; he is Tom the Tinker. I was obliged to put up with the insulting language of one of his sons the other day in Pittsburgh, not thinking it safe to resent it in the present state of things. He threatened the town with Tom the Tinker."

M'Donald gave me directions in what manner, crossing a certain road that led from the house of Holcroft, I could avoid it, by a circuit through the woods, and come into the road again. But before I had got to that point I met two men on horseback, one of whom accosted me by name and himself sorry that he had set out before I had got to his house, that he might have offered me a little whiskey and something for my horse to eat. "But," said he, "I will go back with you to the house." I was not without apprehensions of every man; nevertheless, I thought the safest way was to affect to have confidence, and I suffered him to ride back with me. The man with him accompanied us.

When we came in sight of the house, I knew the farm to be that on which a certain Samuel Irwin, some years ago, had lived and which I knew had been sold to Holcroft. Heavens! thought I, is this Tom the Tinker? Is he to get his sons to help murder me, that he is taking me to his own house? Pretending civility but meaning to put it out of my power to negotiate with commissioners any more? However, I concealed my apprehensions and entered his house. Our conversation turned upon the business of the day, the signing a submission. Holcroft gave me to understand that the people were greatly averse in that neighborhood and threatened death. "That is unreasonable," said the man that was in company. "It is not so with us in our settlement. We allow free liberty of conscience and molest no man for [doing] what he pleases. Every man that chooses to submit, let him do it; and we give him five weeks to sell off his effects and move out of the country." I was diverted with his ideas of perfect freedom but thought that in five weeks probably the situation of the proscribed and the proscribing would be changed without the days of grace to sell off effects and move away.

I could discover in Holcroft hesitation to know what to do. I explained myself fully, informed him of the history of crossing from Westmoreland, with what views, etc. He expressed himself happy in having seen me and wished me to go to the meeting with him and to which he had been on his way, but acknowledged there would be danger of insult. I declined going for this reason and because I was now on my way past the ground. I took leave of Tom the Tinker and came on.

.   .   .   .

Coming to town, I was happy to learn that the people had generally signed the form of submission. It was too late and the hours of signing expired. But it was not for this reason but because I had no solicitude to bring myself within the amnesty, not conceiving myself to have any need of it, that I did not go forward even then to put my name to the paper. I went forward the next day and put my name to it that I might show the people that I would do what I had recommended to them to do, and that it had been my absence only that had hindered me from being among the first.

.   .   .   .

I had heard . . . by individuals from Philadelphia of the impression made upon the citizens by my letter to Tench Coxe; that it was considered as a letter of defiance and had excited an irresistible flame of indignation against me. This did not disturb me much at first, for I conceived the government would understand it also. Marshall Lenox had gone to Philadelphia and knew my solicitude in his behalf when at Pittsburgh. Presley Neville had gone, who though somewhat chagrined because I would not do everything his way, yet when his mind cooled would see things in a more proper point of view and would at all events do me the justice to acknowledge that it was at his instance that I came forward at an early period of the business. Commissioner Ross, who knew my conduct from the commencement, had been with the executive and, in speaking of those in this country that were hostile or offenders, would represent me favorably. On these grounds I was perfectly easy as to men of information near the President, and concluded that from thence just ideas with regard to me would spread and gradually correct the popular error with the militia that were coming forward. I had seen paragraphs unfavorable with regard to me in the gazettes; but I thought nothing of that, considering them as the result of an unavoidable but temporary misconception. I had also heard of the flame by the "Indian treaty" publication which was charged to my account and had raised the resentment of the Jersey militia in particular so that they were hewing me in imagination with their sabres as they came along and bayoneting every bush or other thing upon the road and calling what they bayoneted "Brackenridge." But I conceived it to be the policy of the more intelligent to let the people exercise their minds with some objects and perhaps improve their resentment, general or particular, but not that any person who knew my style would take that publication for mine.[55]

I had more reason to be apprehensive than I was aware. . . . David Reddick, commissioner with Findley from the committee at Parkinson's, returned from his mission to the President, whom he had found at Carlisle with the army on their march. He called upon me and, with great appearance of solicitude, gave me to understand the unfavorable point of view in which I stood with the army and the great danger I had to apprehend from the threats against me, that having occasionally introduced my name to the President as not being concerned in the insurrection, he was silent, but that those about him

55. Brackenridge had published "Thoughts on the Present Indian War" in the *National Gazette*, February 2, 1792, and had signed it with his own name. It contained passages which could be construed as a threat of insurrection.

appeared to have strong prejudices. This brought to my mind an expression I had seen in the address of the President at Carlisle, exhorting among other things "to detect intriguers." Thought I, that savors a little of chevalier Neville. He knows that I cannot be charged with any overt act and may have insinuated there, as he had done here, that I have intrigued against the government. The fact was, the intriguers here were all on the side of government; there was nothing but open force against it.

[12]

The rage of the army against me appeared to increase as they approached the country; at least the accounts received of menaces and death were every day more frequent and determined. It was said that I had saved myself by the amnesty of government, but that should not save me from death without the forms of law. The executive would not be justifiable in bringing me to trial in violation of their faith, but on moral or political grounds there would be no impropriety in the army exercising, at least in one instance, an act of summary though irregular justice. This I understood to be the language, not of those in the ranks of common soldiery only, but of the highest officers.

. . . .

The army was now at Bedford and Cumberland, and the inquiries with respect to me were whether I had left the country, or was it probable I would remain until they could get me in their power? It seemed to be a contest among them who should have the honor of dispatching me. I conceived that the example of the Jacobins in France had infected the mass of the army just as much as it had the people here in Tom the Tinker's time; and I thought it not at all improbable that I should be assassinated.

. . . .

It struck me, therefore, to address the army generally, in a hand-bill which would be circulated through the whole body, whereas, if I addressed individuals, my letters could not be generally communicated in order to correct in any degree the false sentiments entertained of me or to avert the intention of putting me to death without inquiry. Under this idea I drew up a short address and dispatched a messenger with some hundred handbills to commissioner Reddick and others who had been appointed from the last meeting at Parkinsons to wait again upon the President or other commanding officer

with the army in order to lay the state of the country before them. . . .
My directions to our commissioners, to whom I had transmitted my
handbills, [were] to deliver them to the commanding officers of the
different parts of the army to be by them distributed, if they thought
proper, among the troops. . . . Mr. Reddick, in order to serve me,
had contrived that some of the handbills should find their way among
the troops without going through the hands of the officers. I disapproved of having done this, for I knew that offense would be extracted from everything possible and that the officers would say this
was wrong. It was said to be wrong, and I began to be charged with
stupidity as well as villainy in not knowing better than to send
forward papers among the ranks of an army. I was blamed for
addressing them at all. I had considered this army as consisting of
citizens, and I did not conceive any greater impropriety in addressing
them in a camp by a handbill than in their counting houses or
upon their arms in the gazettes of Philadelphia, Trenton, or Rich-
mond. But I was unpopular. I was under the imputation of being a
traitor to my country. If I was not hanged, I deserved to be hanged;
and it was immaterial what I said or did, it would be taken in bad
part. It was said it was a damnable impertinence in me to have the
assurance to write or speak a word to anybody. I scarcely knew
whether to laugh or indulge chagrin at the absurdity of such speeches.
I had thought the recent instances in France, of men being run down
by the clamor of an occasion and murdered without an opportunity
of justifying themselves, might have corrected such precipitancy in
the American mind.

The deputation of commissioners from the country had not answered the end of arresting the march of the army by assurances of
the restoration of tranquility and obedience to the laws. The President
had seen things from a different point of view with me and had not
thought himself justifiable in suspending the march. I presume he had
not a perfect confidence in the submission of the people. It would
seem so from the circumstances of spies traversing the country at
this time in order to gain intelligence on which he could better depend
than on the representations of our commissioners. I presume he also
conceived that the exhibiting so formidable a force in the country
would leave an impression of fear, the best security, in his opinion,
against future opposition to the laws. . . . It would have a good
effect on other parts of the union, where a spirit of insurrection
might exist, to hear that an army had crossed even the Allegheny
mountain to the heads of the waters that run to the west in order to

crush the insurgency that had shown itself in that remote skirt of the government. It would have a good effect in Europe and restore that confidence in the government which had been lessened by the report of the disturbance of the summer. Finally, a great part of the army were anxious to see the Western country, and they might as well come on embodied as they were.

The right wing of the army had now crossed the mountain and were in the Western country. It was like the approach of a tempest to me. I could hear the thunder at a distance; every day new accounts of butchery denounced against me without judge or jury. I began to hear General Neville raise his voice: "The damnest rascal that ever was on GOD Almighty's earth."

The left wing had also crossed the mountain at the distance of thirty miles to the westward. I could hear of Colonel Neville at the table of General Lee [56] and publicly elsewhere through the camp denounce revenge against the "damned rascal," meaning me.

I began to think it would be unsafe to stand it, that I could not have sufficient confidence in the good disposition of the commanding officers, much less in their power to restrain injuries, and that it would be advisable to be out of the way a little until I could see whether subordination in the civil authority was preferable or not. I had the wilderness behind me and, as before I had meditated to escape from Tom the Tinker by going to the East, so now I meditated to escape from an equally outrageous banditti, as I began to think them, by going to the west. My sensations were violent at the time, but they ought to be excused, as I must have thought it very extraordinary in people to have come to support the laws and to be talking of violating them.

.   .   .   .

I lay upon a couch and thought of it till midnight. I reflected that people would always talk more than they would do, and that putting me to death would be more in the language than in the intention of the mass. It was the fashionable speech of the camp, and every one adopted it without meaning to carry it into effect. But I reflected also that this very strain of talking, though not originating from intention of act[ing] with the mass, yet might lead some inconsiderate and unprincipled men to perpetrate what they heard spoken of, more especially as I had heard of the violence of the Nevilles and

56. Governor Henry Lee of Virginia. Brackenridge had tutored him at Princeton.

suspected that the horrid resentment which they appear to entertain against me might prompt them to encourage assassination.

However, after the deep thought of many hours, I sprung from my bed couch and expressed determination that if I was to be assassinated it should be in my own house. It never should be said that I would move a foot from the ground, more especially as in my address to the army I said I would not.

. . . .

It was precisely as I had foreseen. Accounts from the army, of the language of the Nevilles, now began to be that of having me hung. I was diverted with a speech of General Neville's reported to me. When some of the people, alarmed for their situation, had gone forward to solicit his favor, "Children," said he, "it is not you we want; it is some of the 'big fish'—Brackenridge, Gallatin, and Findley— that we want." Thought I, it is high enough to expect to find me in the same shoal of fish with Gallatin and Findley, when I have had a political difference with Findley that has produced a distance which still exists and when I have never spoke to Gallatin in my life, that I recollect, until I saw him at Parkinson's ferry. But the fact was, Findley and Gallatin were obnoxious, perhaps with the judiciary, but certainly with Secretary Hamilton, who acted in aid of the judiciary in the examination of witnesses; and it would have a good effect to involve me in the odium of Gallatin and Findley. I give credit to the ingenuity of the old general in this.

[13]

. . . .

In the examination of all witnesses the great burden of the song was, "What do you know about Brackenridge?" I knew well that Secretary Hamilton would have a predisposition against me. He would rather find the opposition to the law to have originated in the plan of some leading individuals than with the mass of the people, for the excise law being a result of the funding system of which the secretary was an advocate, it would save the pride of judgment to have it thought opposed by the seditious arts of one or a few rather than by the feelings or common sense of many. I reflected also that the secretary would have observed in my letter to Tench Coxe and in some other publications that I was not a friend of the funding system itself. And this, even with a man of integrity, would constitute a bias imperceptible to himself; and I was sensible that the opinion of the secretary, in my case, would have weight with the judiciary.

. . . .

With the secretary and judiciary the wishes of the Nevilles' connections, who were considered as martyrs to the government, would have an almost irresistible influence. I reflected that the drift of my speech at the Mingo meeting-house might not have been fully understood at all; but more especially my management at Parkinson's ferry, the first meeting, was not understood generally, for it was not my wish that it should be generally understood, and therefore the testimony that would of course come forward, with regard to what was said or done on these occasions, would place my conduct in an equivocal, if not in a criminal, point of view. When I add to this the leaning that persons conscious of criminality would have to gratify the government, by testimony against a character that was to be run down in order to gain favor for themselves, I thought an arrest not improbable. But when I also took into view the prospect of favor with government, as to offices of which it would be supposed the Nevilles' connection would have now the distribution, and that an oath on the present occasion would go a great way to recommend, I thought my arrest certain.

. . . .

The way had been prepared; it had been given out that he [Bradford] was a weak man, that he had been gulled into the business, that he had been set up as a thing to be shot at by some behind the scene, that I was the manager of the puppet show, the most dangerous person to the government on the west of the mountain, that Gallatin and Findley were nothing to me. . . . He [*Bradford*] was to be represented to the secretary as deceived, misled by an artful and designing man, whom they wished hanged in his place. The Nevilles had been brought into it and begun to adopt the language suitable to the occasion and which continues to be the rhyme yet, that Bradford was gulled.

In the meantime a detachment of horse, escorting General Gibson who had been exiled, arrived at Pittsburgh. They were under the command of Corporal Cunningham, a merchant of Philadelphia. He had given the orders not to speak to me. I had supposed that General Gibson, who had been acquainted with the commencement of the insurrection, would have explained to them the mistake under which they had labored with regard to me. I had heard of him as the only one of the exiles who had the candor to do me justice on his way out of the country. It is probable he had given his opinion favorably with regard to what had happened before he went away, but it might be supposed that I had acted a different part afterwards. I reflected on my solicitude on his account at the time of the expulsion, when I saw him pass by my house with the dragoons of his train, looking up and laughing as much as to say, "There lives a fellow that is to be hanged." He ought to have recollected that he was chairman of the committee that exiled the first three. But Gibson is far from being an unfeeling or unjust man, but he was under the necessity of giving way to the current against me; it was too strong to be stemmed. He did go so far as to say that, all things considered, he could not conceive me to be so much concerned in the insurrection as I was supposed to be.

The next detachment that arrived was an escort of three or four squadron of horse, conducting in great pomp the younger Neville. General Morgan [57] himself was along. They showed themselves on the southern flank of the Monongahela; they crossed the river; the standards were unfurled and the cornets blew their horns; the guns of the garrison were discharged—it was like a Roman ovation, a species of the lesser triumph.

General Morgan, in the evening, accompanied by his suite and parading near my house with a military gait, was heard to say, "Hang the rascal, hang him."

After night, I was informed by my servants that some of the dragoons were occasionally coming and going and watching the avenues to the house, and that two of them had come into the kitchen and looked into the adjoining rooms. About nine o'clock I had [further] information that two of them had been in the yard and had gone away. This did not strike me much; I resolved it into curiosity or an intention of plundering something. They would naturally think it could be no great harm to make free with property of an insurgent.

However, the danger was greater than I had imagined; that night, about eleven o'clock, I was to have been assassinated. The troops had advanced to within twenty yards of my door when an officer who had been apprised of their inention and in vain labored to dissuade them, having run to General Morgan, who was in the house of Neville the younger and not gone to bed, gave him information. The

57. General Daniel Morgan, commander of the Virginia Volunteers and young Neville's father-in-law.

general and the colonel ran out without their hats; and the general, opposing himself to the fury of the troops, said that it must be through him they would reach me, that I had stood my ground, would be cognizable by the judiciary, and "let the law take its course."

I had dismissed all apprehensions of assassination, conceiving that my adversaries had turned their attention to a legal prosecution. It was not until two or three days afterwards that I heard of the attempt of the troops of cavalry. I had thought myself perfectly secure, at all events, from a detachment under immediate command of the general. . . . I will not say that the Nevilles were usually capable of deliberately contemplating the putting me to death. The father is outrageously passionate but not vindictive or cruel; the son is a man of good temper and humanity but labored under irremovable misconceptions, owing to a variety of circumstances; and their pride had also been wounded by acts of mine which I thought virtuous and think so still.

.   .   .   .

When the matter was thought to be pretty well fixed against me, the great and concluding stroke was to be given. A treasonable letter of mine, addressed to a certain Bradford, had fallen into the hands of my adversaries. It was dark and mysterious and respected certain papers, a duplicate of which I wished him to send me, having mislaid the first copy, that these were so essential I could not go on with the business without them. This letter was now brought forward. "What do you make of that?" said Secretary Hamilton to James Ross, who was present. "You have averred, as your opinion, that Brackenridge had no correspondence with Bradford. Look at that. Is it not the handwriting of Brackenridge?" "It is the handwriting," said James Ross, pausing for some time. "And there is only this small matter observable in the case, that it is addressed to William Bradford, Attorney General of the United States, not to David Bradford."

When a blast, transverse, takes a shallop on the river and throws her on her beam ends with all her sails set, or when a scud of wind takes the standing corn of the farmer and on the field bows the stalks to the earth, so languished my brother of the bar.[58] The old

58. John Woods, attorney for the Neville faction. Brackenridge had opposed him on several occasions at the bar. Presumably it was Woods who presented the letter to Alexander Hamilton.

general [59] stood motionless and speechless and to this hour had been standing had not Secretary Hamilton broke silence. "Gentlemen," said he, "you are too fast. This will not do."

.   .   .   .

It was amusing to me to see the numbers of those coming forward, and passing themselves for friends of government, whom, during the insurrection, I had a great deal of trouble to keep down. They took their revenge now and joined in the cry against Brackenridge.

Some poor fellows did this to save themselves; I had given them leave to do it. They came to me with tears in their eyes to consult whether they would go off or not or stand trial. The army had then crossed the mountain. I directed them to contrive to let my brother of the bar hear them curse me and say they had voted against me at the election; this would be carried to the ear of my adversaries, and they would be represented as friends of government. They did so, and it had the effect.

At the time I had given this advice, I had dreaded nothing but an assassination; I had no idea of having anything to fear from a judiciary process. Now I began to apprehend danger from this source. I looked forward to a trial before a jury in Philadelphia which, heated with prejudice against me, would differ little from a revolutionary tribunal in Paris. Besides, the part I had been drawn in to act was so various and of such a nature that it would take a multitude of witnesses to explain the quo animo,[60] and the expenses of a trial would ruin me. But what alarmed me still more, from a stroke that I received from a sedentary life twenty years ago,[61] I am subject to a delinquency of failing of nerves, especially when anything affects my mind; and I was afraid that my feeling would kill me under a sense of the arts [62] that were practising against me. I bore it with apparent fortitude, but my sensibility was greatly affected. Not that I was uncommonly afraid of death, but I regarded my memory for the sake of my family and was apprehensive that if I sunk under the sensibility of my affections it would be resolved into a consciousness of guilt and

59. Neville.
60. With what mind or intention.
61. Brackenridge suffered a nervous illness when he was a Maryland schoolmaster in 1775.
62. The devious arts.

not into the pain which the ingenious mind feels when it is wronged by the world.

[14]

Men were dragged out of their beds at two o'clock in the morning, not suffered to dress themselves but in an unfinished manner obliged to march, some of them without putting on their shoes, which they had to carry with them in their hands; dragged out of their beds amidst the cries of children and the tears of mothers; treated with language of the most insulting approbrium by those apprehending them; driven before a troop of horse at a trot through muddy roads, seven miles from Pittsburgh; impounded in a pen on the wet soil; the guard baying them and asking them how they would like to be hanged, some offering a dollar to have the privilege of shooting at them; carried thence four miles towards the town; obliged to lie all night upon the wet earth without covering, under a season of sleet, rain, and snow; driven from the fire with bayonets when some of them perishing had crawled, endeavoring to be unseen, towards it; next day impounded in a waste house and detained there five days, then removed to a newly built and damp room without fire in the garrison at Pittsburgh; at the end of ten days brought before the judiciary, and the information against them found not to be regarded. Was this the way to quell the insurrection? Was this the way to make good citizens? Do I blame the judiciary? No. I blame the management of those concerned to injure them. These were neighbors and friends of mine, and that is the secret of their sufferings. It was thought by my adversaries that they might have a knowledge of something against me and that, when alarmed for themselves, they would disclose it. At least I can in no other way account for the representation which had been made with regard to them as suspicious persons. They were examined, but all they could say was in my favor.

.   .   .   .

Hearing that I had been considered as a leader of the insurgents, I thought I must endeavor to support the appearance, as I would be a good deal looked at. And I had just before this time got a large cocked hat and buff underdress with a coat of military blue, and now and then occasionally showed myself in the street, imitating as well as I could the grave deportment and stately gait of a general officer. A variety of detachments of horse had come to town, and I found it was a matter of curiosity to see the leader of the insurgents. I would sometimes hear it said, when not supposed to hear it, "He has the appearance of a military man."

In order to account for this, it was said by some who pretended to know my history that I had been an officer in the late war.

. . . .

It might be supposed that as the danger approached I might become more alarmed and abscond, if direction was given to take me in the day; and for that reason and because it would gratify my adversaries to accumulate humiliation against me, I counted upon being arrested in the night. I therefore lay all night upon a couch without undressing, ready at a moment to obey the mandate and go with the guard that should call me. I lay two nights in this manner, not sleeping much, but consoling myself with reading some of the lives of Plutarch. Reading that of Solon,[63] I meditated upon his laws making it death for a citizen in a civil tumult not to take part, for by taking a part on one side or the other, the moderate citizens will be divided and, mixing with the violent, will correct the fury on both sides until an accommodation can be brought about. It was on that principle I had acted in the insurrection and by seeming to be of the insurgents had contributed to soften all their measures and finally prevent a civil war. But I saw that the law of Solon would apply chiefly to a small republic where the moderate men were known to each other and could explain themselves in the course of the negotiation. I had been treading upon a precipice, making an experiment extremely dangerous. My intentions were laudable but my conduct hazardous. It is true I had been called upon, in the first instance, by a public officer; and through the whole of the scene was in confidence with men that I had conceived would be unsuspected. But I was at a great distance from the seat of government and not in confidence with the first officers, and it might be said that I had deceived others. If the like scene should happen again, I will not conduct myself on the principle of Solon's law. Let people that are to be expelled get out of the country the best way they can, and let the executive and insurgents settle their own negotiations; I will have nothing to do with them.

In the meantime, the judiciary had come to Pittsburgh and the commander-in-chief also. The deputy quartermaster had taken my house for headquarters; not, I believe, because it was my house, but

---

63. The lawmaker of Athens (639–557 B.C.) has been credited with the first decisive steps towards true democracy.

because it was a large one. I was pleased, in one respect, to see written upon my door, "The commander-in-chief's quarters," as it would secure [me] from assassination.* But on the other hand, it would increase the ignominy to be dragged hence under a guard.

I had reduced myself with my family to one apartment of my house, where I meant to remain and not see the general, but unexpectedly [I] was informed that some of the military had entered the outer door and were asking for me. Having nothing but the arrest in my mind, I composed myself for a moment and stepped out to surrender myself, thinking of some words to address the officer of the guard in order to conciliate, as far as was practicable, civility of treatment. I was appalled at the address of General Lee, who, with his suite, had just entered. I had known him when a lad at the academy [64] twenty years ago; and I had often, as being a senior scholar, assisted him in his prelections or in the study of the principles of composition and eloquence, and had never expected to see him the general of an army arresting me for an attempt to overthrow a government.

The general discovered a pause in me to receive his advance and to answer, and asked if he was mistaken in supposing that his quarters were to be my house? I gave him to understand that there was no mistake and, having showed him in to an apartment, withdrew. I confined myself to my apartment. The day after, General Lee sent a message to me, signifying his expectation that, as my house was taken up by his family, I would dine with him. It was extremely painful to me, but I could not make an apology without explaining the delicacy of my situation; and it had been my system to be prepared for an arrest but not to discover that I had expected it. I endeavored to decline the invitation upon commonplace grounds, but he insisted and I dined with him.

At dinner I sat next to General Chambers, whom I had never seen in my life before; yet I hated him. I had heard that the day of the arrest of the inhabitants from Pittsburgh, when the guard was removing them from the first ground to a second at some distance, the captain of the guard, Calhoun of Chambersburg, had lent his horse to my neighbor, Andrew Watson, who had fallen sick and was unable to walk, when General Chambers, coming up, ordered him to dismount with opprobrious appellations. I conceived from this incident that the general had discipline but not humanity. Perhaps at the

* There were still threats to this effect. [H.H.B.]
64. Princeton.

time I did not make a sufficient allowance for that indignation which he felt on seeing one whom he must think a great culprit treated with indulgence. As soon as I could, to save appearances, I withdrew from the table. My mind was extremely hurt; for though every person behaved with politeness to me, yet I conceived them to think me an insurgent, and I felt every moment the absurdity of dining in such company this hour and the next to be conducted with ignominy as a criminal.

Early next morning a subpoena was read to me from Judge Peters,[65] commanding me before him at his chamber to give testimony touching all such matters as should be inquired of me. I considered this as in fact an examination touching myself, and that on the opinion formed from this was to depend my being or not being arrested.

I attended the judge and was referred by him to Secretary Hamilton for examination. I was received by Hamilton with that countenance which a man will have when he sees a person with regard to whom his humanity and his sense of justice struggles; he would have him saved but was afraid he must be hanged. [He] was willing to treat me with civility but was embarrassed with a sense that in a short time I must probably stand in the predicament of a culprit and be in irons. He began by asking me some general questions with regard to any system or plan within my knowledge of overthrowing the government. I had known of nothing of the kind. After a number of general questions, to which I had to answer in the negative, I proposed putting an end to that by giving him a narrative of everything I did know. It was agreed, and he began to write. I gave the outlines of the narrative I have given in this publication until I came to that particular where, after the burning Neville's house, I represented the people calling upon Bradford and Marshall to come forward and support what was done, under the pain of being treated as Neville himself had been. At this the secretary laid down his pen and addressed himself to me, "Mr. Brackenridge," said he, "I observe one leading trait in your account, a disposition to excuse the principal actors; and before we go further, I must be candid and inform you of the delicate situation in which you stand. You are not within the amnesty. You have not signed upon the day, a thing we did not know until we came upon this ground, I mean into the Western country. And though the government may not be disposed to proceed rigorously, yet it has you in its power, and it will depend upon the candor of your account

65. Judge Richard Peters had accompanied the army in order to deal with the recalcitrant whiskey boys on the spot.

what your fate will be." My answer was, "I am not within the amnesty and am sensible of the extent of the power of the government; but were the narrative to begin again, I would not change a single word." I went on. Having passed through the circumstances of the marshall and Neville being privy to my giving my opinion to Black and Hamilton on the effects of the writs of subpoena against delinquent distillers, and Neville requesting me to go to the Mingo meeting house, my examination was adjourned, Mr. Hamilton being called upon to dinner; and I was desired to attend in the afternoon.

I came home but declined dining with General Lee that day, though pressed by several messages. I could not bear to show myself with that company in the doubtful predicament in which I stood.

At three o'clock I returned to my examination. Mr. Hamilton, entering the room where I waited for him, appeared to have been reflecting and said, "Mr. Brackenridge, your conduct has been horribly misrepresented." I saw he never before heard the least of my being solicited by Neville the younger to go to the meeting at Mingo Creek; but having just dined in company with Neville at the house of Major Craig, where I was then examined, he had asked Neville, and he had acknowledged it. This is conjecture.

I went on to give an account of the Mingo Creek meeting. The secretary appeared not satisfied. "Mr. Brackenridge," said he, "you must know we have testimony extremely unfavorable to you of speeches made at this meeting, in particular your ridiculing of the executive." I saw that some fools had misunderstood and had been giving accounts of what I had deduced from the lenity of the President in the case of the Presque Isle establishment and my introducing General Knox and the Seneca Indian, Obeal or Cornplanter, making speeches. I was extremely hurt to think that . . . I should be at the mercy of the accounts of persons who did not understand me and obliged to answer the pleasantry I had found necessary to use to carry off their minds for a time from the object they were upon until I saw them better disposed to hear what I had farther to say. My answer was, "Five persons were chosen to go with me to that meeting for the express purpose of bearing testimony of what I should say; let these be called upon. Is it reasonable I should be at the mercy of the misconceptions or a voluntary misrepresentation of weak or prejudiced individuals?" He was silent. I went on, giving an account of the town meeting of Pittsburgh. I stated it, as moved by me, that we should march and affect to join the people at Braddock's fields. I saw the secretary pause at this and sink into a deep reflection. It staggered him. "Was it any more," said I, "than what Richard the Second did when a mob of 100,000 men assembled on Blackhearth? The young prince addressed them, put himself at their head, and said, 'What do you want, Gentlemen? I will lead you on.' " [66]

My narrative now continued. After some time the secretary observed, "My breast begins to ache. We will stop tonight. We will resume it tomorrow morning at nine o'clock." I withdrew but was struck with his last expression. I was at a loss to know whether his breast ached for my sake or from the writing; but, disposed to construe everything unfavorable, I supposed it was for my sake and that he saw I must be arrested.

Next morning General Lee made an apology to Mrs. Brackenridge that, for the sake of retirement and to be in a less central part of the town, he was about to withdraw to other quarters with some part of his family. I considered this as owing to the delicacy of his feeling, that he wished to be out of the way and not a witness of the circumstance of one with whom he had been acquainted in juvenile years sinking into a melancholy situation just under his eye. I had taken it for granted that he had received a hint from Mr. Hamilton of what was to take place.

Waiting on the secretary at nine o'clock, my examination recommenced. In the course of the narrative, his countenance began to brighten and, having finished the history, there was an end. "Mr. Brackenridge," said he, "in the course of yesterday I had uneasy feelings. I was concerned for you as for a man of talents. My impressions were unfavorable. You may have observed it. I now think it my duty to inform you that not a single one remains. Had we listened to some people, I do not know what we might have done. There is a side to your account; your conduct has been horribly misrepresented, owing to misconception. I will announce you in this point of view to Governor Lee [*the general*], who represents the executive. You are in no personal danger. You will not be troubled even by a simple inquisition by the judge; what may be due to yourself with the public is another question."

In so delicate a case, where [my] life had been sought by insidious men and where, what I felt with more sensibility, my hopes of estimation in the world were likely to be blasted at least for a time, it may easily be supposed that no word escaped me or will ever be forgotten.

66. In 1381 the peasants revolted against the tax. Richard rode out to meet them; and when Wat Tyler, their leader, was killed, Richard called to the group to take him as leader. He was fourteen years old.

My sensibility had been greatly wounded when I waited on Judge Peters with the narrative, to sign it as directed by Mr. Hamilton. It was with difficulty I could write my name. I cursed the circumstance of having to write it five times to the five different sheets of paper of which my narrative consisted. I returned to my house with different feelings from those I had for a long time before.

.   .   .   .

[15]

My adversaries were extremely enraged at the disappointment of not having me arrested. I was diverted with an expression of old General Neville: "The most artful fellow that ever was on God Almighty's earth; he has deceived Ross, has put his finger in Bradford's eye, in Yates' eye,* and now he has put his finger in Hamilton's eye too; I would not wonder if he is made attorney for the states on the west of the Allegheny mountain."

My brother of the bar expostulated very warmly with the judiciary for the astonishing defect of official duty in not sending me in irons to the capital. It is to be presumed they made proper apologies for acting agreeably to their own judgment and contrary to his.

Neville the younger had conducted himself with more delicate but with more dangerous address. I had been more apprehensive of the effect of his influence than that of the attorney. Having failed of a public prosecution, his object has been to establish individual resentment. I have heard of the information he has given with a view to make me enemies. When I am called upon, I will answer as to the correctness of the information given.

Talk of assassinating me had considerably subsided in the meantime. A feint had been made one day as I stood in the door. An officer presented a pistol within a few steps. It was to intimidate; for on my not moving, but looking at him steadily, he dropped it. He was a whimsical fellow; for returning to the public house, he took part against another officer who was abusing me and said I must be an honest man, for I stood firm when presented his pistol. It came to a contest between them, and my champion disarmed his adversary.

Governor Howell,[67] having been by this time a little better informed in my case, had the politeness to call upon me and make an apology for destroying my handbills, alleging nevertheless the impro-

---

* The Attorney General and Commissioner Yates. It would seem that these gentlemen spoke favorably of me on their return from the country. [H.H.B.]

67. Governor Richard Howell of New Jersey.

priety of my addressing an army by sending writings into camp. I affected to acknowledge it to be an error of judgment in me, but I thought it an error of prejudice in him. However, I was greatly pleased with the soldier-like appearance, the frankness of manners, and the eloquence of the governor, and was very sorry that, though my standing was better than it had been, yet even then I could not feel myself easy in visiting his troops, among whom I had many academic acquaintances, having been educated at the college of that state.[68]

Arrangements had been made for the return of the army, and the divisions had moved. Governor Lee gave a dinner to the gentlemen of the village. I had no invitation. He was led to suppose that it would give offense to the greatest part. I smiled to think how my adversaries were reducing themselves and raising me.

I had an invitation to dine with the Governor next day, with his family alone. If this was not a greater compliment, it was certainly a greater pleasure to me than to have had an invitation with the crowd. He did me the honor to request a conference in private the morning following, on the affairs of the country. It was a proof to me that, though he had given my adversaries the compliment of ceremony, he gave me that of confidence.

A dinner was now to be given to the Governor on the part of the citizens. A number of gentlemen, who had called upon me and expressed their indignation at the treatment I had received, solicited me to join in the subscription to the entertainment to be given to the Governor. I declined it on the ground of not having been at the public dinner on the part of the Governor.

A ball was now to be given on the evening of the entertainment. Prothonotary Brison had been always thought qualified for, or at least assumed the place of, a master of ceremonies on these occasions. He was made manager; and whether it was because I had called him a coxcomb or my adversaries managing him, he declined sending the usual card to Mrs. Brackenridge. She was hurt; I saw the flush of indignation in her cheek and sparkle of fire in her eye. I was offended for a moment. "What!" said I, "Are you hurt at this? You insult me because it is on my account you suffer the indignity. Did you not read to me, the other evening, the life of Phocion? [69] After having rendered

---

68. Princeton, then called the College of New Jersey.

69. The Athenian general (402–317 B.C.) who opposed Demosthenes in recommending peace with Philip of Macedonia. Later he was suspected of aiding Alexander in taking Piraeus and fled for his life to the protection of the Mace-

services to the state and accused of treason by the arts of malignant individuals and acquited by the people, suppose his adversaries to have taken their revenge by getting a master of ceremonies to exclude his wife from a ball; would you not think it more honorable to be the wife of Phocion under these circumstances than of a common Athenian, though you had received a card and been called upon to lead down the first dance? Would not Phocion have laughed at the indignity as I do? And would not his wife have laughed too?" By this address to the pride of the human mind I had a philosopheress in a moment, perfectly reconciled with the circumstance.

Excuse the comparison of small things with great, myself with Phocion. It was a rhetorical flourish to save myself from being wounded by my adversaries.

[16]

I have now finished the detail which I had in view. That my information may not have been correct in all cases, that my memory may have led me into error, that my imagination may have colored facts is possible; but that I have deviated from the strictness of truth, knowingly, is what I will not admit. That I have been under the painful necessity of giving touches which may affect the feelings of some persons is evident. But it has been with all the delicacy in my power, consistent with doing justice to myself. If I have done them injustice, they have the same means with me in their power—an appeal to the public. This is the great and respectable tribunal at which I stand. For though I have not been arraigned at the bar of a court of justice, yet from the first moment of obloquy against me I have considered myself an arrested man and put upon by my country. From that day the morning sun shone to me less bright, the light of night has been more obscure, the human countenance presented nothing but suspicion. The voice of man hurt me; I almost hated life itself. For who can say that I have pursued riches? Who can say I have been a devotee of pleasure? Who can say I do not love fame? What then have I, if I lose the hope of estimation? Was I traitor to my country? Ask me, was I a traitor to that class of men with whom I am in grade of education? Would I disgrace the praise of science, the advantage of an enlightened reading, who am taught to know that

---

donians, but they turned him over to the Athenians, who condemned him to drink hemlock.

virtue is glory, and benevolence and truth that alone which can assimilate with the Divine nature? And what greater deviation than to disturb the settled order of a government while the government remains republican? Such owes it and such to be supported; and any man who touches it with any other views than to rub the wheels and springs deserves the anathema of the people.

[*Philadelphia, 1795. The selection includes Volume I, Chapters 1, 5, 6 8, 9, 10, 11, 12; Volume II, Chapters 1, 2, 7, 8, 9, 10, 11; and Volume IV, Conclusion.*]

III

Collection And Recollection

from *Gazette Publications*

[*After a life of political struggle and often personal combat, Brackenridge collected some remains of his accomplishments and called them* Gazette Publications. *The introduction contains his own judgments upon his writing and its impact. Except for his early drama,* Battle of Bunkers-Hill, *the collection consists of work on the frontier. In the conclusion to the collection he finds that, of all the pieces in the collection, the introduction is the least pleasing. Perhaps its deep penetration into the author's knowledge of himself is embarrassing. Or perhaps the introduction did not please because the work itself appeared to take on greater value in the process of collecting it, and consequently the author began to feel the introduction to be "vanity under the guise of humility," as he says. At the end he does think the work may have longer duration than he had hoped when he began the collection. But successful or not, the literary effort was the most important of all activities in his life. And yet he would warn his son against too much attention to polite literature because it seduces one away from the more profitable pursuits of life.*]

Introduction

. . . I do not flatter myself that my memory will survive me long. It is sufficient, at least it is the utmost that I can expect, that it can survive a few years. And even this not without some pains to make it live. For I do not conceive myself to be what I will acknowledge I was once disposed to think myself, a thing endowed with faculties above the capacity of ordinary mortals. But had it not been that I had some idea of this kind, I would not have made the exertions that I have made. For since the discovery of my mistake, I feel myself sinking into indolence and considering only how I shall get through the world, the small remainder of it that lies on hands. It is of little consequence to me what mankind think of my talents, provided I can get ease and quiet living. It may seem then strange that I should collect this trash and put it together in a volume. It is not with a view to a long period of posthumous existence but that of a few years among my immediate descendants, who may take some little pride in preserving the memory of a literary man, and this for their own sakes; for though my fame must fall short of giving luster to a country, yet it may throw a little light on a small circle of immediate descendants and endure, perhaps, for a generation after I am gone. By a generation I do not mean any determinate number of years but the age of a child who may preserve a volume of these publications. For as to grand-children, I give it up. I shall not be remembered by them. So far am I from anticipating immortality, in the language of the poets, that I think twenty years will about do; and I am resigned to this, finding that with all the pains I have taken I can make no better of it. But who could know unless he had tried? But I am willing to give myself the best chance, even for the few years of recollection that may be in my power to add to my name—memoriam nostri quam maxime longam offerre.[1] I feel some regret that I have lost many things occasionally written and thrown by in manuscript or appearing in fugitive pamphlets in print—some of them, which is not saying much, probably better than anything which is preserved. I have no idea that this volume or any part of it will be republished, but it is something to have seen the light at all or to have born to be collected. This I do not believe it will do so as to defray the expenses of printing; but it may go a certain length towards it, and the self-love of the author must supply the rest. Who knows after all but that even an hundred years hence a copy of this impression may be found in an old library among scarce books and be valued because it is the only one remaining. It has been always a matter of amusement to me to be rummaging among old and scarce books, to see in what manner the human mind had employed itself in times past. It is astonishing to think on what a variety of subjects books have been published since the art of printing has been invented. I remember to have heard old Doctor John Witherspoon, Principal of the Jersey College,[2] make this remark and say that he was particularly struck with this in looking over an old library in Britain and finding a treatise in Latin "De humani capitis caesarie." [3]

It is true, what I have collected here consists of nothing but shreds; but I have been always fond of miscellanies, and it was not so much the value as the variety that pleased me. Hence it is that I have supposed these scraps may afford amusement, especially if they are accompanied with observations, as they occasionally will be,

1. To remember me as long as possible.
2. Princeton.
3. From the hair of the human head.

which will throw some light upon the affairs of men and the history of the time.

The Trial of Mamachtaga

[*Usually Brackenridge wrote in haste and later retouched his work for publication. But even his rewriting appears hasty. "The Trial of Mamachtaga" was composed soon after the events which it reports, and was only slightly revised for* Gazette Publications *(1806) and for Archibald Loudon's* Selection of Some of the Most Interesting Narratives of Outrages Committed by Indians in their Wars with the White People *(1808). In the revision Brackenridge added the perspective of more than twenty years but did not reduce the awkward phrasing of the original. Nevertheless this true account renders a realistic story that compels understanding and sympathy for the Indian forced to live in a white man's world.*

Uniquely in Loudon's selection of Indian narratives, "The Trial of Mamachtaga" concentrates on the character of the Indian rather than his deeds. Through the narrator's point of view, which is objective, the reader sees the Indian at close range and is led to an appreciation of his virtues. These virtues are contrasted with those of the mob, who desire to lynch the Indian, and with those of the judges, who appear unaware that Indians can possess ennobling traits. Before the story ends the reader begins to associate the white man with the savage characteristics usually attributed to the Indian.

Shortly after his arrival in Pittsburgh, Brackenridge wrote two narratives of Indian atrocities (also contained in Loudon's Selection*). The following sympathetic portrayal of Mamachtaga, composed three years later, demonstrates a deeper concentration on the sensibilities of the individual, an approach that was to characterize much of the fiction in the nineteenth century.*]

I know the particulars of the following story well, because one of the men (Smith) was shingling a house for me in the town of Pittsburgh the evening before he was murdered by Mamachtaga, and for which murder and of some others, this Indian was tried. Smith had borrowed a blanket of me, saying that he was about to cross the river (Allegheny) to the Indian camp on the west side. Here a party of Indians, mostly Delawares, had come in it, it being just after the war and the greater part of these Indians having professed themselves friendly during the war, and their chief Killbuck[1] with his

---

1. In 1779 the Delaware Indians warred against the United States. Only a few of them under Chief Killbuck refused to join the war. They moved to Smoky Island at the mouth of the Allegheny to be under the protection of Fort Pitt.

family and that of several others having remained at the garrison or on an island in the Ohio river called Killbuck's island and under the reach of the guns of the fort. Mamachtaga had been at war against the settlements with others of the Delawares who were now at this encampment.

I went myself over to the encampment the next morning and found the Indians there. Two men had been murdered, Smith and another of the name of Evans, and two wounded, one of them a dwarf of the name of Freeman. According to the relation which I got from the wounded, there were four white men together in a cabin when Mamachtaga, without the least notice, rushed in and stabbed Smith mortally, and had stabbed Evans who had seized the Indian who was entangled with the dwarf among his feet, attempting to escape, and who [*the dwarf*] had received wounds also in the scuffle; and the other white man also had received a stab. It would appear that the Indian had been in liquor according to the account of the other Indians and of the white men who escaped. Killbuck appeared greatly cast down and sat upon a log, silent. Mamachtaga made no attempt to escape. He was now sober and gave himself up to the guard that came over, affecting not to know what had happened. The seat of justice of Westmoreland county being thirty miles distant and the jail there not being secure, he was taken to the guardhouse of the garrison to be confined until a court of Oyer and Terminer should be holden in the county. Living in the place and being of the profession of the law, said I to the interpreter Joseph Nicholas, one day, "Has that Indian any fur or peltry, or has he any interest with his nation that he could collect some and pay a lawyer to take up his defense for this homicide?" The interpreter said that he had some in the hands of a trader in town, and that he could raise from his nation any quantity of racoon or beaver provided it would answer any purpose. I was struck with the pleasantry of having an Indian for a client and getting a fee in this way, and told the interpreter to go to the Indian, and explain the matter to him. He did so, and brought me an account that Mamachtaga had forty weight of beaver, which he was ready to make over, being with a trader in town, and that he had a brother who would set off immediately to the Indian towns and procure an hundred weight or more if that would do any good, but the interpreter stipulated that he should have half of all that should be got, for his trouble in bringing about the contract. Accordingly he was dispatched to the Indian, and from whom he brought in a short time an order for the beaver in the hand of the trader, [signed by] Mamachtaga (his mark). The mark was something like a turkey's foot, as these people have no idea of an hieroglyphic merely abstract as a strait line or a curve, but it must bear some resemblance to a thing in nature. After this as it behoved, I went to consult with my client and arrange his defense, if it were possible to make one on which a probable face could be put. Accompanied by the interpreter I was admitted to the Indian so that I could converse with him. He was in what is called the black hole, something resembling that kind of hole which is depressed in the floor and which the southern people have in their cabins in which to keep their esculent roots from the frost during the winter season. Not going down into the hole as may be supposed, though it was large enough to contain two or three and was depressed about eight feet, being the place in which delinquent or refractory soldiery had been confined occasionally for punishment, but standing on the floor above, I desired the interpreter to put his questions. This was done, explaining to him the object of the inquiry, that it was to serve him and, by knowing the truth, [to] be prepared for his defense. He affected to know nothing about it, nor was he disposed to rely upon any defense that could be made. His idea was that he was giving the beaver as a commutation for his life. Under this impression it did not appear to me proper that I should take the beaver, knowing that I could do nothing for him, besides seeing the manner in which the dark and squalid creature was accommodated with but a shirt and breech-clout on, humanity dictated that the beaver should be applied to procure him a blanket and food additional to the bread and water which he was allowed. Accordingly I returned the order to the interpreter, and desired him to procure and furnish these things. He seemed reluctant, and thought we ought to keep the prerequisite we had got. On this, I thought it most advisable to retain the order and give it to a trader in town with directions to furnish these articles occasionally to the officer of the guard, which I did, taking the responsibility upon myself to the interpreter for his part of the beaver.

An Indian woman known by the name of the Grenadier Squaw was sitting doing some work by the trap door of the cell or hole in which he was confined, for the trap door was kept open and a sentry at the outer door of the guard-house. The Indian woman was led by sympathy to sit by him. I had a curiosity to know the force of abstract sentiment in preferring greater evils to what with us would seem to be less, or rather the force of opinion over pain. For knowing the idea of the Indians with regard to the disgrace of hanging, I proposed to the Indian woman, who spoke English as well as Indian and was a Delaware herself (Mamachtaga was of that nation), to ask him which he would choose, to be hanged or burned? Whether it was that the woman was struck with the inhumanity of introducing the idea of death, she not only declined to put the question, but her countenance expressed resentment. I then recollected, and have since attended to the circumstance, that among themselves when they mean to put any-one to death they conceal the determination and the time until it is about to be put in execution, unless the blacking the prisoner which is a mark upon such as about to be burned may be called an intima-tion; but it is only by those who are accustomed to their manners that it can be understood. However, I got the question put by the inter-preter, at which he seemed to hesitate for some time but said he would rather be shot or be tomahawked.

In a few days it made a great noise through the country that I was to appear for the Indian, and having acquired some reputation in the defense of criminals, it was thought possible by some that he might be acquitted by "the crooks of the law" as the people expressed it; and it was talked of publicly to raise a party and come to town and take the interpreter and me both and hang the interpreter and exact an oath from me not to appear on behalf of the Indian. It was however finally concluded to come in to the garrison and demand the Indian and hang him themselves. Accordingly a party came in a few days, and about break of day summoned the garrison and de-manded the surrender of the Indian; the commanding officer re-monstrated, and prevailed with them to leave the Indian to the civil authority. Upon which they retired, firing their guns as they came through the town. The interpreter, hearing the alarm, sprang up in his shirt and made for a hill above the town called Grant's Hill. On seeing him run, he was taken for the Indian that had been suffered to escape, and was pursued until the people were assured that it was not the Indian. In the meantime he had run some miles, and swim-ming the river, lay in the Indian country until he thought it might be safe to return.

It was not without good reason that the interpreter was alarmed, for having been some years among the Indians in early life a prisoner, and since a good deal employed in the Indian trade, and on all occasions of treaty employed as an interpreter, he was associated in the public mind with an Indian, and on this occasion considered as the abetter of the Indian from the circumstance of employing council to defend him. And before this time a party had come from the

Chartiers, a settlement south of the Monongahela in the neighborhood of this town, and had attacked some friendly Indians on the island in the Ohio (Killbuck's island) under the protection of the garrison, and had killed several and among them some that had been of essential service to the whites in the expeditions against the Indian towns and on scouting parties in case of attacks upon the settlements.[2] One to whom the whites had given the name of Wilson (Captain Wilson), was much regretted by the garrison. A certain Cisna had commanded the party that committed this outrage.

A day or two after his return the interpreter came to me and relinquished all interest in the beaver that was lodged with the trader or expectant from the towns, that he might, to use his own language, "wipe his hands of the affair, and be clear of the charge of supporting the Indian." The fact was that as to beaver from the towns I expected none, having been informed in the meantime by the friendly Indians that Mamachtaga was a bad man and was thought so by his nation, that he had been a great warrior but was mischievous in liquor, having killed two of his own people, that it would not be much regretted in the nation to hear of his death, and that except his brother, no one would give anything to get him off.

He had the appearance of great ferocity, was of tall stature [and] fierce aspect. He was called Mamachtaga, which signifies trees blown across, as is usual in a hurricane or tempest by the wind, and this name had been given him from the ungovernable nature of his passion. Having therefore no expectation of peltry or fur in the case, it was no great generosity in me to press upon the interpreter the taking half the beaver as his right in procuring the contract; but finding me obstinate in insisting upon it, he got a friend to speak to me, and at length I suffered myself to be prevailed upon to let him off and take all the beaver that could be got to myself.

It did not appear to me advisable to relinquish the defense of the Indian, fee or no fee, lest it should be supposed that I yielded to the popular impression, the fury of which, when it had a little spent itself, began to subside. And there were some who thought the Indian might be cleared, if it could be proved that the white men killed had made the Indian drunk, which was alleged to be the case but which the wounded and surviving persons denied, particularly the dwarf (William Freeman), but his testimony it was thought would

2. In March 1783, militia from Chartiers Creek attacked Killbuck's friendly Delawares encamped on Smoky Island and killed all but a few.

not be much regarded as he could not be said to be a "man grown," and had been convicted at the quarter sessions of stealing a keg of whiskey some time before.

At a court of Oyer and Terminer holden for the county of Westmoreland before Chief Justices M'Kean [3] and Bryan, Mamachtaga was brought to trial. The usual forms were pursued. An interpreter, not Nicholas but a certain Handlyn, stood by him and interpreted in the Delaware language the indictment and the meaning of it and the privilege he had to deny the charge, that is the plea of "not guilty." But he could not easily comprehend that it was a matter of form, and that he must say "not guilty"; for he was unwilling to deny, as unbecoming a warrior to deny the truth. For though he did not confess, yet he did not like to say that he had not killed the men; but said he was drunk, and did not know what he had done but "supposed he should know when he was under the grount." The court directed the plea to be entered for him, and he was put upon his trial.

He was called upon to make his challenges, which the interpreter explained to him and which he was left to make himself and which he did, as he liked the countenances of the jury and challenged according to the sourness or cheerfulness of the countenance and what he thought indications of a mild temper. The jurors . . . were called to the book, being told in the usual form, "Prisoner, look upon the juror. Juror, look upon the prisoner at the bar. Are you related to the prisoner?" One of them, a German of a swarthy complexion and being the first called, took the question amiss, as thinking it a reflection and said with some anger that he thought "that a uncivil way to treat Dutch peoples as if he could be the brothers, or cousings of an Indian." But the matter being explained to him by another German of the jury, he was satisfied, and was sworn.

The meaning of the jury being on oath was explained to the Indian to give him some idea of the solemnity and fairness of the trial. The testimony was positive and put the homicide beyond a doubt; so that nothing remained for me in opening his defense but the offering to prove that he was in liquor, and that this had been given to him by the white people, the traders in town. The testimony was overruled, and it was explained to the Indian that the being drunk could not by our law excuse the murder. The Indian said he hoped the good man above would excuse it.

3. Thomas McKean, elected Governor of Pennsylvania in 1799, supported by Brackenridge.

The jury gave their verdict, guilty, without leaving the bar. And the prisoner was remanded to jail. In the meantime there was tried at the same court another person (John Bradly) on a charge of homicide but who was found guilty of manslaughter only. Towards the ending of the court these were both brought up to receive sentence. The Indian was asked what he had to say, why sentence of death should not be pronounced upon him. This was interpreted to him, and he said that he would rather "run awhile." This was under the idea of the custom among the Indians of giving time to the murderer, according to the circumstances of the case, to run, during which time if he can satisfy the relations of the deceased, buy a commutation for his life [with] a gun, a horse, fur and the like, it is in their power to dispense with the punishment; but if this cannot be done, having not enough to give, or the relations not consenting to take a commutation, he must come at the end of the time appointed to the spot assigned, and there, by a warrior of the nation, or some relative, son, brother, etc. of the deceased, be put to death, in which case the tomahawk is the usual instrument. No instance will occur in which the condemned man will not be punctual to his engagement. And I think it very probable, or rather can have no doubt, but that if this Indian had been suffered to run at this time, that is, go to his nation on the condition to return at a certain period to receive the sentence of what he would call the council, he would have come with as much fidelity as a man challenged would on a point of honor come to the place assigned . . . to risk himself to his adversary. Such is the force of opinion, from education, on the human mind.

Sentence [had] been pronounced upon the convicted [white man] of manslaughter. (In this case the first part of the sentence, as the law directs, was that of hanging, which is done until the "benefit of clergy is prayed by the prisoner"; [4] but not understanding this, nothing could exceed the contortion of his muscles when a sentence contrary to what he had expected was pronounced.) Being a simple man he made a hideous outcry, and gave a most woeful look to the court and country and begged for mercy; and it was not for some time after, that having the matter explained to him and the benefit of clergy being allowed, he could be composed. Sentence of "burning in the hand"

4. The sentence is imposed as a form and is changed to manslaughter when the prisoner asks for the intervention of a clergyman. Apparently the convicted man had not been informed of this legal custom.

being now pronounced, at this moment the sheriff came in with a rope to bind up his hand to a beam of the low and wooden court-house in which we were in order that the hot iron might be put upon it.

Sentence of hanging had been previously pronounced upon the Indian, on which he had said that he would prefer to be shot; but it being explained to him that this could not be done, he had the idea of hanging in his mind. Accordingly, by a side glance, seeing the sheriff coming in with a rope which was a bed-cord he had procured, having nothing else in our then low state of trade and manufacturing, Mamachtaga conceived that the sentence was about to be executed presently upon him, and that the rope was for this purpose, which coming unaware upon him, he lost the command of himself for a moment. His visage grew black, his features were screwed up, and he writhed himself with horror and aversion; the surprise not having given time to the mind to collect itself, and on the acquired principle of honor to conceal its dismay, or on those of reason to bear with and compose itself to its fate. Even when undeceived and made acquainted that he was not to die then, he remained under a visible horror, the idea of immediate death and especially of hanging giving a tremor, like the refrigeration of cold upon the human frame.

Before he was taken from the bar he wished to say something, which was to acknowledge that his trial had been fair and to express a wish that his nation would not revenge his death or come to war on his account. Being asked, as he was taken off by some of those accompanying the sheriff in conducting him to jail, whom he thought the judges to be before whom he had been tried and who were on the bench in scarlet robes, which was the official custom of that time. Being of the Delaware nation, among whom Moravian missionaries had been a good deal and, as it would seem, mixing some recollections which he had derived from this source, he answered that the one, meaning the Chief Justice, was God, and the other Jesus Christ.

At the same court of Oyer and Terminer was convicted a man for the crime against nature, and at a court of Quarter Sessions a short time after, another, a young man of the name of Jack had been convicted of larceny and was now confined in the same jail, and in fact in the same room, for there was but one, with the Indian and the white man before-mentioned. And though, upon account of his youth and family connections, the jury in finding a verdict had recommended him to pardon, for which the supreme executive council of the state had been petitioned some time before, nevertheless he could not restrain the wickedness of his mind and had prevailed upon the white man, guilty of the crime against nature, as he had to die at any rate, to save the disgrace of being hanged, to consent to be murdered by the Indian. The creature [*the one condemned to death*] was extremely simple and had actually consented, and Jack had prepared a knife for the purpose. But the Indian refused, though solicited and offered liquor, but he declined, saying he had killed white men enough already.

A child of the jailor had been taken sick and had a fever. The Indian said he could cure it if he had roots from the woods which he knew. The jailor, taking off his irons which he had on his feet, took his word that he would not make his escape while he let him go to the woods to collect roots, telling him that if he did make his escape the great council, the judges, would hang him (the jailor) in his place. But for the greater security the jailor thought proper to accompany him to the woods where roots were collected, and which on their return were made use of in the cure of the child.

The warrant for the execution of the Indian and of the white man came to hand, and the morning of the execution the Indian expressed a wish to be painted that he might die like a warrior. The jailor as before unironed him and took him to the woods to collect his usual paints, which having done, he returned and prepared himself for the occasion, painting highly . . . [as] on great occasions.

A great body of people assembling at the place of execution, the white man was hung first, and afterwards the Indian ascended a ladder placed to the cross timber of the gibbet; and the rope being fastened, when he was swung off it broke and the Indian fell, and having swooned a little, he rose with a smile and went up again. A stronger rope in the meantime having been provided, or rather two put about his neck together so that his weight was supported . . . he underwent the sentence of the law and was hanged till he was dead.

This was during the Indian war, and this place on the verge of the settlement, so that if the Indian had taken a false step, and gone off from the jailor while he was looking for roots for the cure or for painting, it would have been easy for him to have made his escape. But such is the force of opinion as we have before said, resulting from the way of thinking among the Indians, that he did not seem to think that he had the physical power to go. It was nevertheless considered an imprudent thing in the jailor to run this risk. For if the Indian had made his escape it is morally certain that in the then state of the public mind, the jailor himself would have fallen a sacrifice to the resentment of the people.

[Pittsburgh, 1785]

Ideas at the Interment of Mrs. Bedford[1]

[In a preface to his drama The Death of General Montgomery *(1777), Brackenridge announced that he would exclude women and the effeminate passions from all his works. Life on the frontier and embroilment in its politics led him to abandon his epic approach to life and his grand manner of portraying it. Exposure to frontier life brought out a strain of sensibility which can be observed in "The Trial of Mamachtaga" and which may have been expressed in unpublished poems now lost. He included "Ideas at the Interment of Mrs. Bedford" in his* Gazette Publications.*]*

Whether the spirit doth survive
The body and doth live
In the Elysium of the Greeks
Or heaven of which the Christian speaks,
I know not; but, if there be
Such immortality* to thee or me,
Fair shade, this thing call'd death
And the mere stopping of the breath,
Not being to oblivion brought,
Is a light matter in the scale of thought,
And not the proper subject of a tear.

Why then such shape of melancholy here
And crystal distillation of the eye?
Is it because the form that there doth lie
Was passing pleasing in her life,
And none so fair and virtuous doth survive?
Fair ladies, I will not say none,
Nor even with the dead induce comparison?
But this will say,
The soul that animated that same clay

* The despondent mind will doubt at times, but where there is hope there must be faith. [H.H.B.]

1. The wife of Doctor Nathaniel Bedford of Pittsburgh, who died July 9, 1790.

Was wise and good,
With every excellence, endued,
That could the sex exalt,
Without a foible or a fault:

Uncensur'd and uncensurable,
Her exit answerable.
For pure as innocence and love,
She felt the will of Jove,
With proper fortitude complied
And like an unstain'd lily drop'd her head and died.

[*Pittsburgh, 1790*]

To the Sons of St. Andrew on the Celebration of the Late Festival[1]

Among the inhabitants of Pittsburgh were some of Scottish origin or descent, who on the anniversary of St. Andrew (30th of November) were accustomed to celebrate his festival, on one of which occasions the following was written and appeared in a paper the day following.   [*Gazette Publications*]

If Gude St. Andrew's saul, a wee
    Bit, could be spar'd frae he'ven,
It wad delight his sprite tae see
    How ye did spend the ev'en.

For weel I wat, the sangs aboon
    The lift are scarce as gude,
And Scott's sauls even in the moon,
    Tae hear them wad rin wid.

Wad pit them in the mind o' braes,
    And knows where they were born,
And springs they play'd, and bony haes,
    They danc'd among the corn.

Ah: had I but the soul o' sang,
    My kintra kens fu weel,
The pleasant melody ere lang,
    Wad sound o'er vale and hill.

1. For explanations of Scottish terms, see the Glossary.

My name be heard on Allegane,
And ilka neighbouring burn,
When I am laid beneath a stane
And marrows left tae mourn.

But aw my wish, and aw my vows,
Will no'e gae sick a strain,
As is, "The broom of Cowden knows,"
Or "Tae the Greenwood gane."

For spirit o' sick sang is gane
Simplicity sae sweet
And artificial airs hae taen,
Its place, which gars me greet.

But blessings on the kindly bairns
That keep it up a wee,
By chaunting here among the kernes,
A wee thing o' tae me.

For ay my heart e'en on these braes
Clings tae the pleasing thought,
Rememberance o' the sweet strath-speys
My native music taught,

As when the love sick saul o' ane
Has lost his dearest mate,
He hankers still about the stane
And winna gae his gate.

[*Pittsburgh
December 1790*]

Scot's Poems Addressed to David Bruce

[*David Bruce, a country storekeeper and poet in Washington County, had written some Scottish verse the year of the insurrection. The verse praised whiskey and stated that Bruce was quite willing to pay the excise for all the blessings that whiskey yielded. Disagreeing with this attitude, Brackenridge was nevertheless charmed with the Scottish phrases that allowed him to escape the present ignominy among his fellows, both insurgents and loyalists.*

Overwhelmed with nostalgia for his root culture, Brackenridge replied to Bruce in the same vein, starting a poetic correspondence that lasted off and on for several years. His first effort referred to Robert Burns, who died that year. It introduced

the literary note into the series. Clearly inspired by Burns, the Scottish verse of
Brackenridge achieves a simplicity not evident in his earlier poetry. Like Burns'
poetry, it is autobiographical and concerned with rural domesticity. The satire is
slight, written in good humor. He aims no hard blows at specific objects. The
nostalgic mood warms all that is said. In place of conscious efforts to achieve
the eloquence of classical and Augustine poets, the tendency is lyrical, expressing
less wisdom derived from life than the experience of life itself.]

Whiskey

Your rouse rins blib thro' a' my veins,
I find it at my finger en's:
An' but a gouk that has nae brains,
   Wa'd it deny,
That mony a time, baith wit and sense
   I can supply,

Far better than the drink ca'd wine,
Wi' me compar'd 'tis wash for swine:
Ae gill is just as guid nine;
   And fills as fou':
It is nae very long sinsyne,
   Ye prov'd it true.

That time ye made sae muckle noise,
About the tax they ca' excise,
And got the name o' *Whiskey-boys,*
   Frae laland glakes;
That cam' sae far, nae verra wise,
   To gie ye pikes.
Tho' I may say't among our-sels,
Ye gaed o'er far wi your pe'mells,
On N——— and the gouger W———.[2]
   And ither louns,
Far better ye had drank your gills,
   And eat your scons.

It was kittle thing to take
The government sae by the neck,
To thrapple every thing and break
   Down rule and laws;
And make the public ship a wreck,
   Without guid case.

'Twere safer ye had tulzied here,

---

2. General John Neville, the excise inspector, and Attorney John Woods, Brackenridge's bitter enemy.

Wi' chiels that dinna muckle care
To gouge a wee bit, or pu' hair,
　And no complain,
But a' the tugs and rugings bear,
　Or let alane.
The warst is, but to et a lesson,
If som' ane puts ye i' the session,
To take a prie o' spiritual sneezin
　Frae J——— M-M———n,[3]
What'l say o'er ye a backward blessing,
　When ye're nae willing.

What wha' ist o' ye mak's the verse,
Sae very kittle and saw terse,
That in the Gazzat gies me praise?
　They say tis Bruce,
I canna half sae weel rehearse:
　Tak' my excuse.

I'm mair among unlettered jocks
Than well'lear'd doctors i' their buiks,
Academies and college nuiks
　I dinna ken:
And seldom wi' kintra folks,
　Has I been benn.

Ye canna then expect a phrase,
Like them ye get in poets lays,
For where's the man that now-a-days,
　Can sing like Burns,
Whom nature taught her ain strathspeys,
　And now she mourns.

I dinna like to sign my name,
By that o' Whiskey, fie for shame:
I had a better ane at hame,
　In town or city,
Where a' ware glad to get a dram.
O' ——— Aqua Vitae.

[*Pittsburgh, 1796*]

3. Reverend Dr. John MacMillan, whose influence among Presbyterians was so great that Brackenridge called him the Cardinal. A supporter of the federal government, he refused to allow the insurgents and their sympathizers to partake of the Communion.

Answer to Bruce

There was a clerk, I' the neist door,
Cam' to our town; had fear gilore,
And tauk'd about ane Pythagore,
   Wha had a thought,
His saul wad tak, when life was o'er,
   And ither bught:

And lowp into the bodie o' ane,
Now in the shape o' a wee wean:
And after shaw the self-same vein,
   O' wit and sense,
He had, before death wi' a stane
   Dang out his brains.

I leught and ca'd him a daft chiel,
And thought his head in peat creel,
But now I be'lieve him verra weel,
   And gie him faith,
Ye'r Allan Ramsey or the Deil,[1]
   Upo' my aith.

His saul has soomit o'er the burn,
To tak in you an ither turn,
And be a while in life's sojourn
   Sic as he was,
Near Frith of Forth where he was born,
   And liv'd his days.

I ken ye Allen verry weel,
Though you may hardly ken your-sel'.
But ah! your sang is nae saw shill,
   Nor pipe saw soft,
The voice ye had, as clear's a bell,
   'S a wee thing dowff'd.

But's nae your fau't, my canty gallan,
That ye fa' short o' the auld Allan,
There's neither highland man, nor lallan',
   That's here the same,
But finds him scrimpit o' the talen'
   He had at hame.

That's mair expect'd here i' the west,
Sae near where night taks off his vest

---

1. The Scottish poet Allen Ramsey (1686–1758) is best known for his pastoral
"The Gentle Shepherd."

And his grey breeks, and gaes to rest,
  And the lang day
Is dock'd o several hours at best,
  Sic as on tay.

I find my'self degenerate,
And nae sic aqua as ye gat,
In clachan horns wi' comrades met,[2]
  To take a gill,
And though come stacherin hame fu' late,
  Yet did nae ill.

The lads got gumption by their drink,
And carls could better speak and think,
Tak aff a bonnet wi' a clink,
  And say a grace,
And lug out scripture verra distinc',
  Frae ony place.

But here the drappie that ye need,
Maun ay some wisked brulzie breed,
Gie ane anither's slaes a screed,
  An aften seen,
To gash wi' teeth, or tak in head,
  To stap the een.

Unless it be as folks o' lear,
Say a' things gradually impair,
And human nature wears thread-bare,
  And turns; —Gude help's,
Ae year auld, and twa year war',
  Like the tod's whelps.

Be this as 't may, it does me guid,
To meet wi' ane o' my ane bluid,
I was saw glad a' maist ran wud
  To be thegither,
But I maun now, gae chew my cud,
  And had my blether.

[*Pittsburgh, 1796*]

To Bruce

**A number of years after the preceding correspondence had taken place, and having
in the meantime had no personal communication or acquaintance, several things**

2. A joining together in merriment by clicking spoons made of horns.

appeared from this bard, and on the score of politics, somewhat personal towards me. This drew from me the following, to which an answer was given, on the part of this gentleman, and a rejoinder from me; this was in the summer of the year 1801.   [*Gazette Publications*]

When of an age to run an errand
To town or far-house that was near hand,
At bird's nest, or a beastie's bed,
Aft turn'd me frae the gate I gaed,
More, when I saw the thing itsel,
And ran to catch it by the tail,
As ance a thing just leke a cat,
I saw, and what wud I be at,
But try to grip it, a wild pousie,
And bring it hame to catch a mousie.
Before I knew what I was doing,
Or mischief that the thing was brewing,
A vapour came that had a smell,
And made me noisome to myself.

As fast as I could lift a heel,
Ran hame, and said the muckle deel,
Or some war thing alang the fence,
Had drain'd its bags at my expence,
And rais'd a funk, and made me wet—

They ca'd it something I forget,
That strones upon a man and dog,
That tries to take it by the lug,
And leaves a scent about the place:
That it behov'd to change my claes,
She stipp'd me o' my sark and trouse,
And hung them out to get the dews,
And bade me tak mare care again,
And keep frae things I did na ken.

Soon after this I gaed to Latin,
And read a buke, I kenna what in,
That talk'd o' things that whir in bushes,
Dryads, Hamadryads, Muses,
On tops o' hills wad sing leke Mavies,
And in the shady woods and cavies.
Thought I, it mean be this vile clearing,
And grubbing up the trees and bleering
At burning brush, and making fences,
That scars these out o' their senses,
And drives them frae our fields and patches,

For who sees any now or catches
A moor-land deity or nymphy,
That roosts in trees, or wades in lymphy?
Or hears a musy in the thicket,
Just as you wad hear a cricket?
Maybe in places farther back,
The vestige may na be sae slack,
Where woods are green, and countra new,
The breed may yet remain, a few
May sing to mak' our spirits glow,
Leke them on the pierian now,
Or near that place ca'd Helicon,
Where bonny tricklin' streams rin down.

It was when I had cross'd the hills,
Amang these western woods and rills,
Was sitting listening ae still e'en,
A min't as weel's I do yestreen,
It seem'd to me, I heard the seugh,
O' ane; I kent it weel eneugh:
It was nae inarticulate trill,
Or echo o' the whippoorwill,
But words cam' wi the melody,
I kent the verra air, d'ye see.
Frae the description I had got,
In Latin buke, or Crecian poet.
Ah, hah! thought I, this sang is fine,
It has an inkling of the nine,
It maun be what they ca'a muse—
What was it but the voice o' Bruce.
O' a Lochaber origin
And Scottish air sae very fine,
Thought natural, expression saft:
I loupet leke a man ha'f daft,
To think at last, out owre these woods,
Amang the simmer trees and buds,
A bardie should spring up, a musie,
A genuine Parnassus pousie,
In nature real, and in mew,
Of Arcady a *kitlin' true.*

My wishes led me to caress it,
To stroke the thing and amaist kiss it,
But what my wonder and surprisal,
Without an ill word or divisal,
To find the thing when a' was done,
In verse, and sang begin to strone,
Wi Hogo war then as a fetid,
Or bag o' animal four fitit;

I thought me o' what happen'd early,
When *skunkie* pish'd upon me fairly
When I had ta'en it for a rabbit,
And did na think it would grow crabbit.

Sae frae the verra self same things,
Our gude and evil aften springs,
Our pleasure and our pain thegither.
The bony bard if turn'd dog mither,
And bites and brangles like a bitch,
Or an apossom, makes na which,
Or a racoon upon the creek,
Near where his cabin gies it's reek.
But still the consolation's taen,
Hard words, and language break nae bane.
While I can laugh and take a drink,
I'll be to them that evil think.
Here's to the bardie; fill the cogue,
Or send and get anither jug:
The best way is to laugh at fools:
It is the wisdom of the schools,
For mirth tak's out the sting o' hurt,
And mental wounds are this way cur'd.

[*Pittsburgh, 1801*]

A Reply

Two pipers ilk wi' bag and drone,
Forgether'd in a wee bit town,
Grew unco great; the ane was Angus,
The tither Duncan. Wha can bang us,
Oho' they at playing on the popes?

Scarce had the word gaed out their lips
When up play'd Duncan *Charlie's reel.**

Angus he said he liked it weel,
And, in his turn he played the *Boyne.* †
But Duncan said he was na join
Since revolution spring as that,
Mare than the Devil and black cat,
No play'd for laird or lady Mary,
Wha hated seugh o' Inverara;‡

---

* Aristocracy. [H.H.B.]
† Democracy. [H.H.B.]
‡ The set of the Duke of Argyle, a Whig and revolutionary. [H.H.B.]

And lik'd by nane but laland cotters,
Or what they ca' in glens, bog-trotters,
Wad stick to *Charlie owr the water.*

Quoth Angus it is na great matter,
To my conception or my pleasin,
Out of what mul I tak my sneeshin,
Whether it is a blaw my cheeks,
To gar them poup wha' na breeks.
Or lairds or ladies wi guid beltin,
As muckle pleasure aft as felt in,
The seeing lads and lasses wallop,*
Wha ha' sma claes to hide their gallop,
As in the ha's o' pride, and plaiden,
Where men ha' geer, and madis ha' claden.
Here man is nearer man; the lardie
Is no sae far aboon the bardie,
And she that frisks it wi' her neighbor,
Will na be laith to kiss the piper.
But why should ranters ban and banter,
But as they like blae up their chanter?
The thing is a' but sound and ranting,
What need we care but for our canting?
And no gie hard words, or break crowns,
Because we canna suit our drones.

The same wi' us now canty Bruce,
Two pipers that had different views,
And baith had music in our brain;
Ye play'd up R[oss]; I play'd M'Kean.¹
And sooth, maun a' be dolphin fish †
That cam' to soom about your dish,
And very worst birds o' the heavens,
That listen to my pipe or spring.

Now toleration is a thing,
That's amiable in church and state,
And why should bardies derogate
Frae the same licence in their strains?
While men ha' different heads and brains,
The same things will na seem the same,
And he has the maist sense o' them,
Wha lets anither think and say,

* Dance rompingly, "Walloped it owr the green," Maggy Lauder. [H.H.B.]
† Amphin with his lyre is said to have charmed a dolphin. [H.H.B.]
  1. David Bruce had supported James Ross, the Federalist candidate for governor, while Brackenridge had supported Judge Thomas McKean, the Republican candidate, who won.

And in his turn takes the same way
I did na scirl, and clamour out,
And ca' ye a false loon and lout,
Or say your pipe had lost its drone,
Because ye play'd up Ettison,*
Though a' the sense that man can feel,
O' wrang frae that misguided chiel,
I had o' whilk ye nothing knew,
And ought t' have had still less to do,
Unless like piper to a laird,
At hame in some great castle yard,†
On droupit doup like dog at tether ,
Ye blaw'd your cheeks up to a blether,
And play'd a spring just to his liking,
As bardies did to get a picking,
In auld times when the meal was scarce,
Frae failing ha'rst, or wasting wars.

Ah! no, my canty winsome Bruce,
Ye had na sic a guid excuse.
It was just thoughtlessness and folly,
Though it strake me wi melancholy,
To find my bardie take a part,
Against me wi' his tunefu' art,
And though it touch'd me wi an ach,
Yet, I forgave it for the sake,
O' our relation to the muse.
The mason word has na sic use,
O' brother-hood, as tis same charm,
And whilk is got without the harm,
O' raising, or o' laying De'el.

But I maun bid you now fareweel:
I dinna ken I shall say mare:
'Am ganging frae this thoroughfare,‡
May ay the Muse, to you dispense,
The sowth o' sang, and pith o' sense.
And bony art to wale the words,
That make folk friends, and tighten cords.

[*Pittsburgh, 1801*]

* President of the District. [H.H.B. *The reference is to Alexander Addison, District Court President.*]

† The piper usually plays out of doors during the entertainment but is seen and heard from the hall. [H.H.B.]

‡ About to leave the western part of Pennsylvania for Carlisle, my present residence. [H.H.B.]

Conclusion

In looking over this book, there is no part [with] which I am less pleased than the introduction. There would seem to be vanity under the guise of humility. By the word "exertions" in that preface, I do not mean the labors of my composition but my efforts in life which have been successful to a certain extent. But even with regard to my literary attempts, though I cannot apply to myself the gratulation of the poet,

Exegi monumentum aere perennius,[1]

yet the selections here made may be considered as remembrancers of some short duration. True it is that, having had perhaps too great a desire of distinction in early life, I may have less now than is necessary to application; but my ambition never was for place of office. Nevertheless, I begin to think it had been better to have set less store by the opinion of the world as to my flight or song and to have made my nest with more care like other birds of the grove.

Be that as it may, it has been my amusement to write; and I have set a greater value on the praise of genius than on all else that is obtainable among men. A man of very moderate parts can fill an office, perhaps the better for being moderate; but it is but one in many that can show a single spark of the celestial fire that distinguishes the orator, the philosopher, or the rapt poet. I have always considered every hour, in a sense, lost that was not employed in the cultivation of the intellect, with a view either to the virtues of humanity or the delights of the fancy; for I give the virtues of humanity the first place. But when a man of taste considers how much more he owes to those who have increased the store of literature than to such as have amassed wealth for themselves and others, he will certainly consider the productions of the mind as more deserving his respect than the acquisitions of the purse-proud, even though there may appear a little vanity in the publications of the author, which he has not had the self-denial to suppress or the prudence to conceal.

With a view to mend the matter of my introduction I have added this; perhaps it will be thought unnecessary, for all the notice that will ever be taken of the proemium, or of the collectanea, to which it has a reference.

One thing I will add in excuse of employing so much of my time

---

1. "I have built a monument more lasting than bronze." Horace, *Odes,* iii, 30.

and whatever talents I may possess in what may seem to be of too light a nature for a serious mind, that the taste for playful humor and the habit of versifying . . . [were] contracted in early life from the want of a monitor to direct resistance to the propensity; and at the same time that I present the result to the public, I must caution others to beware of the indulgence. It is not an age or country that will make it the means of emolument or the way to honor. And though I would rather be the poet than the Maecenas [2] as to after-fame, yet it is better to be the Maecenas as to present enjoyment. I would warn therefore a son of mine against too much attention to some parts of what may be called polite literature as not fashionable in our present state of society and as a seducing syren from the more profitable pursuits of life.

[*Carlisle, 1806*]

2. Patron of Virgil and Horace.

from *Modern Chivalry*, Part Two

[*The second part of* Modern Chivalry *was written from 1801 to 1815 in Carlisle, where Brackenridge had moved to assume his supreme court duties. Its two major subjects—the scurrilous press and attacks on the judiciary—are treated in a most haphazard fashion. There is little organization. The tenor of the whole is philosophic; the narrative is slight and erratic. But the mood is rather consistent. As in the Scottish verse, the satire is warmed with good-natured reflection. The philosophic weight is lightened with melancholy descriptions of settlers. Some of these descriptions contain the author's most effective writing. The selected pieces have been given appropriate titles for this collection. They include one of several ballads Brackenridge composed during the last ten years of his life.*]

The American Press [1]

I take the pulpit, the courts of judicature, and the press to be the three great means of sustaining and enlightening a republic. The Scripture is replete with the finest sayings of morality. With a scholar of the Latin and the Greek school, it is delightful to quote in conversation or writing the classical sentences of antiquity, aptly applying them to the occasion, enriching the discourse with apposite thoughts, pleasing the hearer or the reader, and doing credit to the persons drawing out from his treasury such things new and old. But these writings of an oriental cast, the Scriptures, contain pithy observations upon life and manners than which there can be nothing more delightful to remember and quote and more profitable to carry into practice. Reading the Scriptures by young people, hearing them explained and introduced by quotation, sermon, and lectures from the pulpit raises the affections to virtue and helps the judgment in the conduct of life.

The courts of judicature are a school of justice and honor. A great ground of the law are the principles of universal justice. The discussion of council, the verdicts, the decision of the courts have

1. From Volume I. *Observations.*

respect to the great principles of moral honesty. But the sphere is confined, compared with that of the press which has an extensive range, and for this reason ought to preserve the greater delicacy in language and sentiment. Even the war of the sword has its laws. It is not allowable to poison springs or the means of life. In a paper war nothing is justifiable that does not tend to establish a position or determine a controversy; that which outrages humanity is the cruelty of a savage who puts to death with torture or disfigures to gratify revenge.

To know what may be said in a paper or in what manner it may be said, the editor, whom the public alone knows, need only consider what would become a gentleman to say in promiscuous society. Whether conversing in the manner he writes, or in which what is inserted is written,[2] he would be heard with respect and treated with civility. Good breeding is as necessary in print as in conversation. The want of it equally entitles to the appellation of an ill-bred man. The press can have no more licence than the tongue. In fact, at the tribunal of common sense it has less, because an expression might escape a man which might receive pardon or excuse as the offspring of inadvertance; but writing is deliberate, and you may turn back and strike out the allusion or correct the term.

National character is interested in the delicacy of the press.[3] It is a disgrace to a people to have among them volumes of scurrility circulated through their post-offices with a peculiar privilege of centage [4] more than their common correspondence; to have billingsgate,[5] as they call it in a kingdom which we surpass in privileges, placed upon the benches in our public houses or sent home to our private dwellings.

Is this the occupation to which it ought to be an honor to belong; to which a father would wish to put a son, having educated him with the best advantages and giving him, as he had thought, a duty as sacred as the priesthood and with a more exclusive sphere of action than the barrister, having it in high commission by the constitution of his country "to canvass the conduct of men in public offices" and inform the public "where the matter is proper for public information"?

2. In the style of his contributors.
3. Delicacy of the press is in the interest of national character.
4. Postal rate.
5. The coarse papers of England, called Billingsgate after the fish market which was known for abusive language.

It does not follow that because a man takes a paper . . . he approves of all that is in it. It is certainly censurable to continue our subscription to a paper the prevailing tenor of which is defamatory of individuals; but were we to reject a paper because it is occasionally so, there are few papers that we should take at all. The American press has been abominably gross and defamatory, and there are few publications of this nature that have been at all times unexceptionable. "The fool scattereth firebrands," and saith, "am I not in jest?" A man will be astonished sometimes to hear of himself or of others what has not the slightest foundation but in the invention and imagery of the paragraphist. There may be some prototype, filmy origin to the unsubstantial fabric, perhaps not even a vapor but in the breath of the defamer. Is the assassin odious and not the author of anonymous abuse? Yet such is the error of opinion with some that they think it not dishonorable to attack anonymously. It is cowardice in a free country, where the law is equal, where no Caesar exists to make it necessary to conceal the author of the pasquinade. A brave man will scorn subterfuge and shade. An honest man will avow himself and his opinions. Yet how many write in public prints that, were they at the time to count upon being known, they would retract or alter much, both in style and sentiment, of what they subscribe with signatures of fiction.

I feel a concern for the honor of the American press that, as we are before most or all other governments in the freedom of it, we may not be behind in the delicacy with which it is used.

Why Burn the College?[1]

A great uproar had . . . taken place in the village. The doctrine of abating nuisances had been much in conversation, since the town-meeting in the matter of the pole-cat. It came so far that an incendiary proposed to abate or burn down the college. "Because," said he, "all learning is a nuisance."

A town meeting had been called on the occasion and, whether from a wish to see a bonfire or from the hatred of the ignorant to all that places the informed above them, the proposition, however un-

1. From Volume I, Book I, Chapter 8.

reasonable and illegal, had its advocates. It had been actually carried, and a person was now on his way with a brand lighted to set fire to the building.

The alarm was given; and the more considerate, and among these the captain, rushed out to endeavor to prevent conflagration.

Force was in vain, and reason avails little with a mob. The only way to oppose their resolution is indirectly by turning the current of their thoughts aside and to the attaining the same thing in another way. The principal and professors had harangued in vain. It was threatened that if they did not stand out of the way, they would burn them with the college.

The captain had come up and ventured to speak. "Gentlemen," said he, "it is not for the college that I am about to speak; it is for yourselves. Your object is to put down learning; and do you not know that it is put down already? Why will you do a useless thing? It is calling in question your understanding to do a needless mischief."

At this they began to stare, while the captain went on.

"Is not learning put down already? The Methodists are the best preachers. Take a horse jockey, and in two weeks from the jump he is in a pulpit. No need of Latin, Greek, Hebrew, a polyglot bible, systems of divinity, a commentary, a treatise, an essay, or a dissertation. All is plain sailing now.

"All this tends to put learning down, so that you have all the advantages of this without the trouble. Why burn the college?

"The building will serve useful purposes when the professors are driven out of it. All is plain sailing now.

"Politicians say—we have it from their own mouths on some occasions—that though they have no learning, they feel no want of it. Is it to be supposed that a workman does not know whether he wants tools? All this ends when learning and law are put down. Trial by battle must regulate society. We shall then want barracks and hospitals. This building will accommodate invalids."

"I do not know," said a sedate man among the crowd, "whether after all a little learning may not be, in some cases, useful. It is a great help to weak people. I have seen a book entitled, 'Huke's and e'en to had up crippled christian's breeks.'"

"That is, hooks and eyes to hold up breeches. Alluding, by the bye, to hooks and eyes which were in use before buttons. What are called gallowses have succeeded to the assistance of buttons but have not altogether superseded them. Not that I mean to insinuate that the disuse of hooks and eyes lead to the gallows in the proper sense of the word, any more than that learning does. Though many a man that wears buttons has been hung. Perhaps more without buttons than with them. But I mean to say that a young man, before he comes to the years of discretion, may as well be employed in learning to make marks upon paper as playing at nine men's morris,[2] and it does him no more harm to try to read Greek than to trace partridge tracks. The mind must be employed in something to keep it out of harm's way, and a recluse in a seminary is useful if for nothing else at least to keep young people within doors, which the academician could not easily do unless the device of books was used to beguile the hours of study. And though a great part of their learning is but the knowledge of hooks and crooks, yet the exercise of the mind renders them more expert in thinking; and though Latin is of no more use to raise the devil than English nowadays, yet it is a gentle exercise to learn it and makes the boys grow faster. It keeps them from their mothers who are apt to spoil their offspring by too much indulgence. The idea of getting[3] a task accustoms the mind to obedience. Now there are some branches of science that are really useful, such as speaking and writing intelligibly and casting up accounts. Nor is the time altogether thrown away in learning mathematics, especially the theory of the mechanical powers. Some are of opinion that this study has been of great use in navigation and water works. The ancients found their account in it in the construction of the catapult. But at least what harm in letting pedants chop logic and boys laugh in the seminaries? A herring pickle or a merry-andrew[4] is allowed to amuse people, and we do not pull down their stalls. A ventriloquist is suffered to take his dollar from us, and we make no remonstrance. Lectures on moral philosophy are at least as innocent as this. I do not know any better recreation for a lad of mettle than to listen to a dissertation on eloquence or a discourse on chronology and history. It sharpens his wit to talk over affairs with his equals. But there is one reason that serves for a hundred. It is not every one that is born a genius and can do without the help of education. I am therefore for continuing these crudities a little longer. When we can afford it better, we can pull down the college." This speech had a good effect, and the mob retired.

But before they were aware, the flame had broken out in another

2. An old game played by two men, each with nine pebbles, disks, or other counters placed at angles of a figure.

3. Pursuing.

4. Hawkers and buffoons in the marketplace.

direction. The mob, retiring, had entered into altercation among themselves and began to blame one another, some for not going on to burn the college and others for having thought of it at all. In opposition to the last, the first grew outrageous and began to exclaim and to curse and to swear and said, "Damn them, but if they had not burned a college, they would burn or pull down a church." They had actually prepared fagots and were on their way a second time to execute a new mischief.

The alarm was given, the chief burgess and assistants and respectable inhabitants assembled! Great reliance was had upon the captain, from his success in the former instance; and when the two forces, that of the mob and that of the community, stood face to face and were in opposition, ready to fall on, the one to commit waste and the other to defend, he was called upon to come forward and harangue.

He obeyed instantly but was well aware that a stratagem in war cannot succeed a second time; and, therefore, instead of attempting to decoy and turn aside their passions, [he] thought proper to attack them directly by the opposite, fear. "Madmen," said he, "what do you mean? Is it to rob, plunder, and murder that you have assembled? Come on; but in coming you must meet with this weapon," brandishing his hanger.[5] "I am alone, but a legion is behind me and will be with me speedily.

"But as I am at all times averse from the use of force until it becomes necessary, I am willing in the meantime to hear reason. Why is it that you would pull down a church and abolish the Christian worship in the village?"

"It is not our intention to abolish Christianity," said a grave man among them, "but to put down the preacher at this place who is not an American republican but quotes the English commentators in his sermons, Henry's annotations on the Bible, Burket on the New Testament, Pool's Synopsis, Tillotson and Baxter and many others. We wish to abolish these and have nothing but our own commentaries. Are we to be drawing our proofs from under a monarchy and referring to tracts and essays published in Great Britain? Have we no sense of our own to explain texts of Scripture and apply doctrines? It is time to emancipate ourselves from these shackles and every man be his own expounder, or at least confine our clergy to the Bible and the Psalm book or such of our divines as have written among ourselves and are of our own manufacture in a republican government."

5. A short sword used by seamen.

"Religion," said the captain, "is of no government. Wines are the better for being brought overseas, and our best brandies are from monarchies. Where was the cloth of that coat made? Will you reject a good piece of stuff because it came through the hands of an aristo-cratic weaver? These are false ideas of what is right and useful to mankind. The common law is not the worse for having been the common law of England and our property and birthright which our ancestors brought with them; nor is our Bible the worse for having been translated under James the First of England, which translation we still use and from which we repeat all sentences of Scripture. Nor are systems of theology or harmonies of the evangelists the worse for having been written in another country. Why do we use the English language? Is it not because we cannot easily substitute another or have no better a substitute? The Shawanees, or Delaware, or Piankisha may be softer but not so copious or of equal energy and strength. But even if in all respects superior, can we by an act of volition trans-fer it into common use and make it all at once our vernacular tongue?"

The grave man made no answer, but the more violent were still disposed to pull down the church.

The Settler Takes a Wife[1]

A cattle-driver had come from the Western settlements to exchange at the fair stock for salt, iron, and women. In barter for the last article, a cow was given for a girl. The settler went out in the first instance with a rifle, a hatchet, and a knapsack. Having fixed on a spot at a spring head, the next thing was to fall saplings and construct a hut. A small piece of ground was then cleared of the underwood and this formed into a brush fence to enclose it. He returned then to the interior of the country; and the next summer, going out with a hoe and a stock of provisions on a pack-horse, he began his cultivation. Having tamed a buffalo or got a cow from Padan Aram,[2] he had in due time milk in abundance. This put it into his head to get a milkmaid, in other words a wife. The traders in this article usually

1. From Volume I, Book II, Chapter 8.
2. Where Isaac sent Jacob to take a wife. Genesis xxv, 20.

chose those of the less opulent, whose dress answered all the ends of fashion without the affectation. The elbows were bare because the sleeves did not reach, and the folding doors of the bosom were undrawn because they had been always open. There was no occasion for flesh-colored pantaloons, for the pantaloons were the natural flesh itself, discovered through the rents of the muslin by the waving of the wind, like a light cloud upon a bed of air in an April day.

When these virgins, "nothing loath," had been conducted to the bowers mantled with the natural vine, an offspring arose in a few years, such as that from whence the poets have drawn their best fictions. You will have no occasion to read Ovid's *Metamorphosis* to have an image of Daphne or Proserpine, Diana and her nymphs, the Dryads, Hamadryads, or other personages. Just cross over into these new forests and there you have them in reality; maids bathing their snowy limbs in transparent streams, climbing the mountain top, collecting flowers, or gathering the berries of the wood. Nature is here in her bloom; no decay or decrepitude. All fragrancy, health, and vivacity.

The stripling of these woods is distinguished from the city beau; but it will not become me to say who has the advantage, whether the attitude of the presented rifle or that of the segar in the teeth is the most manly? Which looks best, the hunting shirt open at he neck or the roll of muslin that covers it and swells upon the chin? These are things to be canvassed by the curious. I am of opinion, however, that it is better to be clear sighted than purblind, and to be able to see a deer in a thicket than to have need of a glass before the nose to direct the steps where there is nothing to stumble over.

It can be no slur upon the descendant of a Western settler that his mother was obtained in barter, with her hair depending to her girdle or waving in ringlets on her shoulders, and the moisture of her eye brightened with a tear at the emigration; when he considers that in all times and in all places matrimony, to use the pun of Bishop Latimer,[3] has been in a great degree a matter of money; and the consideration of the contract not always what the lawyers call a good consideration, that is affection; but a valuable one, wealth. Even if the circumstance should be considered as less honorable than a marriage settlement with forms and perfect equality in the transaction, it will be forgotten in a century or two and it may come to be doubted whether there was ever such a thing as barter at all.

3. Bishop Hugh Latimer (c. 1490–1555), a major promoter of the Reformation and a wit whose sermons were often as racy as they were holy.

Settling in the New Country[1]

The first thing a settler does when he goes to the new country is to look out for a spring. Hard by he builds a cabin of the stocks of trees laid at right angles and forming a square or parallelogram. A stone serves for a back-wall, and an aperture over it to give vent to the smoke.

The settler brings with him few implements of husbandry because he is poor and has them not to bring; or the carriage is not in his power from the want of draft cattle. An axe, a mattock, a corn-hoe without a handle, perhaps a plough-irons, an auger, and a saw.

His household furniture is a pot, a frying-pan, a kettle, and sometimes a grid-iron. A few blankets and a bed-tick to fill with oak leaves is a luxury.

A cow to give milk is almost indispensable; and the rifle, with a little ammunition sparingly used, supplies flesh for the family. He must occasionally take a turn to the settlement to get a bag of flour and a quart or two of salt.

His horses, if he has any, range in the woods; and a good deal of time is spent in looking them up when wanted for service.

A breeding sow is an admirable acquisition, big with pigs. If he can bring one with him, which is most generally accomplished, he has soon a herd of them, living on the pea vine, that supersedes the casual supply of hunting and covers the sides of the chimney with hams just at hand to cut off and broil.

It is of great advantage to the settler to be able to handle a tool and to lay a stone. It would be advisable, therefore, in a father who means to send out his son when grown up to the new country, to put him some time to a carpenter and to a stone mason. His own smithery he cannot well do, as an anvil, a pair of bellows, etc., are heavy to be carried; but the greatest drawback is that he cannot resist the solicitations of his neighbors to assist them occasionally, and this takes him from the main branch of his improvement and cultivation.

The settlement is usually begun in this manner and carried on by poor, honest, and industrious people. The town on the other hand, at the commencement, is usually a nest of adventurers that have more wit than money and more experience than industry.

A tavern-keeper or publican that passes for a republican to get

1. From Volume II, Book III, Chapter 11.

custom, a horse jockey, a storekeeper, and a young lawyer are the first that you find domiciliated in this metropolis.[2]

And the young lawyer that had got to this place was half starved, either because there was no other to help him to breed suits or rather, which is most probable, because the state of society had not yet so improved as to draw with it the inevitable consequence of valuable and individual property, litigation, and law suits. The small controversies that had yet arisen were determined by arbitration. These related chiefly to occupancy and the rights of settlement or contracts as simple as the subjects of them and involving no intricacy. But the inhabitants, either from the love of novelty or finding the system of arbitration inadequate to the administration of justice, began to wish to have fixed principles and permanent tribunals to govern and guard life, reputation, and property.

Song of Clonmel[1]

What use is in fighting, and gouging, and biting,
    Far better to let it alone,
For kicking and cuffing, and boxing, and buffing,
    It makes the flesh ache, and the bone.
But give me the whiskey, it makes one so frisky,
    But beating, and bruising makes sore,
Come shake hands, my cronies, come near, my dear honies,
    And think of your grudges no more.
We are a set of poor fellows just escap'd from the gallows,
    And hunting a wolf or a bear.
And what with a tail on, except the camelion,
    Can live upon fog, or the air?
Some venison haunches, to fill up our paunches,
    Come see if you cannot produce,
A barbecued pig, a nice mutton leg,
    Or turkey, or bit of a goose.
We have store of good liquor, so bring something quicker,
    And club your potatoes and yams.

2. Pittsburgh.

1. From Volume I, Book III, *Observations* (following Chapter 10). Clonmel is a fictional ballad-singer associated with Tom the Tinker's whiskey boys, whom Brackenridge portrays as being in the woods in their own "madcap settlement" after the insurrection.

We'll make a great feast, and turn all to jest,
　So away with your frowns and your damns.
There is nothing like love, which comes from above,
　And tickles the youngsters below.
It is vain man's own fault, that he so brews his malt,
　As ever to cry out, heigh-ho!
Alexander and Caesar, and Nebuchadnezzar,
　Found out to their cost this was true,
Now who will be fools, to drink at the pools,
　Of ambition and war, we or you?

An Epistle to Walter Scott

[*Returning to Pittsburgh on court duty in September 1811, Brackenridge took up, "by chance," The Lady of the Lake. In this frontier setting, where he had come to make his career by advancing the western country in literature as well as action, his failure to achieve his dream mingled in his sensibilities with Scott's success in romantically portraying the Loch Katrine country. As a result, nostalgia enveloped Brackenridge, and in this mood he wrote "An Epistle to Walter Scott," clumsily imitating his countryman's octosyllabics and pointing up his own crude versification as the living demonstration of his failure. The effect of the poet who cannot release the poetry he feels is itself poetic.*

The classicist in Brackenridge cannot quite let go of Homer and Virgil even as he cries out amateurishly:

> Oh give me Burns, oh give me Scott;
> I want no more when these I've got.

In the "Epistle," Burns and Scott become true descendants of the classic poets, and thus join characteristics of eighteenth- and nineteenth-century literature. The "Epistle" is perhaps the clearest demonstration of Brackenridge as a transitional figure.]

> Full many a rounded year has cast
> A shade upon the period past,
> Since Scotia on maternal lap
> Received me. There, upon the map,
> I see Kintyre,* there was I born.
> Hard fate to be so rudely torn
> By poverty and need of change,
> Away to this a foreign range,
> With parents whom Culloden muir [1]
> And other troubles had made poor.
> But early mem'ry paints me well
> The Bellivalen † hill and dale;

---

* A peninsula in the North. [H.H.B.]

† Farm. [H.H.B.]

1. Culloden Moor is in East Inverness County, Scotland. For other Scottish terms, refer to the Glossary.

The bracken green, the heather blue,
And gowan of a golden hue,
And though se-join'd by length of wave,
I feel a charm some fairy gave
To bind me to my natal soil,
And think upon that distant isle;
An isle where charm of verse is found
To make it an enchanted ground.
For most the ballad and the rhyme
Imparts a charm to every clime;
And not the deeds that men have done
So much the listening ear has won,
As magic of that art divine;
Which springs from the harmonious nine.
Oh give me Burns, oh give me Scott;
I want no more when these I've got,
To make a rock of any sea
Immortal by such ministrelsy.

    Who now need ask, where are the nine,
That sang the tale of Troy divine,
Or later, in Italian day
Gave to the Mantuan [2] his lay?
These fairy footsteps here I trace
On lands from whence have sprung my race.
Here heights are sung, unknown before,
But by traditionary lore.
Who would have thought that Thule's isle [3]
Would be the seat of song erewhile;
And lyric fire, and epic swell
Come with Apollo here to dwell?

    Ah me! that cannot nearer be
To hear such native melody!
Here by Ohio's stream my pen
Gives image to a sort of strain
Which feeling prompts, but Genius none,
So gifted to a favorite son.
My gift is only to admire,
In madness I attempt the lyre,
At hearing this celestial sound
From Scotia's hills and distant bound.

2. Virgil.

3. Polybius imagined that Thule was the most northerly region of the world. It has been variously identified as the Shetland Islands, Iceland, the northern point of Denmark. Figuratively, it is the uttermost degree or point attainable, but Brackenridge is not using the term in this manner. The context restricts the meaning to Scotland.

Of this I dream, and when awake,
I read the Lady of the Lake,
Or throw it by to gain the power
Of sense and motion for an hour,
For such excess too long to bear
Incapable our natures are,
And the delirium must have stay,
Or spring of human frame give way.

   Here silly hills, and untaught wood,
Because a little of that blood
Address me, or I think address
The lonely weeping wilderness.
Have you not something of that vein,
A little of the minstrel strain,
To give us also here a name,
And taste of an immortal fame.
Ah! lonely bowers you give me shade,
But such return cannot be made,
Sweet waters, you must trickle on
Till some more favor'd muse's son
Shall sing of you like Walter Scott
And to immortal change your lot!
Through many ages cast your glance,
Perhaps a thousand years at once;
A lesser time will be too soon
For nature to dispense such boon;
As comets centuries require
To pass off and recruit their fire.
Who knows but this epistle may
To you attract a poet's lay;
To put in verse some height, some stream
Just incidental in his theme.
Oh! might my name of Bracken born
Some ridge where infant lay forlorn
Or peasant built his hamlet drear
Attain the sanctity to hear
It named in one immortal line,
Which turns a harsh word to divine!
But this too much; I cannot claim
The need of such advance to fame,
So far secluded from my race,
And cut off from romantic base.
It can't be said that such a dale
Where deeds were done, is where I dwell;
Or that I vegetate among
The hills which once were hills of song.
Here neighboring to the savage tread
Inglorious I must bend my head,

And think of something else than fame;
Though in my bosom burns the flame
That in a happier age and clime
Might have attempted lofty rhyme.

But thou, celestial, take thy course
With fancy's pinion, reason's force;
Go on; enjoy increasing fame,
Now equal with a Milton's name,
Or him that sang the fairy-queen;
Or other Southern [4] that has been.
Not Shakespeare would himself disdain
The rivalship of such a strain.

Oh! for a theme of ampler space,
Whereon eternal lines to trace;
Embracing sea and continent,
And not within an island pent;
A stage commensurate with power
Of bard and sacred orator!
But this would kind of treason be
To isle of my nativity,
Which claims and has a right to claim
Her bard for her own sep'rate fame,
Since other lands no mention make
Of genius which did here awake,
Or deeds which heroes here have done
However meriting renown.
Much merit here of feeling heart
To make the breast heave, and tear start
Remains unsung; and valor's prize
The golden hair and sky-blue eyes.
Hence I retract the wish, resign,
To Scotia give that harp of thine
To which all melodies are known
That harp has rung or pipe has blown,
Like thine own bard, thy Allan Bane [5]
So full, so various is thy strain,
In torrent numbers, flood of sense
In bounds which judgment well restrains.

No fear of a short-liv'd renown,
Or fading to thy ivy-crown;
For should some hidden fire or force
Of ocean in his changing course
Unfix Benledi [6] from his stance,

4. Others south of Scotland, that is, England.
5. Probably the minstrel in Scott's *Ivanhoe*, Allan O'Dale.
6. Mountain in Scotland.

Yet time at thee shall break his lance;
Or miss his aim and level wide
At thy more solid pyramid!
Go on; add lustre to an earth
So honored by thy magic birth;
For not of mortal art thou born,
O darling son of orient morn!
Go on—and fill the rising gale
With Scotia's early lore and tale;
Make vocal and give life in turn
To every mountain, glen and burn;
As erst in Grecia did the god
Of poesy, his dear abode,
Attended by the sister choir,
That hymned the song or tuned the lyre;
For of Castalia 7 ev'ry dream
Is found, in thy Loch Katrine theme; 8
And Pindus 9 rises to our view
When that we think of Benvenue 10
Or we forget all other song,
Thy inspiration pours so strong.

So far removed, what the reward
Can we bestow upon the bard?
Our praise is vain; what winds will bear
Encomium to a distant ear?
Or will it please, so little skill
Have we, however the good will?
All we can do, we bid the sun
When he his weary course has run,
And in the orient brings the day,
To halt a little at thy lay,
And see if not his beams appear
More cheering when he climbs the sphere;
For joy of heart lights up a grace
And dances in the human face.
And why not morning at her dawn
More sprightly look upon the lawn;
And birds in melody repay
With sweeter imitative lay?
Though not, thou bird of scarlet wing *
Canst thou a tale of Marmion 11 sing?

* A beautiful American bird of a variety of notes. [H.H.B.]
7. A spring of the muses on Mount Parnassus.
8. The wild country of Loch Katrine was Scott's inspiration for *The Lady of the Lake*.
9. Mountain in Greece.
10. Mountain in Loch Katrine country.
11. Scott's *Marmion* (1808) , an adventurous tale of patriotism.

Though carol sweet and matin voice
Is charming at our early rise;
Thy Border minstrelsy [12] fall short;
Thy lay is not of such a sort
Articulate as tongue of men.

What sound is that I hear again,
That winds across th' Atlantic bear
In harmony to ev'ry ear?
With gratulation welcome sped
It trembles on the mountain head,
Which starts to higher majesty,
When rapturous strains like these pass by,
Sit down thou ridge in lower style;
I also wish to hear awhile;
Depress thy erst aspiring head;
Be level with the ocean bed;
That no impediment may be
To this the coming minstrelsy,
The vision of Sir Rodrick * sung
These words and solitudes among:

Sole poet of the present age,
At once the poet and the sage,
Accept this distant homage given
To sounds that well deserve a heaven;
Original, of vigor born,
And dress'd in splendor of the morn,
With all the witchery of shade,
And spell unseen upon us laid.
What is this spell? It is the charm
Of manners from the pencil warm;
And moral observations true,
Of passions which the world subdue,
With drapery that must beguile
Attention by the form and style.

But now no more; enough, enough,
Of these prosaic numbers rough:
We cease th' attempt, since it requires
A poet to tell a poet's fires.

[Pittsburgh, 1811]

* This poem announced, but not arrived. [H.H.B. The Vision of Don Roderick *was published that year, 1811.*]

12. *Minstrelsy of the Scottish Border* (1802–1803), an anthology collected by Scott and John Leyden.

CHRONOLOGY

GLOSSARY

INDEX

A Chronology of
Brackenridge's Life

1748   Born in Kintyre, near Campbellstown, Scotland.

1753   Settles with family in the "Barrens" of York County, Pennsylvania.

1755   Experiences Indian terrors in York County following General Braddock's defeat.

1763   Teaches at Gunpowder Falls, Maryland.

1768   Attends the College of New Jersey, Princeton.

1770   Writes *Father Bombo's Pilgrimage to Mecca,* with Philip Freneau.

1771   Granted Bachelor of Arts degree; presents at commencement exercises *The Rising Glory of America,* written in collaboration with Philip Freneau.

1772   Appointed master of academy at Back Creek, Somerset County, Maryland.

1774   Influenced by Attorney Samuel Chase haranguing the public at Annapolis; granted a Master of Arts degree from Princeton, where he presents "A Poem on Divine Revelation" during the commencement exercises.

1776   Becomes army chaplain; publishes *The Battle of Bunkers-Hill.*

1777   Writes and publishes a second drama, *The Death of General Montgomery at the Siege of Quebec.*

1778   Goes to Philadelphia; publishes *Six Political Discourses Founded on the Scriptures.*

1779   Founds *United States Magazine;* delivers in Philadelphia "An Eulogium of the Brave Men who have Fallen in the Contest with Great-Britain."

1780   Admitted to Philadelphia bar.

1781   Arrives in the frontier village of Pittsburgh; changes middle name from Montgomery to Henry.

1783   Submits first report from the frontier to an eastern newspaper, "Narrative of the Perils and Sufferings of Dr. Knight and John Slover."

1784   Vacations in Warm Springs, Virginia, at the same time President Washington is there, and writes in Washington's honor, *A Masque, Written at the Warm-Springs in Virginia, in the Year 1784.*

1785   Defends twelve rioters accused of attacking the excise collector, William Graham; also defends Mamachtaga, an Indian charged with the murder of two white men; writes "The Trial of Mamachtaga"; marries a Miss Montgomery.

1786 Encourages foundation of the first newspaper on the frontier, the *Pittsburgh Gazette;* elected to the State Assembly of Pennsylvania; his son, Henry Marie, is born May 11.

1787 Acquires endowment for the Pittsburgh Academy (University of Pittsburgh) and passes bills establishing Allegheny County and a church in Pittsburgh; argues for the adoption of the new Federal Constitution; writes his first Hudibrastic satires.

1788 Defeated in re-election effort; starts *Modern Chevalier;* delivers "Oration on the Federal Constitution."

1789 Leaves Federalist party.

1790 Marries Sofia Wolfe.

1792 Publishes *Modern Chivalry,* Volumes I and II, Philadelphia.

1793 Publishes *Modern Chivalry,* Volume III, Pittsburgh.

1794 Tries to mediate in the Whiskey Insurrection.

1795 Publishes *Incidents of the Insurrection in Western Pennsylvania in the Year 1794.*

1796 Composes Scottish dialect poems addressed to David Bruce.

1797 Publishes *Modern Chivalry,* Volume IV, Philadelphia.

1798 Returns to political activity as leader of Jefferson's Republican Party in western Pennsylvania.

1799 Appointed a judge of the Supreme Court of Pennsylvania.

1800 Founds *Tree of Liberty* in opposition to the *Pittsburgh Gazette*

1801 Composes more Scottish poems addressed to David Bruce; moves to Carlisle, Pennsylvania.

1804 Stands by fellow Supreme Court judges in impeachment proceedings; publishes *Modern Chivalry,* Part Two.

1806 Collects *Gazette Publications* and *The Spirit of the Public Journals; or Beauties of American Newspapers, for 1805.*

1807 Attempts to adapt English common law to American society.

1810 Poses for a portrait by Gilbert Stuart.

1811 Returns to Pittsburgh on circuit duty and writes *An Epistle to Walter Scott.*

1814 Publishes *Law Miscellanies.*

1815 Reworks and republishes *Modern Chivalry.*

1816 Dies at Carlisle, June 25.

A Glossary of Scottish Terms Used by Brackenridge[1]

a'—all
aboon—above
ae—one
aff—off
aften—often
ahint—behind
a'maist—almost
ance—once
ane—own, one
aw—all
ay—have

bairn—child
baith—both
bane—bone
benn—into the parlor
beltin—dressings
bigging—building
birk—birch
blae—livid
blaw—blow, boast
bleering—blinded
blether—idle talk, nonsense
blib—blithely
bluid—blood
boney—handsome, beautiful
bracken—fern
brae—precipice, declivity, hill, slope, river bank
braid—broad, or a long letter, a letter on a broad sheet

brake—broke, fern
breeks—breeches
brulzie—a broil, a combustion
bught—pen
buiks, bukes—books
burn—water, a rivulet

ca'—call
canty—cheerful
carl—an old man
carlin—stout old woman, a peasant woman
charter—part of a bagpipe
chaunting—chanting
chiels—young people, children
clachan—clicking noise
claden, claith—pieces of cloth
claes—clothes
cogue, cog—wooden dish, cask
corbies—a species of crow
cotter—cottager
cowshunning—dropping cow dung
crabbit—sour
creel—to have one's wits in a creel, in a basket; to be crazy
cummock—a short staff with a crooked head

danged—dashed, beat
deel, de'el—devil
dinging—beating

1. Brackenridge's usage was neither accurate nor consistent.

dinna—do not
divisal—device
doup—backside
dowff—wanting spirit, pithless
drappie—small drop
drone—part of a bagpipe
droupit—drenched

een—eyes
et—get
ev'en—evening

fairlying—being courteous
fitit—footed
fou—full
fu'—full
frae—from

gae—go
gaed—went
gallan—gallant
gane—gone
gar—force, make
gate—way, manner, road
geer, gear—riches, goods
gie—give
gill—a measure of liquid, a pint
gilore—galore
gin—given, if
glakes, glaiks—fools
glen—valley
gouk—gook, a term of derision
Gude—God, good
guid—good

ha—hall, have
hae—have
haes—had, has
hame—home
har'st, hairst—harvest
hogo—possibly short for hough-magandie, meaning fornication. Line could read, "With the fornicating world, then as so fetid."
horns—spoons made of horn

hurdies—hips or the rump

ilk, ilka—every, other, each
ist—is it
ither—other, one another

ken—know
kerne—rude peasant
kintra—country
kitlin—young cat, kitty
kittle—ticklish, likely

laland—lowland
laird—landholder
laith—loathe
lang—long
lardie—lord
lear—learning
lear'd—learned
leke—like
leught—laughed
loch—lake
Lochaber—place in Scotland
loon, loun—lout, rogue, person of low rank, term of disparagement
loup, lowp—leap, jump
lunder—cudgel
lug—ear, handle

madis—maidens
mair—more
maun—must
mavie—dimunitive of thrush
min't—mind, remembrance, meant
mony—many
muckle—much
muir—moor
mul—mill

nae—no, not any, not
nane—none
neist—next, nearest
no'e—not ever
nuiks, neuks—nooks

o'—of
o't—of it
on—any, on
orsa-versa—vice-versa
owr—over

paik, pike—pummeling, to pummel, a pick
paisley—Scottish town known for shawls, paisley shawls
pickle—a small quantity
pickle strae—bag of straw
pit—pat
plaiden—outer loose garment
plunkie—trick
popes—pipes
poup—pop
pousie—pussy cat, rabbit
prick—rod or wand used as a mark in shooting
prie—taste
prig—quibble or haggle
pu'—pull

qho'—quoth

rede—advise
rin—run
rive—tear
rouse—praise
rugings—beatings

sae—so
saft—soft
sal—shall
sark—shirt
saul—soul
scirl—shriek
scons—a kind of bread
screed—a tear or rent
scrimpit—scanty
sels—selves
seugh, sugh—the continued rushing noise of wind or water
shaw—show

shill—shrill
sic—such
sick—such
sinsyne—since
slae—sloe
sleech—ooze
sma—small
sneeshin—snuff
soomit—swam
sowth—to use a low whistle over a tune
sprite—spirit
spurtle—a spatula or wooden stick for stirring porridge
stackerin—staggering
staid—stayed
stane—stone
stap—stop
stark—strong
stots—oxen
strae—straw
strak—struck
strathspeys—Scottish dance
strone—spout

taen—taken
tae—to
tauk'd—talked
tay—tea
tate, tet, teete—lock of hair
thegither—together
till—to, towards
tither—other
thrapple—choke
tugs—pieces of rawhide
tulzied—quarreled, fought
twa—two

unco—strange, ucouth

verra—very

wad—would
wale—choose
wame—womb

war'—worldly
wardle, warld—world
wat—know
wean—one
wee—bit
weel—well
wha—who
whilk, ilk—each
wi—with
wid—wide, wild

winna—will not
wisk, whisk—sweep, lash
won—swell
wrocken—avenged
wud—would
wyle—choose

yestreen—the night before
yerk, youke—jerk, a term of derision

Index